# TH
# PRINCE
## OF THE
# AIR

THE MEMOIRS OF A
CONTEMPORARY WIZARD

BY

MASON WINFIELD

RPSS Publishing - Buffalo, New York

publisher@rockpapersafetyscissors.com

ISBN:978-1-956688-00-9
Printed in the United States of America

10 9 8 7 6 5 4 3 2 1

First Edition

RPSS Publishing - Buffalo, New York

For Michael Robartes

Don't waste time trying to make him think
that materialism is true! Make him think it is
strong, or stark, or courageous – that it is
the philosophy of the future.
That's the sort of thing he cares about.

C. S. Lewis, *The Screwtape Letters*

# Other Books by Mason Winfield

## *History and Folklore:*

*Shadows of the Western Door* (1997)
*Spirits of the Great Hill* (2001)
*Haunted Places of Western New York* (2004)
*Village Ghosts of Western New York* (2006)
*Haunted Rochester* (2008)
*Supernatural Saratoga* (2009)
*Ghosts of 1812* (2009)
*Iroquois Supernatural,* with Michael Bastine (2011)
*The Paranormal Almanac of Western New York* (2012)
*Spirits of the Niagara Wine Trail* (2015)
*The Rose Witch* (2018)

## *Fiction:*

*A Ghosthunter's Journal* (1999)
*A Paranormal Intrigue* (2017)
*The Lord of the Dawn* (2019)

# Contents

# INTRODUCTION

I opened my eyes. Every joint in my body ached. I couldn't feel my arms. It felt like one of those nights that I had fallen asleep on top of one and cut off the circulation, but this was both of them. I couldn't feel my legs, either. It was like a nightmare of paraplegia. My lower back was one big cramp. It was even hard to turn my head. But I must have.

A horrid snarling exploded like a gunshot. If I could have moved I would have jumped out of my skin. Two hideous, frothing faces were snapping and yowling a foot from my throat.

I was scared and angered into full wakefulness. It was then that I realized that my upper body was fixed in a modified Christlike pose, each wrist held over my shoulders. My back was against something metallic and springy. My butt was on a hard floor, and my blue-jeaned legs spread before me, each ankle clotheslined to a loop beside the foot of the old wooden door.

The two massive dogs must have been sleeping as long as I had been still. At my first stir, they tuned up. How long had I been out? How did I get here? Where was I, anyway? It was hard to think with those demons going at it.

I was in what looked like somebody's working space, probably twenty feet by ten. A tinny work light hung from a beam overhead and gave me all the light I had. From the lack of windows and the concrete floor, I presumed it was a basement. A workbench was fitted with sturdy ring-bolts and stocked with suddenly sadistic-looking tools. Underneath it were folded tarps, acid containers, and mop-up materials. I could imagine all these implements being used upon a human body. Bodies.

Whatever supported my back flexed and creaked with every flinch. Whatever held it was stiff as stone. I could envision a spring bed frame bolted to the wall. The raging dogs were between me and the door, held by their long, heavy leashes to a high bolt on a beam. They were no fun to look at, but I studied them, which enraged them even more.

One looked like a Rott-mix – it had hound-ears and that bulging forehead. The other I'd swear was wolf-Huskie. They were 100-pounders at least. I knew they had been fighting in the rings by their tattered ears and scarred cheeks. I made a vow of hatred against anyone who could have turned loving creatures into monsters like these.

They were in the perfect position to keep me exactly where I was. Their slanting leashes kept them just short of tearing off my cheek or digging into my legs. I credit their bellowing for shooting me some adrenaline. It was also surely announcing something to someone else, someone who had this procedure down to a practice. I didn't have a lot of time. Whoever put me where I was was coming back, probably at the first moment they knew I was conscious.

My head was thick as mud. More than anything I wanted to fall back asleep and forget the ache, but I held as still as I could and tried to remember what had led me to this position. I felt like Hamlet's clueless lackeys in *Rosencrantz and Guildenstern Are Dead*, finding themselves with adult consciousness, independent processing, automatic functioning, cultural literacy, moral compasses, full faculties, full use of language – and absolutely no personal memories apart from the play in which they find themselves ("My lord, we were sent for…"). I flashed back to my life, and aspects of it started to return. I still couldn't remember anything just before I got where I was.

I tried to focus on my options. The best was to stall for time. Still, my foggy mind had a question to ask: *Why had they left me alive?* Only one explanation came to me: *They have no idea who I am.*

I slitted my eyes like I was lapsing back into unconsciousness and did my best to look around without moving. I spotted the little surveillance camera above the bolt that held the dogs' leashes. I had thought there would be one. It was completely out of the reach of a normal person in my position.

The dogs weren't fooled. They set up another round of slavering and wailing. One was so mad at not being able to get at me that it took a snap at the other, which set it caterwauling differently and snapping back. Anyone anywhere close would hear that racket – unless this basement was soundproofed. Guessing its likely uses, I bet myself that it was. I took another squinty look at the devices around me and was sure of it. The point of the dogs was to add to my terror.

*Good luck with that*, I thought. *Somebody is paying.* But I felt weak. Breathing was hard. No wonder. People can die when they are held immobile with their arms up. Most victims of crucifixion have died of suffocation. Only the real tough ones like the Son of Our Lord needed the coup de grâce of the spear-thrust to make the Promised Land on schedule.

Though every sense in my mind and body was shrieking to take action, I had to be patient. I didn't want to bring any new tormentors into this space before I was ready to deal with them. It would take me minutes to recover once I got my arms down and got a bit of blood in them. Should I quell the camera first? That might set off an alarm. Someone at a desk could very well be watching me on a monitor, though maybe not vigilantly enough.

Trying to give no sign that I was fully conscious, I energized my left hand above me, producing what I sometimes call "the Lightsaber," a la *Star Wars*. Usually I call it "the Beam." It's a ray of force that seems to come out the knuckles of my index and middle-finger and extend from my open hand like a light-as-air broomstick. In darkness it looks to me like a rod of teal-colored light, fainter and paler as it goes out. It doesn't cut anything, at least not quickly. It's like a microwave of heat, electricity, and general disruption. It works a Hell of a lot better when I can straighten my arm out. At eight feet, it's an electrical annoyance, a back-off. At four feet, it stops hearts, short-circuits brains, and toasts internal organs.

I angled my open palm forward from over my head, aimed the Beam right into the lens of the camera, and held it long enough to be sure the video feed would go dark. I knew this would look like a natural malfunction to anyone who thought this arrangement was going to hold me.

A new duet of yammering from the dogs made another decision for me. How could anyone think with them acting up at every flinch? Getting them shut up was becoming a matter connected to my own survival. A gentle death was the best the world held for them, anyway.

I turned the left hand down and burrowed the beam into the forehead of the Rott mix. He backed up onto his haunches and put his head down like he had forgotten to live. The other one's frenzy had only a few heartbeats to process itself into confusion. Then I shot the bolt into him the way I had the first. He went night-night in a second and dangled on his leash like he had hung himself.

It's then, and only then, that I could hear "the Chimies," those light, humanlike voices that populate every space in which people have lived long – or died. I don't think they're souls or spirits; I think they are some component of the human essence that stays behind when soul or spirit launches. All I know is that they have a musical, non-verbal tone. At happy places they're merry, sometimes melancholy, as if they miss being there like they once were. At tragic sites, they are anxious, even agitated. They try to warn others, or at least me, when entering rueful space. At moments of crisis they escalate – as they were doing at that moment.

The capacity to hear the Chimies is my one truly receptive psychic power. I tell no one about it, as it would give my potential opponents an edge I don't need them to have. The Chimies had surely been tuning up for the entire time I'd been awake. I just couldn't hear them because of the dogs. From their tones, I could deduce that this was a place in which people had died, and miserably. Was this John Wayne Gacy's abbatoir? It felt like people might be coming. How was I peeling myself off the wall?

My left, the Beam, may look a bit like the *Star Wars* lightsaber when it's in action, but my right – with what I call, "the Axe-hand," or "the Gleam" – works like it, though it's a stubbier weapon. Its range is about the size of my hand. To me it appears as a glow, greeny-blue like the other, but denser. I have never seen anything it couldn't plunge through quickly. It doesn't matter whether it's a brick wall or living flesh. Even individual fingers are cutting tools when I energize it. I still don't know whether the effect of the Axe-hand is heat or super-cold – or a laser or radiation or molecular disintegration or any of the other theories that may come to you. All I know is that it makes holes in things.

I reached up and around with my right index finger, tugged on the chain of the handcuff until I was sure I had it – my hand felt like it belonged to someone else! – and tore it through. It took longer than it should have. The right dropped to my side, the police-style cuff clanking on cement. Blood flowed painfully back into the arm. I tried flexing it in a minute and slapped myself in the forehead with a cadaver-cold set of limp fingers and an edge of the cuff on my wrist. God, did it hurt! Almost knocked myself out.

It took minutes to recover from that first move, during which I realized how my lower back hurt. I'd been leaning against the wall atop something hard and angular. I presumed it was one of the tools like they had all over this place. I was envisioning the head of a sledgehammer.

When my right arm was working again I set about liberating my left. I couldn't reach the chain so I hooked an index against the skin of my own wrist and under the coil of the cuff. Fortunately the Gleam doesn't hurt me. In seconds an inch of curving metal flew off and clinked on the floor. I still wasn't loose. I took another whack at the cuff with a couple more fingers and was finally free of it, taking a little scratch on my left wrist as I pulled loose. I had no idea the process was going to make such crusty edges. It's different every time.

I got some circulation back into my upper body. I leaned forward and severed the clothesline at my ankles with just a pull of my right index, then sat deciding what to do. There was no perceptible commotion outside the room, so I figured I had a few minutes. I thought I could work up a surprise if I had to for whatever first came in the door, but I wasn't looking forward to it.

It took awhile to get up. I had to haul myself with that springy contraption to which I had been spreadeagled. I still had that coil around my right wrist. It would be a while before I could work it off with my left. That was fine. If I got into a close-quarters scrape before I was fully ready it could come in handy as a temple-thumper or a knife-blocker.

I was dying to get out of there – the Chimies were driving me almost as crazy as the dogs had been – but that wicked kink in my back made me curious about whatever I had been lying on for who knows how long. I looked back.

It was then that I spotted what I recognized as one of my shoulder bags against the base of the contraption I'd been fastened to. It was a Patagonia, with pouches, zippers, and a bandolier-style shoulder strap. I remembered it from many a journey, and looking at it actually helped me come back even more. My dream-mind had been through so many eras of my life that it was hard even to remember the decade in which I'd dropped out and ended up where I was.

The bag must have been around me at the minute I was hit, the minute that I couldn't remember. It must have stayed on me when I was transported. At some point it had slipped off and sagged under me. What! Why had they left that on me? Where was I before the world went dark? How had I ended up where I was?

I went back to it and looked into its main pouch. It held an old, wood-covered book as thick as an ancient encyclopedia, with a shallow lock dead-center of the metal bands that belted it shut. It looked like you needed a key to get it open. Like trying to remember a dream by hauling

dropping a hooked and baited chain into the ocean and
ies up – the scenes and the journeys and the adventures
k to me. *Oh, yeah*, I said to myself. *We had been rousting*

*Who knew that was starting a war?*
*How did I end up with that book?*

Chapter 1

# Rousting Witches

1

I should introduce myself. I'm Eric Hawthorne Wood – yes, related to *that* Hawthorne, the author Nathaniel. I drive a manual SUV and live with two cats in a barn with a tower near Saratoga Springs, NY. I run a small walking tour company as a cover for what I really do. I live in the Northeast because I'm hooked on mountain sports.

I'm a wizard.

You're probably either laughing right now or thinking of wands, academies, Harry Potter, Dark Lords, spells… Merlin, Gandalf, Hogwarts, Dumbledore… Ah, no. The real thing's a lot different.

I don't say I'm a wizard because I wave wands or cast spells and make things happen. Most of that stuff is out of folklore and fiction – or pop entertainment, which is where almost everyone gets their impressions about magic and wizards. No, I say I'm a wizard because people like me are the closest things you will ever get to what you think when you hear the word. I call myself a wizard because people like me are behind all the legends and traditions of witchcraft and wizardry that go back to the earliest days of culture.

My gifts are nothing like what you would expect "magic" to be. I don't even like that term. I hate it so much that I usually put in quotes. It's distracting, and it's not very specific. Got a lot of baggage.

I believe in magic, or at least in something that would look to you like it. I don't believe in magical thinking. Everything has a cause. I spend a lot of my time trying to figure out what might be the power-point, the "pedal to the metal" instant of magical events. What's the energy-source?

How does the intention of a human mind exploit it? I'll get to more of that in pages to come. To cut it short, there are sources of power in the world around us that would be virtually inexhaustible if they could be channeled. Atmospheric electricity is only one of them, but for me it's the most likely power-source of human psychokinetic events and spontaneous psychic phenomena, if not magic.

For now, I believe that magic, like psychic abilities, is simply a non-material causal system for occasional material events. Magic is probably nothing more than an enhancement of the hidden powers of the human mind, plus its exploitation of that mysterious power-source. I know our skeptical – read, *materialist* – friends don't buy any of it.

Magic. Psychic phenomena. The scientific method doesn't work to explain either one of them. The scientific method demands that something has to be repeatable, which no human ability is, at least not identically, and under restricted and unnatural conditions. I mean, ask Michael Jordan to score 55 points in a lab. He's not going to. He won't do it every night on a court. Does that mean he can't ever do it? Does that mean he's not a basketball player? That's one of their mistakes, the materialists, at least theoretically.

Magic, like psychic abilities, is in the realm of the arts, not the sciences. Like any human talent, it doesn't work the same way every time. Asking it to is simply incorrect. Denying that it ever does work… That's another mistake.

Just because you don't understand the mechanism by which something happens doesn't mean you ought to deny that it did happen. The materialists are wasting their time there, unless their real goal is befuddling most of society into believing them. There they have done all right.

I do have a few limited abilities that would look to most people like magic. To a parapsychologist, my gifts would seem like massively expanded expressions of *psychokinesis*, "mind over matter," basically the extrasensory physical property of the human organism. I think that probably is what they are. Other people in our world specialize in the information talents, ESP. Still others use the spells and implements you would associate with classic figures of tradition. If they get everything right, they can be really effective, though they have to do a bit of planning. The old world – and many fundamentalists of any era – would have called all of us "witches" or "wizards."

The difference between a witch and a wizard is a quibble. There isn't quite the stigma about "wizard," but for me the term doesn't have the impact of "witch." And whereas the general public is willing to accept the likelihood of a few evil wizards, the image of a good witch usually takes a bit of explaining. I'd prefer to call us all in this community "power people." We have nicknamed ourselves, "the College," I am told, for at least 300 years, and most of our slang spins off from there. What was it before that? I can't find anyone who remembers. Call us whatever you like. There are a lot of us out there. We are all around you. And you'd never guess.

There are witches and wizards in every part of the populated world. I wouldn't say 1% of the human world is a Collegian, a power-person. I wouldn't say one out of a thousand – not at all. One out of ten thousand, now you could be getting close. One out of a hundred thousand, I'd say that's at a minimum, at least based on the number of them I know in my home region of the upper Hudson Valley. You have a lot of us around. And we don't declare ourselves, almost none of us. Not the real ones.

By the time of the events of this book – the mid-1970s to 2020 – Western society no longer tries to repress this sort of stuff because it, at least the "serious" people, no longer believes in it. Yet among the alternates, the hippies, the counterculture, there are a lot of folks claiming to be witches and shamans and occultists of all types. It's actually undergoing a new renaissance, though I'm not sure how much people really believe in it. But most of the real people like to stay covered up.

We Collegians, if we chose, could show the world that there is something to what we do. We could blow people's minds. But things would change, and almost all of us like things the way they are. This we have figured out.

No sensible person would advertise a gift like ours, at least in the general society. We nickname non-wizards "Townies," in the College motif, or "Muggles" since Harry Potter became such a smash. Yes, we hang out. Yes, we go to movies. Yes, you should have seen the parties on *Game of Thrones* Sundays.

Human nature being what it is, we do have a few showboats in our loose community who, at least when they're drunk or otherwise high, like to show off. Their secrecy survives, again, because the world doesn't believe them, even when they show off. Most people can witness almost any type of magical miracle and tell almost no one because they're afraid everybody will think they're crazy. We can be such herd animals. Plus, this world is so damn material. It has to believe something to see it.

People in the College – the Arts Majors, anyway – even have a little fun with the Townies now and then, putting on some minor display of something and then acting nonchalant about it. I was a master at that kind of jive when I first started developing my abilities. Since many Muggle individuals can't believe what they know they saw, they often act a little kooky. It's really funny to see the double-take. It's hard to keep from laughing.

But where was I? Ah. Me.

When I read books I like to know what people look like, so I'll tell you that I'm a white guy, kind of tall and angular. People have been telling me for years that I look like James Taylor on the *Sweet Baby James* LP cover, the record that really broke him. They even nicknamed me *JT* during my brief spell in college. I don't agree with that. Taylor's way handsomer, and he might be a little taller. But I see the general resemblance. Our body types and skull shapes are just about identical. I could be his brother that way. I like my hair in that sort of a long shag, too, like the real JT used to. I'm a diehard for the hippie era.

Taylor spent a few summers in Saratoga Springs, he and Carly, in the early 1970s, which was a bit before I moved here. People around town got to know him pretty well. They say he's as advertised: a composed, genuine, down-to-earth being. He does SPAC – Saratoga Performing Arts Center – every couple years, and during the few days around each of those shows, tourists in cafes or pubs or shops came up and addressed me as if I were him, at least into the early 1990s. Some just asked for autographs on something and then ran away nervously, which had to be a hoot when they found that I'd signed it, "Eric Wood."

I quit calling myself Eric Wood a long time ago. I can't tell you what I call myself now. I had to take on a new ID. I still keep my first name, a testament to a Swedish-American grandfather, and I prefer people to use the full word, which is sort of a reflex, possibly to avoid echoing the old school-days joke that provoked more than a single fight. (*Rick Wood,* they'd say without much expression. Then they'd raise eyebrows, make knowing winks, and say, *But his sister wouldn't.*) Nobody's pulled it since junior high and I still hate the memory of it.

I had to cut a lot of ties when I got launched on this pursuit in life – and being a power-person, a Collegian, is a pursuit, a path that excludes a lot of others. It was too dangerous to be associated with my family any more. It was a great pang in me for the first twenty years, them thinking I'm a drug-waste. Now my parents are gone, and the rest are convinced I'm off the planet due to an accident in which I was reported among the killed, and I decided to leave things that way. The emotional loss to me and to them, though, is way better than having harm come to them, as it surely would have as a way to get to me. As the Godfather says, "When they come, they'll come at what you love." The Longhouse witches do it that way, too, at least they used to: They kill everyone close to you one at a time. Then they get after you.

Whether or not you know what the young James Taylor looked like by memory, there is one thing that would shock you if you saw the two of us together today: We are close in age. He's aged normally, if gracefully. I look like I might be 25.

By now the JT comments are coming to an end. Fewer people remember that first LP cover, but I still look as much as I ever did like the man on it. As I write these memoirs in 2020, the season of the Covid, I am pushing 70. And I'm one of the younger ones in our College.

You may be wondering how this comes about. I can't develop it all for you this early in my reflections, but most power-people develop an extended life span. This more or less freezes our looks in almost every physical regard like the vampires of *True Blood*. Most of us stay agile, and we don't get seriously sick any more. Ah, but a lot of changes come over us, at least the best of us, with the added years. Whatever I may look like, I am no longer the youth I was.

I think we get this way because of our channeling of the force we use for our special gifts. It has an enervating, preserving quality on the physical form when it finally kicks in. The *Star Wars* theme of "The Force" is actually a very good one for thinking about what I mean. It's mythologically very accurate for the power-word representing the life-force of the world, the Universe, living beings, and even what we might call magic. It's also such a popular term that people are going to know what I mean when I use it. We most often call it *Source,* though. That's another thing I'll develop later. But back to how the trouble got started. Oh, yes: *Rousting witches.*

2

I drifted in the treetops in the jelling light, the world around me all smoky blue and needle-green as if the very air was soaking colors out of the wood. They were far from uniform, the high conifers and aspens, and I had to focus to keep from sticking or bashing myself on tips or boughs.

No matter how many times I go with the Glide, it never stops being surreal. We humans, most of us, experience only a shallow vantage of the perceptible world. Try flying like a bird – a very slow one – and see how your perspectives change. Even the view from a drone doesn't do justice to what I experience. I feel the breeze on my whole form. The sounds are different. It's always cooler up high. It's a bit of work, too. It takes energy.

I have to look out for a lot of things, though. My concentration needs to be ahead of me. That night it was was divided.

I was trying hard to be quiet, and going ridiculously slow. I wanted to be invisible from all perspectives, even the distant one. The last thing I needed was some punk with a .22 thinking he's got The Mothman lined up.

It would have been disastrous, too, to lose sight of my friend and colleague Danny Montour forty feet under me. I wished again that I had thought to ask him to wear something light. I was lucky to be able to track him by the thin foot-trail he paced or I'd have completely lost him.

Once the tree line fell away to the west, and I caught a pang-inducing glimpse of the late July twilight, the reddening sun slanting toward the ink-green Adirondacks. I was filled with the longing for the gentle, spiritual things of life, for peace and poetry and reflection. For a heartbeat I thought of how delightful it would be to plop down in a high pine, watch the day shade to its sleep, remember all the lines I could from the great nature verse I've read, and write in my journal. I couldn't think about it, not even a second. I had to look out for the anthropoidal shadow I spotted slipping into the grove soon after my friend started hoofing it in. At my last sight of it, it was darting tree to tree, ever closing upon Danny. I had to ride shotgun above him.

If you saw me and Danny Montour on the street you'd pick him to be my bodyguard. Tall for a Mohawk, Danny is that odd combination of an informal apprentice to the Native Medicine People and a mixed-martial arts instructor and competitor. He projects physical authority to a surprising degree for a man his weight – a lean 185. He would whip almost anybody in a street fight. He's tough, fearless, and gifted. He's not average, but he's physically normal. I'm a little more than that.

This gift I call "the Glide" is one of the few abilities I have. I don't streak like a bird, though I can hover like a bee. It's mostly just a lightening of my form. Sort of like that comical image, both a balloon and its passenger, from one of E. T A. Hoffman's tales, I drift like a dirigible like I hear the Christian mystic Joseph of Cupertino and some of the ascended masters of Asian tradition did. I can guide it a bit. I don't have Superman's speed or control, but that evening I was taking his position, virtually dog-paddling among the branches, sometimes tugging myself along. It was tense and scary. If the beastie spotted me it would realize it was being set up and duck out. I'd never catch it in this thicket. Then it would hit us at the worst possible moment, maybe right when we were dealing with its hosts. These things aren't Scrabble whizzes, but they're real good at that game.

Critters like the thing I presumed I was trying to track figure in legends all over the world. The old-timers might have called this one a demon, a djinn, or a rakshasa. Most of the ones people see these days and report as paranormal beasties are just apparitions, back-off signs protecting treasures or sacred places or wizards' lairs. The serious – fully-material – ones come in a couple general types. When people spot one of the big bipeds at a distance they think they're seeing Bigfoot. A lot of the time they probably are. But anyone unfortunate enough to get really close to one of the ones I'm talking about would see a sizable animal-form critter, outwardly mammalian, but a morph of features from other familiar earthly species that might even include insectoid ones like mandibles or a stinger. All the others I've heard of have been like that. One I took out in the 1980s in the Cascade Mountains was like a gorilla with the double-jaws of a giant camel spider. It was just disgusting. Terrifying.

We often call the big ones "Trolls." They are more focused and purposeful than any natural animal can be trained to be. It takes a bit of energy to get one of those working for you, but when you need a confidential and utterly single-minded security agent to put the clamp down for a few hours in an outdoor setting, the Bigfoot-style critter will fill the bill. It's a great intimidator, too. Just the sight of one tends to spook even groups of people, even most Collegians. The fact that the folks we were after had a thing like this to protect them said something.

I spotted the big shadow again about fifty feet from my friend. If Danny was the center of a clock face and his winding footpath led to midnight, this bogie came in at four o'clock. Then it circled around and started coming in from two. Its goal was surely half cutoff, half bushwhack. I dropped a little lower. I hovered right over Danny, admiring his steadiness and trying to keep up with him soundlessly. He has a lot of guts, I've known that for a long time.

The critter darted like a big rabbit. I'd have to really wound it with the first strike or Danny and I were in big trouble. I swooped and tugged myself lower until I was twenty feet over the forest floor. Expecting any sensible predator to come in from the blind side, I was drifting above and just behind Danny. As long as there weren't too many branches in between, I could drop when I got a clear shot at the bogie and lance it with the Beam while it had its sights on him.

I quick-dodged a broad maple limb that could have clubbed me unconscious and lost sight of the critter. I panicked. If I didn't locate it I would have no alternative but to land near Danny, try to look like an unarmed human, and draw it out. In a few seconds I looked back to where I had seen it last and spotted it frozen in place in the undergrowth ahead of Danny to his right, by a big tree along his trail. I had thought the critter would pass right under me to get at him; instead, it was going to let him go by and hit him, maybe even from the side. Why hadn't I thought of that? I couldn't let it get within twenty feet of him. I decided to stake it all on one throw.

I spiraled slowly down and around the stem of a giant red pine toward the clump of foliage under which the critter crouched. Out of its line of sight, I was hoping to get a good bead on it and light up its excuse for a brain. I just couldn't see it well enough. I had to shoot for a bigger target.

I dropped a yard or two closer, focused my intention, extended my left arm like a fencer, and shot out my Beam. I could see it in the gloom, a one-inch wide blue-green rod, fading to white and then invisibility. I swiveled it into the critter's core from eight feet up.

The thing went crazy. The bushes surged and thrashed as though the stems themselves had come to agitated life, as though they were appendages from its own back. I swirled my Beam around like a stirrer, swizzling the critters's innards and surely making a Hell out of them.

It lifted its head and spotted me. It was gross. It had indeed an apelike skull and body, but with a bony, commentless face like an assassin bug, with a sloping forehead and nearly side-mounted eyes. It shot up at me like a Jack-in-the-Box, and I caught a glimpse of something switchblading open and heading toward me. Who thought it could jump like that?

Reflexively, I energized my right hand – the shorter, more destructive weapon – and hacked inward in a karate-style open-hand move. Inches before it reached my throat, the edge of my palm tore through what looked like a horny asparagus-stalk, taking off the nozzle and spilling the tobacco-juice fluid with which it had surged. The ugly brute fell back clear of its cover, landed on its back, and twitched.

Determined not to underestimate it again, I braced for more action, but that lunge had been its last spasm. I touched down.

So it had had a weapon other than its heavy arms. Invisible at a distance, it was sort of a *rostrum*, that combination stinger/sucker, that came out of its chin and had been kept folded into the fur of its breastbone. It was the same shape and type of substance – biological – of other things that have gotten through my defensive Glow – more on *that* later. The idea of that giant, warty, uncircumcised cock plunging into my ribs or neck was revolting.

Danny came up and dealt a couple deft whacks with something to its substitute for a skull, really an extension of an exoskeleton. The last of them caved it in like it had been caught in a vise. He had been carrying one of his ancestors' most distinctive close-quarters weapons, one of the ball-and-stick "turnip" war-clubs. I'd forgotten he had that thing. He could fold it inside a shirt sometimes and you couldn't even see it on him. He was wicked good with it, too. Maybe he would have been all right against this thing after all, at least if he had seen it coming.

We glanced at it and saw a familiar process beginning. The thing started folding its limbs like a dead bug. We knew then that it would start to fade, and in an hour be gone from our environment. The process is always fascinating to watch, though we had no time for sightseeing.

I was glad I had Danny to navigate through the twilight. I hate to make this sound like a stereotype of the Native American trail guide, but Danny can find his way anywhere in the woods. We were still mighty careful. These people didn't seem significant enough to have more than one of these beasties, but that would be just how they'd get you – underestimating them.

We crossed an area of thinner vegetation that held maybe a dozen small depressions. I could envision unmarked graves. "Lotta bad here," said Danny. "You feeling it?"

I didn't say much. I keep everyone, even my allies, thinking that my receptive aptitudes, my ESP, are nonexistent. But the Chimies were tuning up. They sounded furious and agitated.

Danny led us through what looked like an orchard that had been leveled and then neglected for fifty years. Before long I spotted a little run-down structure that had to be our destination. Surely once somebody's cider-hut if not a "roughing-it" cabin, it looked at least a century old. It would have been invisible from the air and I doubted that anyone but a handful of insiders even knew about it. These people must have parked in concealment and used a trail to get here. We were at least a mile from a paved road.

As we closed on the tiny, decrepit porch, the Chimies spiked. They were so frenzied that they were almost whistling. I had to tune them out so I could think – and hear. Danny heard a bit of chanting coming from within the cabin, and he nodded at the door. This was the place. I threw on the Glow.

Danny's one of those guys who gets his core into any dynamic move. He threw his shoulder against the door and crashed it off its rusty hinges. I burst in and took a quick scan of the interior.

We had shocked the would-be-witches – three old, bespectacled hippies, a man and two women. They looked scared and owlish, their lenses glinting in the gleam of the ring of candles on the rough wood table before them. They had been sure their Troll would protect them. The guy managed to get a hand on a shotgun he kept somewhere beside the old fireplace, but I made a quick backhanded slash with the Beam that caught him on the wrist, and that was the end of that idea. He and the weapon hit the floor, him on his knees, clutching the arm. The two others stood beside him, backed against their own chill fireplace. I didn't

26

show them any power of any sort, at least not that they could see, but I kept my left hand trained on them like the Warrior pose in yoga, like it was a loaded weapon. They knew the law had arrived.

The three kids were pinned under an upside-down baby pen. They looked about four, though I'm no expert on kids, and I barely looked at them. They were all dirty. They had soiled themselves in every potential way, and the already musty place stank fearfully, having the oddest effect on my mood. They didn't know what to make of our sudden appearance and the reaction of the witches. Their terror was actually pathetic. I was afraid they'd have heart attacks. They could have even thought we were there to take part in whatever was coming. Danny stepped between them and the witches and talked to them comfortingly. He told them over and over that they would be back with their families soon.

In my years of entering and extricating myself from situations, I've seen deception of all kinds. I'm used to big trouble coming in unassuming packages. But from the beginning I had the feeling these witches were also-rans, Muggles, hanger-ons, "Junkies," as we sometimes call them – "Adjunct Faculty," in the College motif. I just couldn't believe that a serious Collegian would get involved in something like this.

Plus, they were utter cowards. They blubbered for their lives, all three of them at once. I've never seen terror like that, and it seemed so inappropriate in people who had been so callous to their victims, and in the name of what? It was as if the potential consequences of their escalating game had never become real to them until the second we stood them up. Their begging was painful. It confirmed what I'd thought. Real pros would be manning up and taking their last shot as well as they could.

*How long has this gone on?* I said, working myself up. *How many was it? Do you even know? Did you have any pity for them?*

Danny just looked at me. I could see him whisper, "Just do it." But I was frozen. For the first time in my life I thought about the real horror of killing someone who was not trying to kill me.

During the hour-plus cross-state drive to get to this place Danny and I had already discussed breaking up the ceremony and turning the witches over to the authorities. That seemed enough justice to us both. They weren't going to be enjoying what was left of their lives. But the Native Elders at the conference at which I had met Danny had told us without explanation that that wouldn't work. I wasn't sure why, but we could calculate. A call to the cops would leave us open to being involved. The witches could identify us. They would probably tell the cops we had something to do with the killings and make us persons of interest. Then we'd have to do some fast talking, if not make tracks. Danny was right. It had to be done. If he did it, there would be clues somewhere, and that's not his role with us anyway. If I put them bye-bye my way... Different story.

The only way I could face up to this situation with these people was to imagine the glee on their faces in the rising energy of a baneful ceremony – that, and the terror of the children they or someone had done for here in the past. It still wasn't easy.

I spotted a handful of wood-and-stone implements inside the ring of thick candles. They looked like cigar-sized, flint-pointed spears or unfinished atlatl darts made in an authentic pre-Contact style. They were too stubby to make good weapons. They rested like surgical tools ready to be used.

The man stood to my left. He was middle-sized, grey-haired, and bespectacled, in khaki shorts and a faded purple polo shirt. I drilled him in the heart with my Beam and he dropped, probably without knowing what was coming. He looked more shocked than suffering. For all he knew I was making a grand gesture like Charlton Heston in *The Ten Commandments*, bidding the waves to part. Nobody can see the Beam when I fire it up.

The woman in the middle was another grey senior, and in a wacky old EMS T-shirt, that one popular in the 1980s of a tree with its root system that makes the sketchy image of the wizard-hat, face, and beard. With the virtual follow-through of the shot into the guy, I put the beam right through the forehead of the wizard on her chest. She barely knew what was coming. I think she was still astonished by the man's dead-drop. Had she never seen an Arts Major work before? It added to my sense that these people were Muggles. I think half the people who get into this darkest form of "magic" really don't have full belief. If they knew what they were doing, they wouldn't do it.

The last of them was the worst, a short, wide, short-haired greymalkin like many you'd see at the local co-op or behind the wheel of a Prius with a "My Other Car Is a Broom" bumper sticker. She looked like my own grandmother had for most of my former life. She had seen the others drop under my bolt. Her hysteria was mind-numbing. She knelt. She cried abjectly. She tried to crawl toward me and grabbed my feet. I'd never seen anyone behave like that. I didn't have the heart to kick her off me, but this was weird. Myself, I'd rather have just died than act like that before almost certainly dying.

I told her I'd kill her if she didn't get off me and stand up. Hah. My little joke, I guess. *Of course... Kill you anyway,* I should have added. She did get off me and stand up, but she wouldn't shut up. *He made us do it,* she kept saying. If the "he" she meant was the man I'd just taken out, he could no longer disagree. Danny gave me that *Give me a break*-look.

*One phone call would have stopped him,* I snarled. *One phone call.* She could have been the ringleader for all we knew. We still didn't have the pecking order sorted out. It was then that I got the sense of something looking at me from the mantle behind and beside her. I spotted a fragile-looking device made of painted earthenware, as odd and out of place as the stone-tipped stickers. Like a combination of a mask and a headband, it could have fit over someone's face and brows. Whoever wore it could have peered through its goggle-eyes, spoken through its adder-fanged mouth, and been crowned by its city-skyline corona. It reminded me hauntingly of images of a pan-Mesoamerican deity I'd seen somewhere, maybe in a museum or a book, maybe on a tour. For some reason I remembered that this figure was associated with wind, rain, and sacrifice, and said to be specially pleased by the tears of children, the more the better. I had no doubt what would have been coming here. It was worse than a simple death.

I made a pass with the Beam. The woman gasped and dropped.

I turned to the mantle, looked right into the hollow eyes of that mask-like thing as if daring the spirit behind it to come out and face me, and came down on it with my energized right, the Gleam, exploding it into fragments like a cup fired against a wall.

3

We stood outside the ill-fated cabin debating what to do. We were both scared. We had to get out of there, but if there were any more people around like the ones we'd just done for, the whole thing might just start up again the minute we left.

A cell phone call came in from Danny's father, one of the most respected Mohawk Elders in the Northeast. The senior Montour was letting us know that a friend was about to call the troopers to send them to our location. He would report having heard suspicious noises in the cabin behind us while off-roading that afternoon and thinking that it could have something to do with the missing children. Before okaying the call, Ed Montour wanted to make sure we had our work done and were clear of the place.

We asked him to give us half an hour. It could take us every bit of that to get back to my fairly new and trouble-free SUV, all-wheel it down the dirt road, and reach one of the busier thoroughfares.

We felt safe leaving the kids under their weighted playpen. The way the whole countryside seemed to be mobilizing, it might be only minutes before help burst in. Even as we came to the nearest busy road, Route 8, I saw the first trooper going back our way, lights flashing. In these parts they're used to way-out winter rescues. This summer one would come upon three little kids with wild stories and three old hippies dead, as far as anyone could tell, of simultaneous heart attacks. Ah, life does have its coincidences…

We did pass the body of the bogie we had sent to its rest. It was already so much decomposed that the bushes onto which it had lapsed were starting to spring back. The Trolls all do that when somebody takes them down. It really does make me wonder if somewhere there might be a sort of genetic lab that cooks these deadly things up out of DNA or natural parts, sends them wherever they're wanted with a *Star Trek* transporter, then fades them back when they're no longer needed – or operable. That way there's nothing to give the game away, which would be one reason the blasties appear in folklore and not in zoos. I've asked for an explanation of that many a time of the most seasoned people I know and I've never had an answer that suited me. Maybe somebody knows, but nobody tells.

All I can tell you about where we were is that we were west of the I-87 and north of the New York Thruway. The forty-minute foray to the Interstate was visually one of the most sublime drives of my life. I kept looking for likenings for the dusk's steady course through the craggy tree-line. I finally settled on the impression of an inky mane under the stroke of a fiery comb. That was just an intellectual exercise, though. The poetry of the experience was wasted on me.

That morning I'd been mountain biking in northern Vermont. I was planning to break up my drive home, swoop in on the annual conference of Native Elders in the midstate, catch a few talks, hang out with the speakers, and maybe even crash on a cot. I was expecting a peacefest. Instead I got sent with Danny on a vigilante hit that had to be ASAP.

I've had my share of clashes. So has Danny. The recent one had left us sickened and depressed. How many missing children had ended up at the place we had just left? I think for the first time the realization of what could be lying hidden in the countryside came over both of us. If a killer-cult could escape us – me, Danny, the College, the Native Elders – for so long in our home region, what did we know about anything?

As if he felt my despair, Danny was quiet for the first half hour, folding within himself. He looked as put out as if he felt betrayed by someone or something, and I was hoping it wasn't anything I did. He came out of his funk as the 45-mile-per-hour two-lane dipped us into a hollow. "Pull over here," he said.

"What!" I said. "Now?"

I looked over to see how serious he was and found Danny fumbling through his daypack on the floorboard between his legs. I slowed us down, looking about for cars, people, or houses. I stopped at the bottom of the hollow and pulled halfway onto the narrow shoulder. The midnight-teal was all around us. Overhead was a narrow channel open to the sky through which I could see gleaming bellies on some of the clouds.

Danny came up with a little cloth bag that looked like it was heavy for its size, plus an old-fashioned wooden Y-slingshot with those thick rubber bands holding the leather pocket. "Pop the sunroof," he said. "I've got to do something."

"What?" I said. "Here?"

"I think the Little People are out," he said. "Can you feel them?"

I couldn't, and I don't know for sure they exist. I don't cast spells, and I don't peer into other realms. I see no gods, spirits, angels, or Heaven. But I've known Danny most of his life – don't forget he was 25 that night in 1993 – and I respected him enough to process what he'd been talking about.

Most people who ever think about the Little People – fairies, in short – have the impression that they are nothing other than aspects of mythology, and of Celtic and Germanic societies. Most people would be shocked to know how strong Little People traditions are with many Native Americans. For Iroquoian/Longhouse People like Danny's Mohawk, the Little People are nature-beings who form attachments to sites and sometimes human families.

Danny had been one of the Native children who could see the Little People, at least when he was little. He used to play with them, too, they say, though he can't remember it now. His family always had to yell for him to come in when it was bedtime. There was a lot of woods around the family spread in Stillwater, but people never worried about him when he was out because the Little People were looking after him. His grandfather the healer Wes Brant was said to have had a lifelong friend among the Little People. He crossed over when Danny was two, but everyone presumed his friend might have shifted his protection to Danny.

What's certain is that the Little People are as sacred as deities to some Native Americans. With the Longhouse Nations they're rumored to love haunting dawns and luscious twilights. They gravitate to sublime spots in the landscape, including tiny waterfalls like the one I could just see twenty feet off the road. They also love shiny, translucent things like crystals, and some mystical Native Americans like to pay tribute to them when the opportunity presents. What Danny had was a bag of marbles.

He half-stood through the open sunroof, perching his hips against the neck rest of his seat and firing a few loads of marbles, three to four at a time, in high arcs over the little waterfall. I could hear a couple of them drop through the distant foliage like the first beads of a sudden heavy rain. It didn't seem like it would do any harm, but... Didn't Danny have any sense of what kind of moment this was? We had just killed three people at the home base of a potential murder-cult! The whole county was on the lookout for anything goofy, and we were stopped on a state highway shooting marbles into the woods! I chuckled to myself, in spite of my apprehension. Native people often have a sense of bliss about some things that bother white guys, even wizards.

During the rest of the drive to the I-87 we debated heading back to central Vermont and the annual conference of Native Elders at which I'd picked Danny up. The events were basically over, but the thought of being around peaceful people and having a debriefing with the Elders was tempting. The blubbering of that last witch still echoed in my ears. I think I just needed to hear someone say that I had done right. We were also tired, and our homes were the same distance south. We ducked the bridge over the Interstate and hopped onto the southbound ramp.

A wicked shower started up a minute after we hit the route they call the Northway. The deluge lasted only a few minutes, but the road stayed slick and treacherous. The lights of the vehicles set up a starry glitter on the hoods and puddles, and still people sped. I had the best bad-weather car on the road and even I dropped into the right lane. Danny went quiet again and I thought he'd nodded off. I had the chance for a few more reflections.

In the College we nickname a murderous ritual-with-a-goal, basically sacrifice, as "blood work" or even "a blood drive." It was big in the pre-industrial world, and Sir James Frazer (*The Golden Bough*) did a pretty good job of explaining why. Today's Collegians know what a dead end the practice is. I think just about all the people who do it these days are Muggles, working in the mistaken belief that they're doing magic. The more extreme the offering, the better the chance of the spell working, or at least that's how they think. Their goals are usually selfish: healing, money, love, or just being baaaad. It could be argued that they might be channeling *Source* when things go right, but there's no way you can justify that as working with it, and most of the time all they do is play a grisly game of make-believe with wretched offenses against innocent people. It's a dirty little secret that even today cults like these account for quite a few of the human disappearances. Muggle law enforcement knows all about it.

This Adirondack posse was clever enough to be unpredictable – or else there were several. I never went hunting for them because I'd never had a lead on them. Muggle law enforcement does a way better job of tracking them than I could, anyway, and it would have no trouble handling people who weren't College. If the crew's usual fare was hikers, hermits, and hobos – people who are missing but not immediately missed – nipping a couple kids was a major escalation, sure to rouse the whole Northeast.

How the Medicine People had divined the situation, I can't tell you. Maybe it was, like the old *Star Wars* motif, by detecting "a disruption in The Force." Maybe they heard the same Amber Alert I'd heard that afternoon and then sent out their feelers. How they could figure out so much about where the children were kept, that's still a mystery. Without so many august Elders in one place at the right time, it still probably wouldn't have been that way. They were from all over the Americas.

I reflected back on that meeting in an office off the hall of the campground. At the moment of my arrival the tall, lean, photogenic Danny was in deep conversation with most of the speakers, and he motioned me in when he spotted me through the half-open door. I would describe the scene better for you if I had a better mental picture, but I was too shocked from what I was hearing, and it was all wrapped up within minutes. I knew one of the men present: "Hawkie" Jacobs, one of the upstate Elders, a middle-aged Onondaga with the swooping tattoo of a bird splashed over his cheeks and one eye. I remember another sixty-something who looked vaguely famous. They said he was a Cherokee from the Southwest, but they introduced him with a white-guy name, and he looked like he had plenty of white in him. Tall for a Native, he was in jeans and a beat up leather cowboy hat, a long grey pony tail sprouting from under it. One Elder I couldn't forget was a deformed little guy with a long black mane who was supposed to be a Mayan from the Yucatan. He was wearing a multicolored shawl sort of like a poncho, and one of his arms was shriveled and atrophied. He talked through an interpreter who talked to someone else in Spanish, and thus his words were related into English. I think it was that Mayan all along who had sprung the deal. Danny told me that he was one of the most powerful shamans any of them had ever met.

In the big picture, the Elders were convinced that we had an opportunity that would not soon come again. They knew the region in which the ceremony was to be, but they wouldn't know the site any closer than twenty miles until the rite started getting energetic, so they had to have their own people nearby. That was me and Danny. That was why we had to go at once. Indeed, we didn't get the call with any more precise directions till we were twenty minutes from the site, which made it a real emergency.

Ten miles from our exit traffic was strangely heavy. What was every-body going to or from? Was Phish doing a late show at SPAC?

Something low and glowing-eyed tried to scurry across the three lanes and I didn't have time to miss it. Pinned into the middle lane, I couldn't have budged, anyway. The tire right under me hit it. I grieved for the little creature, whatever it was. The sickening thwack of its walnut skull beneath my wheel made me fear that it wasn't killed quickly and could be still limply struggling, waiting for a death-stroke under what to it could have seemed a hallucinogenic array of careening meteors. I could see Danny beside me make a little motion of prayer, nodding his head into his half-clenched hand. I breathed a blessing, too, on the creature's inco-herent soul, with the prayer that it might come back to a joyful life in a more fortunate form.

I felt like decompressing without the obligation of making my own dinner. I also felt like unwinding with company. I invited Danny to join me at a restaurant-pub in town where I knew we could get a healthy lay-out. He'd been telling me how hungry he was but preferred to get home and settle in. I dropped him off at his Stillwater digs and took the back roads to Saratoga village. I expected him to tell his dad everything and go straight to sleep – or else burn some sage and tobacco, call in a few of the family's Native friends, and hold a ritual of praying late into the night.

# Chapter 2

# *Who Knew That Was Starting a War?*

1

I know many of the restaurant people on Broadway Avenue because of my endeavors running my little ghost walks company. They're all used to me coming in after tours, chilled, windblown, and hag-ridden, settling in behind a book, a journal, a sketchpad, or a laptop.

Hoping to put the trauma out of my mind for the rest of the evening, I took to the bar of one of my favorite places, made my order, and hauled out my notepad. I'd picked up a couple new stories from the region and wanted to go over the cryptic notes I'd made while the interviews were fresh. I was also rereading Dion Fortune's *Psychic Self-Defense* for the tenth time.

In Saratoga Springs the pubs and restaurants like their bars on the north side, at least on Broadway. The names, owners, and ornamentation will change over the years, some chronically, but that bar will stay where it is. The one before me was so imposing that I felt like I was seated before a pipe organ in a grand cathedral or a bookshelf in the Oxford library.

At this place the pub feels pretty much like a space of its own. It's secluded from the dining area to the south by a bank of pew-like booths and low-hanging light fixtures. Most of the servers go through the kitchen to get from one to the other. I sensed a few tables still in use, but it seemed a slow night for a Saturday on the threshold of race-season.

The handful of people around me were after-hours restaurant staff, unwinding like I was and closing out the night with a drink. You could tell them by their black shirts, green aprons, and khaki skirts or slacks. The only other person not obviously a server was a large, pale, puffy young man standing at the bar a dozen feet to my right. I thought he might be one of the back-room staff, a busser or dishwasher. He was in the dumpster-dive clothing of an urban rapper: shorts, sneakers, and a light hoodie with the sleeves cut short. This was surprisingly light dress. The evening had taken on a chill. Most of the restaurant people had their sleeves down, and some were in sweaters.

My attempt at anything but sipping and gazing about was a tough go. I had a lot to struggle with. I had just killed three people. I could hardly think about anything else.

I may be an enforcer – a Linebacker, we call them – and we see that I can be an avenger, but I'm no assassin, and sure as Hell no executioner, and I don't like thinking of myself that way.

I've been in many a fight. I have killed – plenty – almost always in fights, basically kill-or-be-killed situations that I was fortunate enough to win, ones that come on so quick that I can hardly think before I act. My opponents almost always initiate the clash. They are perfectly prepared, and they are not always simply human. Some of them have lived many lifetimes already. And still I've never liked it. I can't ever kill without a feeling of guilt.

What do you call a killing without the seal of the law behind it? There may be a couple terms people would use. At least one of them would be *murder*. Some of us talk so tough about what the bad people deserve. When they're right in front of you and it's your finger on the trigger, it's not so easy. Killing someone, no matter how much they deserved it, is mighty serious business when you have time to think about it. It's actually horrible. And, with those people… I couldn't get the screaming out of my ears. The only way I could find any peace within myself that night was to realize that I had been sent by Native Elders, whom I trusted. I believed I had acted with *Source*. And still I questioned myself. Could there have been another way?

With that guilt, too, there's the lingering dread in this highly technical age about getting detected and accused. Even a wizard needs to worry about that. There isn't a jail that could hold me, but would you you want to be on the run your entire life? I calmed myself a bit on that score.

Even if someone could finger me or Danny near the site, no one could prove that I could have killed anyone with the Beam. No poison, no blood, no skin markings… They wouldn't even believe in the existence of something like a Beam unless I cared to show them.

And who were those people Danny and I had settled? Could they have been more than I thought? Whoever had dialed up that Troll had some clout. And what was that mask-like thing they had? I had smashed it so soon after spotting it that I had given myself no clues about it.

I reminded myself again that the night, July 31, was Lughnasa, one of the four old Celtic power-eves, a high point of the year for anyone spiritually tuned, at least anyone of Western ancestry. The Elders had made that point to us before they had sent us out that afternoon. Lughnasa is sometimes stereotyped as a witches' sabbath, but that didn't say much about the authenticity of our victims. Anyone who's ever looked at a Llewellyn calendar could figure that out. It didn't say anything about their affiliations, either. Like the other Celtic fests, Lughnasa has long been conscripted by Wiccans and Neopagans for ceremonies, virtually none of which seem sinister to me in any way. But Lughnasa is an ideal night to pair the power of a rite with that of the cycles of the year and generations of tradition. Power's power, as they always say. Plug in when you can.

The petite blonde bartender swirled up with my veggie/pasta dish and took me out of my brooding. I had never seen her before, which made me think she was new. Tanned like an outdoor athlete, she had blue eyes and an angular, Saxon-or-Slavic-like nose. She looked like many a Skidmore student staying in town for the summer. The name *Kayley* was engraved on the plastic tag on the strap of her green apron. *Kayley*, I said to myself. *A good one for Lughnasa. Ceilidh* in Gaelic – said the same way – is a night of music, storytelling, and poetry.

The big stranger I had first noticed standing to my right took the stool before him and asked our server for "a smoke." She said she was not a smoker. Next he asked for water, which she supplied. He loomed over the glass, looking down at the marble countertop.

In the next half hour, at least eight servers appeared and reappeared at the bar, and I bet the stranger asked every one of them the question he had asked Kayley. I couldn't help spotting him out of my eye-corners. His voice was chalky, back in his throat, and surprisingly high. I tried not to listen to him, but everything he said stood out against the hum of other conversations.

He spoke like someone who might be borderline learning-disabled. Plus the Tourette's. Yes. Four-letter ones. Reflexively. Like drawing a breath. "Shit," he said shortly after taking a seat and noticing that no one noticed him. He looked around and followed it with a gusty, "Fuck," the way someone might say, "Wow," hoping to draw conversation. People can say all those things at the same volume in a conversation and nobody notices a thing. With him, they came out of nowhere, and they were penetrating. Off-tempo. That's probably why I remember so much so clearly.

There is something blurry about him otherwise in my memory, though. To this day I don't have a good impression of his features. He had short, lank, mousy brown hair, and everything about him was big and broad. Other than that, I couldn't pick him out of a lineup of other thick, pale, bespectacled men.

In a few minutes the two servers who had taken seats between us had gone with their checks into the kitchen. "How *you* doin'?" the man called with powdery enthusiasm. He had to mean me. I was the only one within twenty feet of him. I nodded back that I was OK.

"You got a smoke?" he asked.

I shrugged. "Not a smoker."

"OK," he said. Then he sat back and gusted forth another round of F- and S-bombs.

He leaned forward, elbows on the rests. "I have had a real *shit* day," he said, addressing the top of the bar before him. Then he looked to me.

"Sorry about that," I said with an avuncular smile.

Our server returned from a foray. "I have had a real *shit* day," the stranger said.

The gal asked something softly which had to have been, *What's the matter?*

"Coz I had to get set up with a shelter and food stamps," the man said sourly. "First you go there, then they tell you to wait, then they tell you to come back, then they make you wait again. Took the whole day."

The young lady left him to pour something for one of the other staffers. The fellow looked about again and asked how to get to the Price Chopper.

It seemed funny for him not to know how to reach the giant grocer a hundred yards below us on Broadway. It was the foundation of the same small plaza that held the social services offices at which he claimed to have spent too much of the day. It was lit up like a stadium at night, and someone could probably see the glare just by stepping outside. I pointed out the door, showed the guy which way to walk, and told him to look for the lights.

In five minutes two young lady servers came back to the bar, and he asked them the same question he'd asked me. They gave him the same answer in different terms. Both pointed straight out the front door and motioned to the left with their delicate tanned hands, one chucking a thumb and the other an index. He seemed to process it. Then he asked if either of them had a cigarette. Neither smoked.

He delivered another round of aimless bio-curses. He sat for minutes holding the wine, beer, and spirits list like a mask inches from his nose, watching Kayley all the while. I didn't like the way his eyes tracked her ass. Then he called to her. "Can I set up a tab?"

"Sure," she said, watching a pint fill. "What would you like?"

He laughed shortly, then said, "Well, that's a little hard to answer."

That caught my attention. I wouldn't have thought he had that in-nuendo in him. In ten minutes I made eye contact with Kayley and mo-tioned to her to step to my left, farther out of earshot of the blocky stranger. "Make sure you have somebody with you when you walk to your car," I said softly, nodding to my right.

"That's so nice!" she said. "I'm closing. I will make sure to."

In a few minutes the doughboy got Kayley's attention. "If I do get a tab, when do I have to pay up?"

"Well, tonight, if you're going to drink," she said with a little laugh. By then her off-duty colleagues, two women and an athletic-looking young man, were seated to the big fellow's right well clear of him. They watched everything.

"I got food stamps," said the fellow loudly as if it was a badge of power. Kayley said something softly that was doubtless, *You can't use them for drinks.*

"That's what I was afraid of," he said. "Fuck. Shit. Well, I guess I better get on back to the shelter. Shit. Fuck."

It seemed like only moments later that he addressed the still fans high overhead. "Ah, I need some lovin.' I need somebody to take me home. I need somebody to take care of me." The three off-duty servers looked anywhere but at him.

"Why don't you see your mother?" said Kayley softly. "Where's your mother?"

"She's *dead,*" he said so abruptly and stupidly that people drew breath and nearly laughed. I had to fight a chuckle of my own and was glad not to be nearer to him. He was a terrible actor.

I was shocked to notice how thick his frame was. His elbows were like most people's knees. His full-body coat of blubber made him absolutely voluminous. Otherwise, I'd seen waste cases like him before in Saratoga Springs. The tourist who sees only the surface of the village would be surprised at the share of them we get. Right off the Northway, Saratoga is one of the last outposts of urbanism between Albany and Burlington and a way station between New York and Montreal. People who wear out their options in the Big Apple can hop off the Amtrak or the bus line and end up on our less cluttered, two- and three story town. For city-dwellers, Saratoga probably does feel like the wild West. It has its intrigue, and it has danger, as does anywhere, but there's also opportunity. People aren't as suspicious as they would be in big cities. People feel like they can get away with things here because of it.

At 11:30 I settled up and made eye contact with Kayley, nodding toward the big man to my right. "Don't forget what I said."

"I'm not sure I can get anyone. I have to close, and just about every-body's out."

"I could look out till you reach your car."

"I'm leaving at midnight," she said, nodding behind her as if to the mid-block parking area just behind the storefronts on Broadway. "I'm in the really old Saab in the lot in back. Under the trees at the far end."

"I'll be watching," I said. I wasn't interested in the girl, but I am a protective being. I took a walk through the sublime little Congress Park like I was sightseeing and came from the south to the lot behind the restaurant a few minutes before midnight. I spotted the Saab and stood under tree-shadows sixty feet away. In a few minutes I saw a slender form emerge from the back of the restaurant and step quickly. A big, blocky form was following at twenty feet, hand out as if appealing for someone to stop and converse.

*Yep, the new girl,* I said to myself as she was nervously fitting in her key. New in this place, maybe new in this town. The perfect target. What is it with our species? Even the least of us senses it. And then, as the only person in the world that night to willingly talk to the man − it was her job − she made herself a focus.

"She still doesn't have a cigarette," I called with authority, sure it was going to take no more than that to back the clown off. I closed boldly and got between him and the girl's car. I sheltered her like an umbrella, waiting to hear the door open and close. The man stopped ten feet away and looked toward me curiously, lot lights glinting on his spectacles, like he was peering over me and studying the girl. I glanced back to check on her.

My world exploded into light and percussion. I felt like I was tumbling in a giant clothes dryer open at one end to a floodlight − either that or spinning in the funnel of a tornado and being battered by dozens of brilliant lanterns. I couldn't see, I couldn't hear, and I found it hard even to think. I nearly blacked out. In an instant I recalled myself. *Of course,* I thought in a flash. *A setup. All along. A Sunday-punch. The girl.*

Then came the blows: thundering, hammering, one after the other. I was being attacked by either a machine I have never heard of or a fellow member of the College, an Arts Major, even what we call a Linebacker, an enforcer, like me. I collapsed into something hard and metallic, likely the car I had taken for that of the waitress. I had the quick impression of one of those boxing robots, this one Hulk-sized, rocketing jabs; but these strokes were not punches. They were shivering, descending, rage-filled blows from something with forearms dense as tree branches. The first square shot from any one of them would break a neck or shatter a collarbone. I was alive because I must have reflexively pitched on my defensive Glow. Still, the blows were rattling me and tossing me inside my protective bubble.

Blinking and squinting, I fought for consciousness, redoubling the Glow, dodging and feinting within it, and taking as deep a breath as I could. It was hard seeing anything after being snow-blinded by something, evidently, the girl had done, but that one inhalation helped me gather myself. I wasn't feeling lucky to have been driven against the body of the car since it cut off my moves, but I see that I was. The roof and hood had taken much of the beating intended for me. I found my feet to an extent and got a sense of the direction from which the hammering was coming. I glimpsed a blocky, featureless, shadowy form over me raining log-like limbs.

*Perfect*, I said to myself like the warden in *Jurassic Park* saying, "Clever girl," when he realizes he's been jobbed by the second raptor. *Act like such a dope that nobody thinks there's another level to you. Make somebody else look like the target.* Then the girl – the one the real target thinks he's protecting – hits. Or somebody. Then out comes Kong.

In spite of the shellacking, my mind spun with instant possibilities. Maybe the girl was in the College, with at least one aggressive power – that psychic bang-flash – of her own. Or else she had just helped set the whole thing up for a third party lurking near the car. Maybe she really didn't know she was being used in a setup. I swear, my chivalrous nature is going to get me killed someday. Maybe the pair were a hit-team, reeling in their victims like they had me. I smiled against myself even as I ducked blows, envisioning a vaudeville act/co-ed wrestling tag-team with the stage name, "The Chick and the Chump." I hoped I would live long enough to tell someone. It all went through me in a flash. The girl, like the goon, had been more than she looked.

As sight returned to me, I studied my attacker. It was indeed the doughboy from the restaurant who had closed within two feet and was showering forearm-strikes that rocked me within my thin cocoon. His form hadn't changed. I doubted that his SAT scores had improved, either, in the meanwhile, but he, too, was way more than he had looked. He was surely a Collegian, and an Arts Major. His powers seemed, like mine, from within him – a dramatic amplification of the human psychokinetic faculty. The force of those blows was superhuman, and he was showing no signs of tiring. I wondered even as I rolled against the side of the Saab if I was fighting some famous Linebacker whose name may have been legendary even outside the College. He was that good. Any one of his blows would have dropped a moose. The car behind me was taking a beating. More than once I heard cracking glass.

Once I glimpsed his face as he reared back into a gleam from a street-light. The low-lidded eyes were as impassive as I had remembered behind his glinting glasses, but his teeth showed in determination, possibly even anger, at the lack of effect of his mightiest swings. I got the odd image of one of the old Moche pots depicting a warrior with club reared and a very similar expression, a rigor-mortis grin. That was one more reason not to die here, my mind streaked. I didn't want to leave this world with that face the last thing I saw.

Another deep breath cleared my mind. I finally fully dodged a blow by ducking under the level of the car hood. The stroke that missed me caved in the metal, and I got off a long slash of the Beam from my left in the general direction from which the blows were coming. It should have taken the legs out of a normal human being at the range I presumed the goon was standing. I'm sure he got a taste of it, because everything went still.

A form like a felled polar bear rolled on the macadam. *Now we get to have a little fun*, I thought, starting to be able to see. *Find out who you're working for.* Then I remembered Goldilocks and turned to see what she was up to. Another light-grenade went off, and I was back where I had been.

I don't know what I did, but I know what I would have done. I would have thrown the Glow all over myself and lashed out everywhere with the Beam like a fencer fighting multiple assailants in the dark. If anyone could have seen my Force, which I hear no one does, I'd have looked like a crazed Jedi dueling an invisible attacker from inside a light-tornado.

I don't know how many minutes later it was that I came to myself, recovering my wits and my sight, alone in a shadowy parking lot. I was leaning on a Saab that looked like a major league baseball team had gone at it for bashing practice. Maybe that's an understatement.

My first thought was to get away from the car lest someone think I was the vandal. It's funny how those high school instincts stay with you. My next thought was of Danny Montour.

I could only sense that this occult assassination attempt had to have been the response to our actions earlier in the evening. Even as I punched in Danny's number, I worried. Had they already gotten to him? I was trying to remember where I had parked my car in case I had to dash to it.

To my immense relief, he answered. He was having a peaceful night. A couple Medicine People had come to the family farm in Stillwater. They were passing the pipe with the Montours and talking over what had happened. I related my experience quickly and told him to watch out. It seemed like he had enough power-people around him to be safe for the night.

Maybe that was the plan: Take me out, then go for Danny. If they get him first, they know I'll be on the hunt – with advance warning and bloody intent. If they get me by surprise before anybody knows what's up… Well, he's the easier target for people in the College. Despite his personal toughness, he's not an Arts major. He's a trainee. A Special Student.

48

I'd been hit like that, out of the blue before. I'd never been blindsided like that when I wasn't involved in the transport or the negotiation for an object up for sale. It had to have something to do with the witches.

I had thought of those people as a cult of wannabes, Muggles, Junkies, hoping to stamp their diplomas to the College. They were also sicko-psychos. How could you do anything like they had done and were preparing to do again if you didn't half-want to anyway? If they'd been College they'd have known that wouldn't get them anything but used.

But there was an X-factor to be considered: that Troll. Somebody sent it. And it takes guts – forget the depravity involved – to run off with somebody's kids for any purpose. The whole society, including people like me and Danny, will be after you. But had these people even been the kidnappers? They didn't look real spry to me. How had they gotten the kids here? How did they get them in the first place? How many other people like them were out there?

Who thought a hit on a couple loser witches would stir all that up? *Who knew that was starting a war?*

I knew someone I had to call.

# Chapter 3

# The Invisible College

1

You have to be wondering to yourself by now, *What would an occult war be about?* What would  set the unseen wizards fighting?

I have to take a little time-out and explain away a few of your stereotypes about this occult community, the one we call "the College." Surely you have them. Some of you are surely still thinking in terms of good witches and bad ones along the entertainment model. Some are working selfishly and Satanically, and some are working for the good of life and Nature. Right?

You probably think there might be a Tolkienesque/Harry Potter-like echelon of "good" and "bad" witches. Returning Dark Lords and the like. Probably even H. P. Lovecraft's echelons of Elder Gods and "Great Old Ones" come to mind as string-pullers fighting proxy wars. I see why. All your impressions about magicians come from entertainment sources: books, movies, TV. For reasons I'll give you later, this predilection for oppositional contrast – this need to see things as good guys versus bad guys – is almost surely a legacy of  our Western mind. I wish it could be that way in reality. Simple. You'd always know which side you were on.

Maybe there really is such a Zoroastrian arrangement behind the big picture of it all, but it's simply not evident to me. No, the thing that brings all of us together in the College, as we call it, is commerce, in essence, *money*. Good old green. Yes, commerce drives almost all our interchanges – and our all-too-frequent feuds.

When I'm talking about this bottom-line system, I mean it only to include the members of our College who generally live in and hail from the developed countries of the American and Eurasian landmasses. There are surely occult power-people who live on their own and get by in their own ways. There isn't any guessing their numbers. They don't get involved in College business or its intrigues.

The societies of Elders of many of the world's preindustrial traditions seem to me to have other motives, too. In the old days they were on the lookout for their societies, possibly down to the tribe or village. In our age these indigenous Elders seem to be done fighting culture-wars. They seem to me to be on the lookout more for the whole planet, and on behalf of animal life and the natural world. A lot of them don't take the life the channeling of *Source* might give them. Yes. They hit about 80 and decide they've had their day and just check out in the name of a higher vision. These indigenous Elders aren't as united as I wish they could be sometimes, but collectively they match up pretty well against any power I know of on earth, at least anything metaphysical.

But for us, in the College… We don't come out of a single united cultural tradition based on spiritual wisdom and religion. For us, the unifying purpose is plain and utter commerce. Possession. Turf. Money. Control. The commodities of power, which is to say, *choices*.

That's all money is: choices. Oh, money may have a physical presence. Cash. Coins. But money, you see, is an abstract. I know you all have pieces of paper sometimes that we call money. But in a general sense, what you have in a 401K or the stock market is also considered money by a lot of people. I bet George Soros or Hillary Clinton never even carry cash. But they have a lot of money. They just use cards or digits for it.

You can't eat, wear, or bed dollar bills. Not even twenties. You can use them to buy things you can eat or wear. If you have the status that wealth usually brings, you will probably not have trouble finding someone willing to go to bed with you. You can even pay for it. Choices.

If you have no money, you cannot choose to go to a fine restaurant. Drive a fine car. Live in a fine house. Join a country club. That's how it looks to me. Choices. But when it comes to the occult community of power-people we call "the College," you are probably baffled by this. Why would basically "money" rule interchanges between wizards? Well, two reasons.

One is that, other than a personal passion like love, anger, jealousy, or self-protection, commodity is the number one motive of human behavior, at least collective behavior. That's my observation, anyway. That's what just about every large-scale human conflict that has ever taken place has been about: basically, money, or whatever represents it in that day and that part of the world.

People tell you that there have been wars about religion, hatred, race... Hah. It's the commodities of possession: power, land, gold, the throne... Stuff that represents the choices that money brings.

Oh, wars are always in the name of something. It's like political campaigns or NFL locker-rooms the week before the Super Bowl. Anything to whip up the troops. Sports teams are always playing the "respect" card, trying to make themselves feel like underdogs because that's a very comfortable position for competing. Warriors – like footballers – are seldom philosophers.

People are always looking for an ideology, a rallying cry, an ethos that justifies what they want to do all along. If they don't have one handy, they'll make one up. Don't fall for the slogans. If those didn't work, they'd find other slogans, and in the end they'd do the same thing. But that's just the window-dressing. The stronger culture – usually the higher-tech, more urbanized society – always does what it wants. What it tends to want is to *have. More.*

I can think of only one war in history that may have truly been fought over religion: the Crusades. And even that's arguable. It's still debated if the call of Pope Urban II was the major factor in mobilizing thousands of disenfranchised – by *primogeniture,* "first son getting everything" – young knights of Europe. They had nothing to do and no prospects. They had motivation to keep what they could take in a 'justified' war.

That's history. It's money. Territory. Power. Possession. Trade.

The Conquistadors were after gold. The Wars of the Roses were over the throne. The French and Indian wars were over the fur trade. The Japanese attack on Pearl Harbor was over an oil embargo. (Duh. An island nation can't exist without trade. You cut them off, you're going to get a lash-back. Same with England anytime anyone tries it.)

The other reason that basically money runs our turf wars is because we all have to preserve undetectable wealth, often for generations. A lot of us are paranoid about running out of money. Most of us, at least the older Collegians, know we don't understand the economic system of the day we're in. Like old hippies dreading the internet, we really don't think we could make money any more.

2

Our College has a jaunty slang. Most of it's based on the motif of the American university, and, like slang everywhere, it's not totally consistent. Things would get really confusing for you if I broke you in on all of it right now. But the theme of the college permeates our slang to the extent that I can't keep up with it. I keep laughing with memories of fifty-year-old jokes and scenes I couldn't explain to you unless you really get this.

One thing that might help you with the general motif of our College is to keep the image of "the college" – preppy and liberal arts – on a hill firmly in mind, at least if you can think of the hill metaphorically. Cornell will do. A year or two after my own entrance into our College I did a semester there as a special student, so I think I can comment. The city of Ithaca rings it below.

The college kids may not all be privileged at home, but when they're in this community they belong to a privileged culture, one that has its own unique understandings. The faculty and administrative personnel of the college may travel for other academic responsibilities, but they have anchors, like homes or fine apartments. They all come down from the hill when they want something and move quite freely in the general society, but then they go back uphill.

The college on the hill has its own version of grunts: maintenance people, dining hall workers, etc. There may also be hanger-ons, people who are not of the college community but who might like to associate with it. There are never a lot of these, and they may be weirdos, but they do exist. Maybe they're interested in forming relationships with some of the students or professors. Maybe they think some of them are hot and all of them are cool. There's no law against them coming to the libraries or the student cafes, at least until they start trouble. It usually doesn't get them anywhere. None of them really get the college, no matter how much time they spend with it. They'd have to be of it.

Now, take the citizens of the community at the foot of the hill. When I was in school the students called them "townies." No matter how often the students and teachers come into town, not many of the townies get to know them too well or have any great idea what they think or do. Their academic experiences and often highly specialized concerns are so far removed from the lives and speculations of the townspeople that it would be difficult for them to talk to each other.

There is a real gap there. So. You get the picture. At least it was that way when I was at Cornell.

Think of our College like that.

The wizards in our motif represent both the students and faculty of the College. The people who run things, usually the really old ones, we often call Alumni or even Trustees.

Non-wizards are the Townies in this motif. We also call them *Muggles*. Yes, we make endless Harry Potter jokes. Yes, we watch TV, go to movies, and read books. Some of us may do them all more than most people because our occupations generally don't take up that much of our daily time. Mine for sure doesn't.

3

I should tell you that our College is only one aspect of the world's power-people. You need to know how it operates.

Our College is a loose association of once-natural people who live mostly in the United States and Western Europe, including the Mediterranean and Scandinavia. We occasionally hang out together, mostly based on experiences of working together. We've had this association for centuries, at least. I've only been around the College for fifty years or so, and I don't know all the Collegians. I go to parties and gatherings – "Mixers" – and at every one I spot people I don't know, even in my home region. It's kind of exciting that way. But our ties are basically economic and social. We get to know people by working with them, and then we hang out and meet their friends and colleagues. But that's not the whole picture.

Our occult world-within-your-world – this whole society you know nothing about – has basically four components: Information People, Knowledge People, Muscle People, and Spirit People. Yes, information and knowledge are very different things. We have our nicknames for them all, mostly based on the College-motif.

I should tell you about the Spirit People first. They are the outliers. We nickname them, "Religion Majors." A part of me thinks I should not confuse you by even mentioning the Spirit People here because they are not really of our College. They are the one group you have heard of, though, if you have any exposure to literature or other entertainment.

You might stereotype all wizards as "spirit-people," but you should hang out with them. You'll see that many of them are remarkably average, just isolated from the mainstream by the possession of some unique talents, as well as quite a few secrets. The world looks different to them than it does to you, but it's not as if it really affects them all internally. I myself have an introspective streak, but I'm nobody's mystic. I don't belong guiding anyone else to reach their higher level. You'll see that as this book develops.

The spiritual keepers of every world tradition are what I mean by Spirit People. The world's indigenous elders, the original Shamans, the Christian mystics, the Sufis, some notable Rabbis and cabalists, the Buddhist monks... I can't mention them all. Every preindustrial world tradition I've ever heard of has them. They are like us Collegians in many ways, but not of us. The best of them are as good as anybody.

The goals of the Spirit People are not personal, like ours in the College – which I've told you tend to be pretty material. In the old days the goals of the Spirit People were mostly societal. These days their concerns are usually species-wide, if not on behalf of all natural life, the good of the earth, and the balance of our part of the Universe. They're not involved in the commerce and the interaction that makes our College run. I'd expect some of them to look down on us Collegians for a lot of reasons.

A lot of these indigenous Spirit People are so powerful that they could live until something kills them, but many of them are so noble that they choose only one life. The Tibetans and the ascended Hindu masters and many African and Native American Elders are like this. They just go when their time feels like it ought to be up. They go when they feel like they've had all the life they personally deserve. They go when they feel like every breath they take is one someone else doesn't get to draw. It's as if they don't gain the power they have without transcendence. That transcendence makes their goals unselfish.

Very few individuals trained in those ancient, very noble traditions ever enter the business climate of our College. If they do, they come in as freelancers, and even outcasts. When they spring to us, they bring the knowledge and talents from their old disciplines with them, at least what they've learned of them to that point, but they usually leave their societies all the way behind. Some doors close when you walk into ours. And very few of them are true masters. They split that outfit because things weren't working for them the way they wanted. What do I say? We're all human.

Some of the true Spirit People will enter these pages, but most are far from the daily life and transactions of the College. We bump elbows with them. Once in a while one of them turns up at a party. Sometimes somebody has to go run and ask one of them something. Some of us are friends with them. I hang out with some of the Native Elders of the Northeast. Most of the ones I know are Mohawk or Algonquin. They have their flaws, like all of us, but the ones I know, once they find themselves, are truly transcendent beings.

We come to the Information People. This is where our world, our College, really starts. These Information People are basically brokers and auctioneers. We have our nicknames for them. Most of the time we call them *Suits, Trustees, Administration, Alumni,* or, since they do so much with commerce, *Financial Aid Officers* (*FAOs*). The Information-people do the record-keeping and price-setting that keeps our world running. They aren't often as personally gifted as people like me, or at least they hide it if they are. They don't all have ESP-gifts, either. They can tell you things because they read them or wrote them down or see them. They get things done because they are real good coordinators. They keep track of valuable items. They make arrangements between buyers and sellers. They rely on a lot of other people, and everything relies on them. Without these people we'd have very little organization or communication among us. We'd all be on our own. Some of the Suits seem to develop very long lives. Maybe it's because they handle a lot of power-items ("diplomas"). Maybe some of them are more special than they advertise.

The Knowledge People tend to be those (*Duh!*) who know things. They fall into a couple categories. Some of them can make things happen because they know how to use rites and tools, but this isn't really a feature they're born with. They need a little time and preparation to do their operations, too, but some of them get to be very powerful in our world. *Source* flows through many of them. They're just as likely to get the long lives as anyone else in our world. I wish I knew for sure what that's all about. Maybe it's because they channel *Source* through their items and rituals. I'll talk more about this later.

My fourth category is the Muscle People. I won't use that term much more in this book. They embody the power – *Source*. They enter the College only accidentally and not through a program of devoted study, though their abilities usually develop significantly if they last long enough or if someone takes an interest in them. They don't often use any physical muscle to get their work done, and they aren't all geniuses. They aren't all even normally-developed adults. They are psychic freaks who have innate psycho-physical abilities that would look to most people like magical talents. As for who inherits these propensities, it just seems like one of life's tossups. Maybe we all have some, and some of us have more.

This is the category I occupy. Like dancers or painters or writers or athletes, people like me execute. We start with natural talent and hone it through guidance and practice. It's not just knowledge we shouldn't be able to have. It's a force, and we channel it through us. It comes out quirkily, in special, unique abilities. When we work in the College's activities as basic enforcers, peopl;e use a lot of nicknames for us, like *Jocks*, *PE Majors* (Phys Ed), *Frat*, or *Greeks*, all based on stereotypes from the American college motif. Most often they call us *Linebackers*.

I'm a Linebacker. I have psychic abilities of the physical variety. I'm dangerous. When the other side sends their Linebackers into a situation, I'm one of the guys we call up. Every one of the Admins, the FAOs, the brokers, the Suits, has a couple of Linebackers he or she can call in.

The last three categories above, all but the Religion Majors, facilitate the commerce. It would work like this.

Somebody in the College or out of it – we do business with some VIP Townies – has decided to buy or sell something, almost always for a very high price. Usually it's a hot item, something the world thinks it's lost or never really believed it had. Somebody expressed interest in buying it, maybe a long time ago. Once it shakes loose, it goes on the market. The Information People – the Suits, the Administration, the Trustees, the FAOs – have to get word out, even tracking down prospective buyers.

But the world has a lot of deception. Ours is no different. Somebody – one of the Knowledge People – needs to make sure the item is what it's advertised to be. This is a vital and complex process. Our College has a whole range of people who specialize in validating ancient items out of context. Most of them have gifts that the world would call psychic. The Knowledge People we use for the high profile items have to have impeccable reputations.

Then the Suit/Trustee needs to figure out a fair price for the item in whatever era the process commences and start the long-range bidding. Once the deal is made, he or she has to handle the transfer of the gold, money, jewels, or whatever is used as payment.

Finally, somebody else, usually the Linebacker, needs to babysit the item in transit from seller to buyer so nobody thinks about nipping it. When a Linebacker works like this, we often call them "Campus Tour Guides" or even "TG's." This Linebacker needs to be somebody nobody wants to mess with. I may not look like it, but that's me.

4

As long as people have been around, there has been an economy. In exchange for things or services people want to have, they are willing to give other people things or services they are willing to do without. That's called barter when it's just things. They've always traded services for material goods or currency. This is basically what a job is. Economies might even predate human beings.

I heard about an experiment with a captive community of chimps that the researchers were trying to teach about money. It seemed a little abstract to start with the stock exchange, so the experimenters used bananas. The chimps learned that if they did certain things to a machine in their cage, it delivered them a banana. They could accumulate stockpiles. Before long the researchers noticed that the male chimps were doing most of the work with the machine, but the females were piling up bananas. After exhaustive observation, the picture came clear. The females were holding out on the males for sex. The males had to pay for their action with bananas. I laughed when I heard about that. They don't call it the oldest profession for nothing.

But bananas would be the most perishable form of wealth imaginable, and that was a little too above-ground to be the best example. In the College, it's almost the opposite. We have to preserve wealth secretly, and across generations. Some of our Collegians live *very* long lives, and some of them never think they have enough. We need an underground economy, particularly in hard and physical objects – things that can survive the centuries, things that will always be worth something, things that can easily be hoarded. The situation calls for exceptional measures.

For longer than I have been alive people have been coming to brokers in this underground world I call the College and asking them to find or sell for them a certain something. In the old days, people who approached Collegians were more commonly buyers of services: generals hoping to win battles, aristocrats hoping to gain the throne, lonely people looking for lovers, or sick people wanting to be healed. That figures. The world believed in this stuff more.

Now it's almost always the buyers of items, and most of them are in the College, or else among the true elites of the Townies/Muggles. For that you need brokers. Deal-makers. Specialists in all parts of the process. All of us need people keeping track of things, I guess, including buyers and sellers. As I told you, we have our nicknames for the brokers, mostly based on our running though quite flexible "College" motif. They arrange the deals. These are the Information people I introduced earlier.

A good broker/FAO is a good auctioneer, almost always at a distance. A broker has a commission coming, so he or she has an interest in a high price. The broker also has a debt to the buyer, though, to advise on a fair price. Nobody does business with you if they think they're going to get screwed every time. There are always other brokers.

A good broker/FAO is also a good record-keeper. A broker has files on the whereabouts of known power-objects, which he/she maintains across centuries and updates consistently whenever there is a change. The broker keeps a list of contacts who have expressed interest in certain items. When any sought-after object is found... or shakes loose, maybe with a little help... The broker starts making calls. It could take decades, if not more, to get the deal made, and I'm sure the financial arrangements adjust with the times. I'm also sure that some of the bidders are no longer alive when the object "graduates," as we say in the college motif, and the next in line comes in.

A lot of broker/FAO-types aren't even power people in our College; they're just people like many of our buyers. They have normal physical and sensory abilities and natural life-spans. They are simply "in the know." Information is its own kind of power. They pass on this information in clans and families, at least if they aren't power-people themselves. Some families have been brokers for generations, which is realistically the only way it could work in our sort of a world. The Arts

Majors/Linebackers look out for these families. They become utterly trusted friends if not virtual family members.

I work exclusively for a single broker. He's the smartest and most capable person I have ever met. He keeps records of interested parties, validates items, establishes a decent price, arranges for the sale and transport, takes his cut, and pays people theirs. There's often competitive bidding, and he runs that like an auctioneer – at a distance, and across lots of time, I suspect. This is a long game we play.

5

An Invisible College needs an invisible economy. You must be wondering about the type of items in this high-stakes occult black market.

Off the top, most of them are obscure. You would never have heard of almost any of them unless you're a lit buff or a history nerd. They're ideal for this type of market. The Muggle/Townie world never misses what it doesn't know exists. It doesn't recognize it, either, which is handy if you happen to get busted when you're carrying one of those items.

Some are not really artifacts. They are precious because of their material. Gold, jewels, that sort of thing. Most of the Mesoamerican and Andean gold the Spaniards took had been made into exquisite artifacts that were melted down into ingots to be transported. Minerals and some metals are virtually impervious to the effects of time, and they seem only to go up in value. There are always takers for that sort of a deal. You sell a chunk of gold or a jewel when you need some cash. It's lasting, untraceable wealth.

Some of the items are significant historically but trinkets otherwise: Alexander(yes, *the Great*)'s flagon, or the head of Charlemagne's *francisca* (a sort of tribal/national throwing axe), special only because of their age and their owners. These have their own complications, which I'll dwell on soon.

Some are works of high art that mainstream museums would kill to have: urns, paintings, statues. Wars of which the world has had too many are wonderful opportunities to acquire these things. Everybody thinks they are lost or destroyed. Hah. We have bought and sold a lot of them. It's a ton harder these days to transport the big items, but we manage.

The Muggle world might have heard of some of the other things we deal with, but it considers them lost. Some of the fabulous items in world literature and legend fall into this category. Arks, Skulls, Grails, Tablets…

All these items represent a very good way to maintain wealth across the generations. If nobody knows it's there, no overzealous government will try to tax you on it or be perpetually wondering how you live 200 years with no overt source of income and manage to stay comfortable, if not luxurious. If nobody knows it's there, some band of activists won't try to liberate it on behalf of their precolonial ancestors. Especially since the end of the 20th century, nations and cultures have become zealous on behalf of their antiquities. If we had something of Charlemagne's, do you think France isn't going to want it back?

But other items are negligible for substance, legacy, or crafting. They could be stones, crystals, bones, or brutishly carved icons. Their real richness is metaphysical. I would love to know their history. Sometimes nobody knows. They're just powerful. They channel *Source*.

Socially, politically, commercially, or sometimes literally, things like these can be weapons. They're flash-drives of information – or loaded guns – for people who know how to use them. If you gain one of these things, you have become a lot more powerful yourself. These are the items we have to watch out for, at least in my line of work. These have their complications, too.

You've never heard of most of the artifacts in this last category. Some of them are so old that they may not even have names anymore. The cultures that made them are gone, and the languages in which they once were named are dead. I cannot think of a way to make you understand how powerful – metaphysically and ultimately physically – some of these objects you will never hear about can be. One of these might look pretty rude to you, but it could be a real weapon for the right Collegian.

But many others in this category are proverbial to anyone who's had a decent exposure to literature. Think of some of the legendary objects in world tradition: Excalibur, the Spear of Destiny, Aladdin's lamp, the Golden Books, the Philosopher's Stone, the Ark of the Covenant, the Crystal Skulls, Roland's Horn, the Emerald Tablet, the Holy Grail, or the Four Treasures of the Gaelic *Sidhe* (Shee).

Some are surely almost completely fictional, or distorted out of all recognition. If there ever was a material artifact at the root of some of these legends at their fullest development – like the original Excalibur (or *Caliburn*, "hot handle") – a look at what's left of it would disappoint you. They never did look like like what you would expect them to based on the movies, and the centuries would take a toll on them.

Other totems are no longer intact enough to be useful in any sense. Maybe they just need the right key to unlock them, and that's why they look powerless. But almost any of them famous enough for you to have heard of could be in existence somewhere. Legends build upon legends. Something is always at the root.

There are, of course, fakes, some of them overt. There are dozens of recently-made – within a century – Crystal Skulls, for instance, that have no relationship to the original Thirteen. The famous one, "Max," the Mitchell-Hedges skull, I think is the real deal. I don't think it's *the* Skull, the top dog, but it's one of the power-Thirteen. A couple others are surely in the possession of various Native American nations. I think the Iroquois Nations have one, and they're keeping it somewhere in up-state New York, and they aren't saying much about it. The rest are un-recovered.

There isn't just one alleged Spear of Destiny, either. That, of all of the fabulous famous, seems most likely to me to have been lost. Why would anybody bother to keep it? There would have been no reason for anyone to hang onto the spear – or is that, *Spear* – after Longinus ran Jesus through. Nobody knew how special He was supposed to be till the Councils of Nicaea and Ephesus settled on it centuries later. I doubt even Longinus would have remembered which spear it was. And it wasn't made to be powerful anyway; it was a standardized, mass-produced Roman legionary's weapon, either the *pilum* that the heavy infantry used for short-distance throwing or the *hasta*, the thrusting spear that the Romans used pre-Golden Age when they fought more like the Greek hoplites of Homer. I can't think of a logic by which that item, even the real one – or is that, *One* – would have any mojo.

Some of the legendary power-items of literature and occult tradition might not be material things. Very often something portrayed as an object is in fact likely to be a concept: a technique, a secret, or a code. I think the Philosopher's Stone and the Holy Grail and maybe the Emerald Tablet are very likely to be in that category, maybe even the Ark. If someone offered to sell me a Grail, I would "check the transcripts," as we say.

When you do get the chance to see one of the real power-items that is an artifact, it will never look much like what you expect. Ancient artifacts are often humble in appearance, and history has been hard on them. Jewels fall off. Paint fades. Etchings thin out. If the Mongols are closing in, the fine points of art preservation go by the wayside. You don't stop and scour your track for that lost filigree.

Also, when a power-item shakes loose – "graduates," or "is expelled," as we often say – the prospective dealers have to be wary. If you're pulling for Superman, you want to be sure nobody sells kryptonite to Lex Luthor. Sometimes an agreement is made by all parties that certain items cannot be dealt to certain people. Those "certain people" are often proud, formidable, and easily irritated. (*You* try telling a 500-year-old something he/she doesn't want to hear.) They may take things into their own hands. They'll just about always try to cover their tracks, too. Most of the time you never really know who's behind things.

There are other types of collectors. Some of them are just Muggle curio-hunters, but others are absolute hoarders. Hoarders? That has to make you wonder. There's an old anecdote in the sports community that might explain it.

An already-legendary SEC football coach who had the top three quarterbacks in the nation was in the hunt for several other prize prospects. Most of them would never get the chance to play for him. "Don't you have enough quarterbacks?" a sportscaster asked him. The old coach said he could never have enough. If he had them, he didn't have to play against them.

That's an analogy for our world. There are Collegians who buy up totems they can't or won't use because they are afraid of other people getting hold of them – people who might be able to use them. You see again how material wealth is an advantage, even in our College.

Since all of this is so far underground that you don't even believe me, you would agree in theory that special chaperones would be needed to transfer and deliver any very valuable item. That's where I come in. I'm a Tour Guide. I'm in Campus Security. I and at least one other Linebacker work for my broker chaperoning items from one place to another. This might sound like grunt work, but it is a very valuable aspect of the enterprise. Nobody's going to pay you for an item you can't deliver in one piece. That shouldn't surprise you at all.

When one of these items that has a legendary cachet is on the menu, I get paid a lot more to babysit it than anything else. Transporting one of these is a job that may take an indefinite time out of my schedule, but it will set me up for the whole year. Or more. Most of us would feel like we'd won the lottery for the commission – the "Grant" or "Scholarship" – I got for just one of the jobs I've had. That's where most of the adventure comes in, too, at least for me.

Chapter 4

# The *Source*

1

You have seen me use a couple of my powers. You have a circumstantial understanding of the way we live and interact in the College. You have to be wondering how I came to be included in this occult community that at least most of you never had any idea existed. The story is not a quick one, but in retrospect and based on what I know of both occultism and human psychic abilities, it makes sense to me. At least, it fits a pattern. It's also related to the development of my most radical ability: the Gleam, the Axe-Hand. It's the only one for which I see direct precedents.

For somebody who's going to end up a wizard, I was a surprisingly average kid, maybe a little too average for my family and the historic Connecticut suburb in which we lived. My dad was a doctor, one of the old-style general practitioners. He did pretty well, but there wasn't a ton of fun-money to go around. My parents believed in opportunity, and they saved so the three of us could have it. We all went to independent high schools and good colleges. My brother and sister went to graduate schools.

One thing that wasn't average about me was my curiously strong right hand. At no stage of my life have either my forearm or the bones in it ever been big, but at about 14 I noticed that I had never met a twist-off container that got the best of me. It became a family proverb: Screwtop Eric. Right-hand Rick. It was actually funny. Nobody wondered too much about it, though.

Everyone who plays a bit of tennis has a lot of strength in the racket hand, and most of us thought it had to be that. I was always around the game as a kid. My mom had been a teaching professional at clubs all over the Berkshires. I never really took to tennis. I was more into soccer and skiing. My brother Phil – three years and two grades ahead of me – (I have a late birthday) would have been the one you'd think would have the grip. He was a truly fine player. He cleaned up all over the Northeast as a junior and everybody in the Berkshires tennis community knew him. It's hard to tell how far he could have gone had he followed his tennis instead of his law career. But Phil was a lefty, and jars and other containers are made for righties. In short, no one was as surprised at my right hand as they should have been, including me. Just a quirk, I thought. One incident stands out in retrospect, and I realize it might have been a sign of something.

I was on a ski trip in New Hampshire during my junior year in high school. I'd managed to slip into the basement bar with my brother and his four college buddies. It was the first time I'd ever had a drink in a pub, and I was deliriously happy, even if it meant putting up with Phil's wise-offs, 90% of them aimed at me. His friends were really nice to me, but he was so sharp that people couldn't help laughing.

I stood on the right at the end of the line of my brother's crew. I fell into conversation with a man at the left end of his conversing friends. He was the boss of a group of plumbers on vacation with their wives. All were broad men who had turned a lot of wrenches, but this guy was huge. Six-five, he had to be three hundred pounds. He was a pleasant fellow, though he had some stereotypes about people and politics. He had marked me – a longhair – as a dope-smoking lefty and seemed to appreciate the chance to talk peaceably with one. He was curious about why we all think what we do. I wasn't as far left as he thought, but he was so far right that the center looked extreme.

Somehow we got onto the subject of gripping strength, and the contests started. I beat his colleagues in succession rather easily. The first guy, you'd have thought I took him by surprise. The boss was last. To feel the massive, meaty hand and those banana-fingers starting to compress inside my grip was remarkable. He was astonished. It was actually funny to watch those pea-sized blues roll in suspicion, then dawning realization. I made sure not to hurt him. I just sent a message. My strength was so good that I had the illusion that the smaller size of my hand might even be an advantage. It felt harder, more concentrated.

But I never made much out of the matter. I certainly never set up grip-off matches to embarrass bigger men. I'd show off a bit at parties if someone couldn't master a corkscrew or a twist-off. I loved making it look easy. "Tennis player," I'd say with a little nod, though I virtually gave the game up after high school.

But the story of my entry into the occult fraternity you have already heard plenty about really starts one fall night in my first year at a preppy, competitive school in the Five Colleges region. I wasn't a great student in my high school, but the school was great. A B- there was worth an A+ from many other places. Plus, that school had a pipeline to a number of New England colleges, including the one I'd chosen.

I was as confused a freshman as there ever was. I didn't know what I was doing in college in the first place, much less what I wanted to do in life. I did know that I envied stylish, artsy people who traveled a lot, and I had the vague impression that I might want to be one of them. What kind of career that would lead to – or would lead to it – I hadn't considered.

Confused and ambitionless I might have been, but lonely I wasn't. At least a dozen people from my high school, half of them fellow freshmen, were there on the day I arrived. We hung out and looked out for each other for the first few weeks. We met each other's new friends, which was wonderful. After that most of us saw less and less of each other, but one high school friend who stayed close that first fall was a lady art major who had actually dated my older brother. On a Friday night in late September I had met her and her then-boyfriend at a party in someone's off-campus apartment. From there the three of us set out on the town.

It was a big night for gallery openings in Northampton, and after our first one we became a foursome. The newcomer and my woman friend evidently shared a class, and they talked like old pals. I was uneasy with her joining us at first. I was surprised that my friend knew her.

I'd seen this woman before. Everyone had. She was a striking figure about Northampton. Five-eight or -nine and with shoulder-length straight honey-brown hair, she had regular if plain Anglo-Germanic features. She was not a bad-looking woman, but she did almost everything to keep herself from being pretty. She embodied that bad combination – for one's social life – of odd and conspicuous, of standout and stand-offish.

I remembered seeing her weeks before I met her. I went to hear Fairport Convention at the Iron Horse in Northampton and spotted her standing in the shadows close to the stage, nodding in her own trance. That night she was in a sort of Andean poncho and a dorky black felt cowboy hat with a single upraised feather.

I'd seen her several times after that. She didn't fit into any of the familiar life-guises – hippie, artsy, preppy, jock – in the socially-stressed climate of most American colleges in the decade. Face it: Everyone that age is either looking for clan colors to fly or flying them without knowing it. This woman stepped out of all that. Outrageously defiant in style, she reminded me of the Victorian Feminists, but they had their own style, and her motif seemed to be the absurd one of 60s Westerns – or *The Beverly Hillbillies*. She dressed like a Native American, like a TV farmer.

I don't know how long she'd been in the Five Colleges district, but it was long enough – and she was conspicuous enough – to get nicknames from total strangers. "The Squaw" is one I remember. Earlier that fall one of my wry friends spotted her at an outdoor art exhibit and jested that she dressed herself out of the Good Will bin behind the offices of *National Geographic*. After awhile the nicknames went from "Cochise" to "Pocahontas," all with the Native American theme. Some days it did look like she could have stepped off the Navajo Reservation.

She was independent, too. She came and went as she pleased: coffee houses, college libraries, a cafe here or there, and the occasional party or concert. I never saw her with anybody. I never saw her attempt to speak to anyone, at least socially. She looked older than the typical college kid. I couldn't tell the age of older people very well – I was 17 and eleven months myself – but I would have taken her for 35.

The guys I knew would have ribbed me pretty hard for double-dating with "the Squaw," and I confess to being shallow enough at that age that it would have bothered me. None of us dreaded anything more than appearing to be weird. We dreaded even being seen associating with anyone who was weird out of fear, maybe, that the condition might be catching.

My opinion of the woman changed quickly once we started talking. Her name was Dana Lambert, and I found that I had been right to pick her for a transfer or even a graduate student. She was both. She was so poised and interesting that I started to suspect that the matter of the dress was just a joke I wasn't getting. She knew history, archaeology, anthropology, art… She seemed to have good friendships among the artists, patrons, and gallery-owners. To them she wasn't a weirdo.

I still found her off-putting. That night she held her sandy-gold hair back behind her brow with a rolled red handkerchief knotted at her nape, which I didn't find flattering. She was in denim overalls, which you did see occasionally on the hippie crowd of the day, and a flannel shirt-jacket. She did look like Elly May.

We had started touring galleries at about 7:30. By ten Ms. Lambert knew of a party in walking range, an afterglow of one of the openings. It was a spectrum of ages and careers. My two friends and I were the youngest people there. After that it was a college party at which I managed to get stoned. I was already tipsy with wine from the various openings, and I don't recommend that combination.

By midnight the four of us had resolved to finish the evening in my friend's room listening to an LP that she had just acquired, one I was really looking forward to hearing. However, the girl's door was locked. She had misplaced her keys, and her roommate was nowhere to be located.

The door featured one of those sturdy metal L-shaped handles. "Oh, let's just bust in," I said jestingly in the dim-but-light-enough hall. A surge of dizzying authority came over me, and I gripped the handle and twisted down with my right. Something thunked and gave way inside the locking mechanism. The handle flopped limply, and the door gaped open. I had shattered the locking mechanism. It had been easy.

The pair with whom I had started the evening looked at me with drop-jawed amazement. "I wasn't expecting that," I said, embarrassed. Dana Lambert didn't say anything, but she seemed to notice something.

The rest of the evening went as planned. Lounging on beds and beanbag chairs, the three of us got stoned – again. Dana, the newcomer, didn't touch the stuff. Everybody picked an LP from the collection of pop white-kid music. The guy recommended something by Quicksilver Messenger Service. Our guest came up with Stevie Wonder's *Inner Visions*. I've always found every beat of that to be fascinating, and half the dorm rooms you visited in those days seemed to have it on hand. My friend was a jazz fan, and an LP by Ronnie Laws found its way to the turntable. I picked Hendrix' *Axis, Bold as Love*. I sprawled on a beanbag chair and grooved out.

The newcomer, though, looked at me with new eyes, sitting pertly at the chair of a desk. She had shed the flannel shirt and that hankie-hair-

76

band. She made better eye contact with me and addressed more of her conversation to me, too. She asked my thoughts on art, music, human nature, and even spirituality. Those are pretty penetrating questions to be asking a freshman. Though I found it fun to be drawn to talk about myself, I was a little testy. She didn't seem to be approaching me, but I didn't want any awkwardnesses about deflecting advances from The Squaw. I realize now that should have been my first clue that something was up. Why would anyone but another freshman be interested in what any freshman thinks about anything?

Other than my two friends spending a night in a room they couldn't lock, there were no repercussions to the matter of the busted handle. We all told the truth to the two maintenance men the next morning and they thought we were pulling one over on them. My woman friend actually pushed it from the standpoint of a deficient locking system in the whole dorm and the feeling of a lack of privacy in her room. You could see the pair quietly steaming. They had had a lot of surprises in their years on the job, but it still seemed impossible that a single young man could have done that sort of damage one-handed. They were convinced that half the football team must have pranked us while we had been out. It seemed clearly an act of spontaneous vandalism. It was also such a simple repair job that the matter rested as a curiosity.

Other than a few hellos about campus, that was all I heard of any of the people from that night for two weeks. But on a Wednesday morning in early October, I got a note in my student union mail box – after 50-plus years I remember the number, 2355 – from Dana Lambert, inviting me to an early-evening party that she thought I might find interesting. It was in Saratoga Springs, and on a week night. The drive each way was about two hours, but she had a car and was happy to go for it. I was happy to ride along.

2

So: I get a surprise invitation to a party in a town hours away in my first semester in college. It's from a woman I'd never thought was attractive, and my first thought was, "Why me?" My second was, "Is this going to get embarrassing?"

If the genders had been reversed, I'd have been suspicious. But as it was, I wasn't afraid of anything except foiled expectations. Dana Lambert didn't seem crazy – actually the reverse, in spite of her dress. She was the least-crazy person in my circle of friends.

Our paths crossed in the Student Union a few days in advance. I felt a little nervous, but she didn't seem to detect a thing. She said that on the first Thursday of every month there was a pickup party at the home of a professor emeritus from Union College. Anyone who heard about it – and any guest of theirs – was welcome. She had a standing invitation because she had done a summer internship with the professor at Breadloaf and had become good friends with him. She was inviting me because she was sure I would meet people I would enjoy. I liked the idea of an eclectic crowd.

My first surprise came when I met Dana in her old Peugeot in the campus parking lot. Gone was the headband, the hat, and the overalls. She was in a khaki skirt that showed off a pair of athletic legs and a blouse that revealed a womanly bosom through the gaps of the slick denim jacket. Her hair fell around her face in a frame that accentuated her features. She also had on a bit of makeup. She looked a lot prettier and more feminine.

I remember asking her as we drove what she was doing at our college. She said that she was employed by a man she called something like "Yopp" Simon as "sort of an art appraiser." She was taking grad classes in art history and preservation at two of the colleges in the district, including ours. She was an apprentice curator at a third college's small but highly commended museum. She was working on a special exhibit of artifacts from one of the Middle Eastern cultures.

It was my first trip to Saratoga Springs. We parked on one of the older streets a block or two from Broadway. The area looked a little depressed, and the professor's house could have used a new coat of paint. What I've learned about architecture since makes me understand it as a Victorian/Italianate structure with columns on the porch and one of those charming, slender towers that makes you want to just hole up and read in the study at the top. Inside, though, the house was immaculately tidy and decked with spare antique furnishings and woodwork. The walls were painted in sumptuous deep shades, and the many fine works of art mounted on them were exquisitely treated. I was clearly in the home of a connoisseur.

The first thing every young straight guy probably does at a party is to check out the available women, which I did with a single scan. Skidmore hosts a load of beauties, but this wasn't the undergraduate bash I had envisioned when Dana had told me about a come one, come all party with food and wine. I saw when I got there why there wasn't a mob of takers. Someone who had no connection there would have felt adrift.

The party-goers – it was more of an open house – seemed to be students, professors, art dealers, and friends and colleagues of the host. People were lighthearted and cordial, but truly professional. No one raised a voice, even when they laughed. The situation was testing me. I was the youngest person there. I was on my guard not to say or do anything dopey. Freshman-ish.

We came upon a fortysomething longhair in a blazer, studying one of the professor's paintings like he would bore holes through it with his eyes. Dana spoke to him, and the pair fell joyously into conversation. I could have stood and listened, but I took it as an opportunity to scout around.

I've always been one of those rare people who doesn't get antsy when there's no one to talk to at a party. I went to refresh my glass in a dining room, its piny walls ringed with chairs. A table in the center upheld a magnificent light spread: sliced cheese, hummus, pâté, smoked salmon, crudités, dried fruit and nuts, and bread waiting to be broken. Three older, artsy-looking men and a woman of college age stood talking over the open bottles of wine better than I usually drink. Happy to worry about no one commenting on my 17-year-old appetite, I took a seat right by the vittles from which I could attack the layout without rising.

"I wish that Dana wouldn't be so popular," sighed a woman beside me. "I've been waiting to tell her something all night."

I almost jumped. I hadn't noticed anyone but the people I'd spotted in the room. I turned to see a stylishly dressed older woman on the seat to my left. She reminded me of a portly Martha Graham. How had I not noticed her entering and taking her seat? One of the scarves or throws she had on should have flicked me as she settled.

She looked like she could have been a beauty in her day, and she certainly had flair. From an observation about "Charlie's new painting," she launched into a long diatribe about the state of the arts that didn't need anybody to listen to it. Her accent was untraceable, though her voice was light and lilting. She drew out her phrases like someone spinning taffy by hand, needing to gauge, savor, and weigh each word. I remember so little of her conversation because it barely included me. She drawled on about Bauhaus, that I do remember. Then she went on about the Arts & Crafts movement, the Celtic Twilight, and 19th century dance and opera. I would say that we spent ten minutes like this, her talking and me nodding.

I reached over to the table for another couple pieces of broccoli and looked back to find her gone. The narrow dining room had several doorless arches that led into other rooms, but I was still beginning to doubt my observational powers. *Off finding someone else to wear out,* I said to myself. I won't say that I disliked her, but… She looked impressed with herself.

I looked through an arch into another room and spotted Dana and the same dapper longhair regarding another painting. It was then that I realized that the fourth member of the conversation at the other end of the buffet table – a short, dark-haired man scrutinizing bottles – was included only by his position.

In his thinning grey cardigan sweater, white shirt, narrow black tie, and specs perched over his head like the visor of a helmet, he reminded me of the French Existentialist Jean-Paul Sartre, whom I had been studying in freshman philosophy. He spotted me, nodded and, with a tilt of the head toward the bottle he was holding, recommended the Pinot Noir. I found a new cup, crossed over, and let him pour me a taste. I nodded back after a sip and he filled it with at least six ounces.

He asked how I knew our host and I replied that I was the guest of someone who did. He asked me about my circumstances, then on to my studies and my interests, and we were off.

I can only imagine that I was incoherent. After all, I was 17 for another week, one of the youngest members of my freshman class. I was also a little giddy on one and a half glasses. That was all it took in those days.

I talked about art, the world, and what was on my mind. I don't remember exactly what I said because I didn't know it was a conversation that was ever going to make any difference. It was a long time ago. I remember very well how it would have gone because I remember myself pretty well at that age. I was no genius, but I had a creative mind, and I'd had a great high school education. I was fairly well read in a scattershot sense, too. I tracked what interested me. I remember today what I was into then.

What interested me the most, I said, was the merging of a lot of different arts. Music that drew influences from painting. Film that took off on poetry or philosophy. Writers who had interested me included the Symbolists. I liked Rimbaud and Novalis and de Nerval. I liked progressive rock and jazz fusion, and almost none of it was in the hit parade. I mentioned Yes and Tangerine Dream and John McLaughlin as contemporary artists people might have heard of. I also liked Claude Debussy and had just started to listen to Erik Satie. Filmmakers like Roeg and Fellini had utterly fascinated me.

What I liked about all the artists I had mentioned was the way they had incorporated archetypes. I remember saying that I was interested in the way these eternal memory-forms keep holding power for us as they come through in the arts. I was particularly haunted by the figure of the Harlequin. I thought it was a spin off of the archetype of the Shadow. I was obsessed with figuring out what it had to say to me and what it ought to say to all of us.

The man listened so respectfully that I wondered if he might be an artist or teacher himself. Then he asked if I meant Plato's or Jung's archetypes, and I told him I kept them both in mind, though I knew Jung's work a lot better. I really had read Jung in the summer after high school. Plato I knew only in interpretations.

Jung was a great favorite of his, the man said, and casually shocked me by speaking of him in a way that suggested that he had known him. The incongruity of a man who looked 50 in the mid-1970s knowing a famous 85-year-old who had died in 1961 didn't hit me. *How did you get to know Jung?* I said with a good bit of awe. I respected Jung as a human being as well as an idea-maker.

He and Jung had crossed paths in Vienna, the man said, regarding the identification and then the exchange of a certain work of art. The pair had met a number of times after in various parts of the world. He had actually loaned Jung something that was highly meaningful to him, he said, with the understanding that it would be returned after Jung's death.

*An artifact?* I think I said. It was remarkable, in retrospect, how smoothly he avoided telling me much about it. He told me that he ran a very old family business as a sort of antiques dealer and broker for out-of-the-mainstream items.

*A business?* I must have said.

At about that minute Dana Lambert rounded the corner beside her artsy-looking friend. She reacted with delight when she saw my companion. "Jaap!" she crowed, the J like a Y. "So you found each other." We nodded wryly, having just made half an hour's conversation.

Dana's companion turned out to be her former summer school professor. With them came an older gent she introduced as "Charlie" Vesel, the host.

Professor Vesel – I have never brought myself to call him anything but "Professor" – was a magnificently cultured person, an art dealer, architecture professor, and expert evaluator of old pieces. About 60 then – at least he looked it – he was a trim, middle-sized man with thick, round glasses. Bald on the top and grey on the sides, he had immense dignity and no pretensions.

I never got to know the longhair. He seemed interested in Dana and a little competitive with me, which didn't bother me at all since I wasn't thinking of our outing as a date. Before long he and Dana sashayed off with Vesel to look at a new acquisition, and Jacob Simon and I continued our conversation. He had a remarkable way of making me feel like an equal. I should have found it quite interesting and even ironic that a man of his years and experience was listening to a man of mine. I don't think I understood the things I talked about well enough at the time to be expounding on them, except intuitively.

One thing really drew me out. I think it was when he asked what I found in common to all the authors and directors and composers and artists who had interested me. I guessed, I said, that it might be the link to Symbolism, to the reach for some defining factor behind the sheer appearance of the world and the longing for transfiguration to something beyond it. The world was fascinating to me, I said, and I was trying to figure it out, but what I could access of it seemed a little humble – disappointingly material. I couldn't believe this was all there was to it. I sensed, I said, that the world and the life around us might be teeming with messages and symbols, could we only break through our materialist mind-sets and learn to pick them up. That was what I was embarked upon.

*Transfiguration,* he said as if weighing the word by the letter. "That's a lofty goal."

He asked me where I thought I was going to be fulfilled in the world with those kinds of interests. I said I thought maybe I'd like to work with a bunch of multidisciplinary artists, maybe an experimental troupe, to write, act, direct, and even choreograph – which would mean that I'd probably end up teaching by 30. We both laughed. I guess I was a mystical kid.

I noticed at that point that the party had thinned. It was indeed pushing ten. Professor Vesel reentered, elbow to elbow with two people. One was the stylishly dressed older woman I had spoken to earlier. (*You already know Bella,* said the professor.) The other was a tall, dark-haired, pale man in a black mock-T and a really cool tweed sport coat that looked both traditional and expensive. I couldn't decide if he was 50 or a truly degenerate 30-year-old. He was introduced to me as Albert Someone (I forgot his name). He nodded and quickly turned to say something in Simon's ear that the woman should have heard, and all three laughed. I didn't think it was about me, but it's undeniable that it could have been. In my jeans, sweater, and running shoes, I'd been feeling underdressed for the preceding two hours. Sensing this was my invitation out, I thanked the man I had been talking to for the conversation. He alone had been maintaining respectful knowledge of my presence through his stance. I finished by addressing him as "Mr. Simon."

*Jaap*, he corrected with a twinkle in the eye. "My father was Mr. Simon."

He stepped out of the small circle and handed me his card. He invited me to his office any time I was back in the area if I wanted to hear about the item he had loaned to Jung and talk a bit more about his business. I saw that the address was in Schenectady.

I walked with Dana to her car, enjoying the mist that had taken over the streets and made the Halloween decorations on the porches even more surreal. "Have a good time?" she said brightly, unlocking the doors.

I could only nod. I was still buzzing. It had been the most socially stimulating evening of my life to that point. These people had all seemed educated, travelled, sophisticated… Even the ones who didn't seem to like me were interesting.

As we crossed into Massachusetts, Dana told me that Jaap had been impressed with me. That I couldn't see – other than the fact that I didn't get as silly as most freshmen around free alcohol. He'd found me an imaginative and speculative young man. That I could see. I was.

I remember asking Dana what she knew about the nickname Simon answered to. *Jaap* sounded to my English-speaking ear like such a wacky, undignified monosyllable. She didn't have a good answer, but I found out later that it's an old Dutch hypocorism – a shortening, basically a nickname based on the name – for Jacob.

Dana and I found a lot to laugh about on the drive, and the idea of a few sips and some music at her apartment seemed a natural. Before long we were trading back rubs and commencing some surprisingly comforting sex.

I was pretty inexperienced with lovemaking. I'd had a couple girlfriends by then, but none were long relationships, and the young women weren't much more experienced than I was. I had the emotional insecurity of most men of my years on the planet, but it was counterbalanced by the total physical confidence of a youth of 17. You don't know how to do it, but you don't have any doubts that you could if you did.

Dana made love without an absolute and possessive passion. It was more like making love was a function of health that she had to do once in awhile like any other. Nevertheless, I found her nurturing. She had an august sense about her that was simply enveloping. She made me feel like any screwup I might make was forgiven, like she'd seen it all before.

Of course, I got a look at her by candlelight. Most women would pay a lot to have her body. As we lay together in the afterglow, I asked her why she would hide herself under the overalls and hankie-hats. She said it was because she wanted to discourage approaches from students. They all seemed like children to her. That should have been a clue as well, though I didn't take it.

4

Dana and I crossed paths on a number of occasions, including amorous ones, the rest of that fall. By the holiday break she was done with our school and moving on to her life thereafter. There wasn't any drama about it for either of us. She was interesting, a good friend, and a great lover. She was still a frequent flier between Northampton and the Capitol District, and just before Christmas she invited me to Schenectady to spend an hour with Jaap Simon. She had some visits to make at a few of the galleries, and she could drop me off at his office. I was with my family in Connecticut at the time, and, since the idea seemed interesting to me, I hitched into Northampton one morning and went with Dana for an overnighter in the Hudson Valley.

About ten the next morning, Dana dropped me off outside Jaap Simon's three-story Victorian-era brownstone in the historic district called alternately, "The Stockade" and "The Old Dorp." She told me to just let myself in and go up the stairs to Office 7.

As with Professor Vesel's house, the exterior was a bit neglected. That, too, was just a blind. Full of antique items and decked everywhere with likely original woodwork, it seemed never to have been gutted and redone like so many of the big upstate buildings in the Capitol District. I was surprised to pass so many fine and portable pieces – clocks, lamps, tables, and chairs – left unguarded in an urban setting. I was also surprised to pass a handful of apparently empty offices with the classic wood-framed doors with chest-high glass panels.

I tapped on the pane of Simon's second-floor office door, heard his voice inviting me in, and showed myself past a cluttered receptionist's desk. Simon's long rectangular meeting room was a wizards' den. Marvelous curios decked the walls, shelves, and table-tops. It looked cluttered, but I had the feeling he knew precisely where to find anything he wanted. The armchair I took was an ornately carved ball-and-claw masterpiece. As before, I felt completely at home talking to him.

"Things come to me…" he started out. "It's as if they find their way to me, and I'm appointed to find out where they really belong." It was the first time that I noticed the trace of an accent in him suggesting that he had been raised as the speaker of another language. It was more fuel to the ancestrally-Dutch theory. I wondered if the last name might mean that he had Jewish heritage.

Simon told me that he was a freelance broker of art and antiquities. It was a highly discreet business. Most of what he dealt with was both so obscure that the world knew nothing about it and so pricey that only wealthy collectors were involved. He directed all processes in the sale of these unique items between parties who were hoping to remain secret, even from each other. He was uninvolved in anything but the exchange of the item. He arranged for things to be verified, valued, transported, and delivered. He was known for record-keeping, clear judgment, and discretion. He summed up his job description as "sort of a long-range auctioneer." It had clearly made him a wealthy man.

He had some vital talents for this type of service, he said. He was good at assuring deliveries. He recruited reliable people to assist in the delivery, which was not always as easy as it might sound. He established fair prices for items and was trusted for that in his field. He was good at keeping records for long periods of time. When an item came up for sale he knew right who to contact. He was also confidential. Much of the time, he was the only person in the world – besides the owner – who knew where any certain item was. He was the go-to guy, at least when it came to European and American antiquities, and particularly in the cross-Atlantic transport.

Most of the time, he said, he never handled or even saw the items that were being exchanged. He still liked to keep an office, he said, motioning about us with his short, broad hands. He needed it less and less as time went on, and he could see an era coming that would make it needless. He still thought he would keep it. He liked coming to his office.

One group of people he worked with were specialists in evaluating out-of-context items, he said. The others were capable and reliable transporters – people who took items from sellers to buyers. He paid his people by the job, he said. Different jobs went for varying rates, depending on the item and the deal. He made an offer and they accepted or declined. Some people worked only long enough to get that one really big job and then retired. Others were with him for a long time. He was ready for anything. Nothing really surprised him. He got to be a very good judge of people.

"If you were ever looking for something to do," he said, leaning back comfortably in his chair, "I have a job coming up that would be just right for a young man testing the waters. There's no big deadline on it. You'd get some travel, and you would be paid pretty well for your age and experience. You would just need to be reliable. We could try it out. Think about it as long as you need to. Maybe you could make it your summer job."

Of course, my ears were alert for the lingo or the possibility of drug- or jewel- or weapon-smuggling. It was the 1970s. I voiced my worries. I made it clear that I didn't want anything to do with anything illegal. I wasn't a smuggler. A mule.

Jaap Simon sloughed that off with such a casual wave and nod that I believed him completely. Oh, no, he emphasized when I asked, none of the items themselves were illegal or conventionally dangerous. Almost all of them were either utterly mysterious or ancestral curios and family possessions from estates and collections. "Things like these," he said, waving about his office like someone shooing a fly. "Would you be afraid to travel with any one of these?"

I had been looking into the lacquered eyes of an exquisite little wooden chipmunk, one of four peeping out from the pinecones, chestnuts, candles, and fir boughs of the Yule display on the table before me. I could have fit it in my pocket. No aspect of it frightened me.

Someone had already paid whatever price there was for their acquiring, he added. The current holder could have sold the item to a neighbor and no one would have been the wiser. If he or she wished to unload one of these items to an interested buyer and profit through Jaap's own professional services, well… There, he was happy to oblige. Every part of every exchange was done willingly. He chuckled to himself again.

"Imagine it," he said. "Somebody digs up an etched stone in their garden. A metal detectorist finds an amulet. A family spots something odd in an attic, maybe an inscribed walking stick that looks really old." He looked at me. "Nobody knows what they are. Would you be afraid to fly one of those from Paris to Berlin? Would you be afraid to drive it from here to Boston?"

I wouldn't have. But at the mention of the American cities, another thought came to me: the illegal antiquities trade, particularly in Native American artifacts. A lot of those weren't turning up accidentally. Even in the 70s we knew what pothunting was. I said as much.

Simon looked at me as directly as he had all during the meeting. "If you were to go to the National Trust in England and tell them you had Excalibur, what do you think would be the reaction? What if you went to Tel Aviv and offered them the Ark?"

I conceded that I couldn't think of anything good coming of it for anyone.

"What do you think any of those items would look like today," he said, "even if you were sure you had one?" I had to agree with him there, too. Nobody would know what you had.

"I make this promise to everyone I employ," he said, "I would never involve anyone in any transaction without informing them of all the complications, at least of any I could foresee."

I thought rapidly. I saw that there were so many moving human parts to his system that he could't risk running anything truly contraband. His story held. Besides, he looked way too smart – and he'd been in this way too long – to get involved in something that might put him behind bars.

I was starting to be stunned by the simple brilliance of the whole scheme. I had already been stunned by the sum he had mentioned for this first arrangement. "Are there other people like you out there?"

"Oh, yes, there are," he said. "There are always finders, buyers, sellers, and facilitators. But not many have been in business as long as I have. And very few would have my reputation for reliability. In every part of the process."

I took a minute to digest all that. He kept going as I thought. I looked like the type of guy, he said, who might take to a freelance career like this, at least for a few years. I liked the art. I liked the ideas. I liked the ancient cultures. I liked the world-capitals. I wanted to travel. Also, I seemed to him like the sort of person who would be trustworthy. Now there he was right. I am as trustworthy as any person I have ever heard of.

I was tempted. I was also embarked on a program of college study that was delaying my adulthood at least a few years. I sensed that I needed the incubation. I was also interested in my courses, at least the history and arts. I liked my circumstances.

I thanked him for his faith in me. I took his card again and agreed to reach out to him if I was ever interested in this kind of employment. He said he had enjoyed our conversations and welcomed me to check in any-time I was in town.

I waited outside, looking about The Old Dorp. I appreciated the time to think. It was a tame and sunny day for mid-December. The snow had retreated after a couple of days of thaw and rain. Only a few white banks at the curbs and the sides of the buildings were to be seen anywhere in the city. I had probably been standing for ten minutes when Dana pulled up. She must have noticed my head spinning. "You guys talk any business?" she said.

I don't remember what I replied. I think I just said that Jaap Simon was a cool guy. He was so direct, even blunt, in his language and so composed as a person, that I actually started modeling my own manner after him. I do remember being astonished by his trust in me, offering me what seemed like a lot of money based on nothing but the faith that I would do what I said I would.

In the spring of what would have been my second college semester, I was on a plane crossing the Atlantic, on the first of my errands for Jaap Simon. You have to be wondering why I would upend my life, frustrate my family, and pitch my future into question.

5

There was a glorious blonde attending one of the Five Colleges. She was a freshman, beginning to question her time in the adolescent hot-houses many preppy colleges can become. It was that era, the 1970s. A lot of people who might have been happy campers in another time were struggling with the changes that were coming over society and conscious-ness, all symbolized by the music.

Perhaps regrettably for the destiny of my heart, this woman saw something in me in the late fall of my freshman year. We started dating before the January term and had a three-month affair. Maybe I had stars in my eyes at the start. My previous gal pals had been artists or hippies. Nicolle was the first "golden girl" I'd ever gone out with. She had a lu-minous smile and the sleekest legs and butt I've ever seen. She was a runner, a skier, a climber, a tennis player... She could even play guitar and sing. She was one of life's winners. She was the type of girl everybody was after, and she attracted attention – good attention – wherever she went. She could have been with one of the stars of the school. Upper-classmen, frat men, the quarterback, the heir... Enough of them had asked her out. It was more than that, though: more than the image.

No one is nothing but a type. If you ever get to know someone you had once stereotyped, you will see that. There are layers to everyone, whether or not you turn out to like them. Nicolle had depth: compassion, gentility, and courage. She was wonderful to be with.

Me... I was a blundering social oaf who couldn't control his impulses and who had a lot to learn about respect for others. I was so far from ready to join the adult world that it's embarrassing to remember. The thought that I might eventually become a more complete person must have been what Nicolle saw in me. She just "got a kick" out of me. She also thought I'd be a great father.

I knew she was beyond me even then. I knew I'd love her as long as she'd let me and that then she'd leave and tell me not go with her. I loved her with an adolescent desperation that you might be able to imagine. It was a thirst for something you knew you were never going to be able to hold, and you were going to have it only a little longer. One episode among many stands out.

I remember being at a ski show at Stratton Mountain where Nicolle was working as a representative, meeting and greeting people who came to the Fischer display. I got talking with a Rossi rep from Colorado who didn't know I knew her. He watched her greet a customer who walked up to her bearing a ski, and he nodded in her direction. "My daddy told me once that some women's rock and roll and some women's a whole symphony." He nodded again. "That little lady... She's the conductor." I quietly agreed.

Another reason to remember the day is because a crew of us did the mountain after the ski show. Nicolle and I got separated and I found out later that she had fallen in with some of the factory team racers. I'm a son of the Northeast and an all-sports mountain man, but I'm no international competitor. That night beside me in a hot tub she was beyond herself with admiration for the talent she had gotten to ski with. I couldn't hide the fact that I was feeling a little inadequate. *What are you doing with me?* I as much as said.

She looked at me, her brows furrowed. "You're tough," she said after a bit of thought. "A lot of these people have been at something so long that it's easy for them. I'm not sure how tough they all are." I remember thinking that was one of the nicest things anyone had ever said to me. Nicolle was not a flatterer.

She was quitting college. She had signed up for the Peace Corps. She was leaving for Tonga in June. Her Stateside training started just after Easter. I briefly debated going with her. She did invite me, and I was undergoing my own questioning at the time. Maybe I didn't love her enough. Maybe I didn't love myself enough to believe that she could ever love me. But I didn't go with her for two reasons. One of them was that

I thought she wanted a man who would lead his own life, not hers, and that, if it was our destiny, maybe we'd have a few adventures and meet up again. The other reason is because I am that sort of person.

Chapter 5

# The Occult Economy

1

As for the chaperoning that people like me do… Most of the time, you simply get something from point A to point B. It's basically smuggling, just even less likely to get you in trouble with the Muggles since most of the time the item you're packing looks like a piece of junk – and you have serious help from the home base, in my case, from Jaap Simon. Getting through airports, terminals, and customs isn't that big a problem. The temporary concealment of items of almost any reasonable size and form is pretty basic in the College. So are quick mental persuasion tricks if somebody happens to call you on something. Some of those are so effective that it's comical.

Some of the time… It gets a little dangerous. It isn't always or even often, but you never know. In fact, you have to know your item. If there's any mystery about that, well, that's when you can run into problems.

If you're the one riding shotgun, you have to be on edge constantly. There's a lot of competition for these things we carry, at least the high-priority ones. Losing bidders may decide to take a shortcut and head the item off at the pass. One of them is very often suspect Number One when a clash happens. Suspect Two has been known to be the buyer who hopes to nip the item in transit and then call for a refund of the sum that's changed hands for an undelivered package. Sometimes even the seller gets involved in the game: Gets to sell his cake and have it, too. Getting the item like that almost always involves taking out the Tour Guide – someone like me. (Sometimes we call moves like that a little too lightheartedly, "a prank" or "a hazing.") I object to being taken out. Strenuously. I have done so in the past.

You may be wondering about now why someone would send just a handful of barehanded agents, sometimes even a single one, to deliver a small, portable item worth hundreds of millions. It's a reasonable question. But think about this for a minute: How would you protect an item that the world forgot if you don't want to remind it? Call Blackwater? A Brinx truck? Surround it with a posse?

The security has to be undercover. Your potential thieves – "Recruiters" – are all people in the College. Brinx or Blackwater might be able to handle them if they came in with uzis and land mines; that they'd be expecting. But the potential pirates of your in-transit article would be other power-people. (They would be the only ones who know what you are trying to move.) They would be Linebackers like me. A Muggle security crew would have no preparation for the way people like us would come in. None. They wouldn't know what hit them. There might not even be any need to hit them. The item would simply be missing.

Even insurance would be useless to guard against your losses. Trying to insure the Holy Grail would be like trying to sell someone the Brooklyn Bridge. They'd laugh at you like you're loony. Besides, our point is to be secret.

What would you do if your item gets nipped? Who would you complain to? The law enforcement community is no help to you. You can't alert them. Even if you could get mainstream – Muggle, Townie – help, they couldn't do much for you.

So put yourself in my shoes: Campus Security. A Tour Guide. A Linebacker. You're a solo flyer. You have to have a strong sense of independence. An escort like me needs to be more than a simple somebody nobody wants to mess with. There are always going to be people who want to mess with people like that. Some of the wickedest fighters and assassins in the College are kinda thick – just very good at fighting – and they get tested all the time. Some of them are such goons, anyway, that they would attract too much attention in an airport. The real trick is being able to adapt to changing circumstances.

Also – and this should go without saying – the escort needs to have integrity. The broker, the person who arranges for the sale and the successful transport of an item, has to be able to count on the escort to both not back down when there's a confrontation but not simply cut with the merchandise and run. Or fake getting rolled over. Or make a deal of his/her own with some of the many willing parties out there.

I'm told through the grapevine that that's one reason I've become a top tour guide/Campus Security agent fairly quickly, meaning within less than a century: The idea of betraying anybody I work with has never seriously occurred to me. I guess that would make me unusual, and not just in the College.

2

So we've been through the transport and babysitting of the items, at least the introductory material. There's another component of the equation, though: verification. In the College we call that, "Checking the Transcripts." This is the only thing that makes anyone willing to pay the big bucks.

Whenever one of these high-stakes, sometimes very ancient items goes up for sale, there will always be a cloud around it. The mainstream world considers it lost, if it believes at all that it had truly existed or had ever been what it was rumored to be. There may be several parties claiming to have the true item. I don't know how many hunks of metal there are out there posing as the Spear of Destiny. The ones I've seen don't look like Roman military artifacts. The one Hitler had sure doesn't.

"There's one of those born every minute," you'd say to yourself if someone tried to sell you the Emperor Ashoka's *bindi*, the dewdrop gem worn over the third eye. No one is shocked that many people would try to sell you the dagger, the *pugium*, that Brutus used on Caesar. What if somebody tries to sell you the sunburst jewel that appeared on the band of the headpiece of Vlad the Impaler – the original Dracula – in his famous portrait? I guarantee you that the price for any of these artifacts would be extreme.

No one in our College is surprised to suspect that none of the ones offered would be the real item, but that the true one might yet be out there, and that someday its holder will be willing to part with it. The real trick is verifying that the item you want to buy is authentic. The verification is a very important art. How would you go about it?

"Turn to the professionals," you might think. Art historians. Archaeologists. Anthropologists. But there are two really good reasons not to go that route. Think about it a minute.

The first good reason not to go to a mainstreamer is that he or she couldn't help you with a truly obscure object simply passed to them across a table. Mainstreamers can't prove much about items that are taken from their sites and out of their cultural context. That's not the way the work of any of those disciplines is done. A lot of the time they couldn't tell you if it was even made in the same century as the real item. You can't Carbon-14 date an inorganic object, which most of our artifacts are.

A mainstreamer could probably tell you if the item you had was a conspicuously poor fake. They could tell you if the age, workmanship, style, or materials ruled it out. But ruling it in? Brutus' pugium? Ashoka's gem? There's no material way to prove that the item in hand wasn't even a contemporary copy of the real item. Everything artistically, culturally, and historically could be right about it and it still wouldn't be the real deal. That would make all the difference, at least when it comes to a metaphysically powerful totem, which some of our items are.

The second good reason you can't go the mainstream route is that — at least in the 21st century — the academic communities are the last people you'd want knowing about your article. Any one of them would turn you in, even if it's not the treasure you think it is. The sheer possession of an artifact would provoke an outcry.

Anything of Ashoka's would be considered the property of the Indian nation, if not the world. The Greeks would go to war over Agamemnon's crown. Pavarotti would be singing operas about the Ides of March if Italy found out about its missing dagger. In short, a whole society would be all over you.

Most of the wizards in our College would prevail over that sort of pressure. They'd catch wind of the bust long before the marshals crashed in. There would be nobody home — and possibly a scary booby trap for whoever showed up depending on how mad you had managed to make them. Whoever finked on them... That could be nasty. But they'd have to move, and in a hurry.

Some of the old Collegians get real cranky and protective of their domiciles. They get attached to their possessions. They get to like certain estates or even simple flats in the old capitals of the world – or the resort areas. Most of them have several of these manors about the globe, but they despise being uprooted, especially in a hurry. They keep a lot of their most prized possessions in or near those digs, as well as some of their stocks of treasure. Even I like where I live, and I know I'm going to have to move in a couple decades. Not looking forward to it.

So how would you go about validating a very old, very contested, incredibly valuable, potentially dangerous item if you were in our College?

Extrasensory Perception is sometimes called "the Sixth Sense." ESP is basically getting information about things that are not immediately perceptible in time or space through the acknowledged five material senses.

Some people say there are four major categories of ESP. Some people say there are six. For me, there are only three primary ones. Two are relevant to the type of work I do in the College.

Some people read living people's minds. They can know some of the things other people are thinking, at least when it's people they can read. It's a type of ESP we call *telepathy*.

Some people can pick up things nobody knows. They know things that just *are*. We call those people *clairvoyants*. Those are both special gifts. They don't seem to overlap much. You're good at one or the other.

Some people in the second category specialize in finding out things nobody knows about physical objects. We call that *psychometry*. The Greek roots are often translated, "soul-measuring," but it makes more sense to me if you say, "Evaluating by use of soul/spirit/psyche." These people get information about inanimate objects through their own ESP. It's just their knack.

Even this last category, psychometry, may have at least two sub-categories that I've observed. Some people are very good at tracking the human associations of an object. I suspect that this might be an aspect of what to me was the third major category of ESP, *mediumship*: talking with or getting information from disembodied entities ("spirits"). These folks can get a feeling for the people who may have fashioned, owned, or handled an artifact just by sensing its energy. If something was supposed to belong to Helen of Troy, these folks can tell you if it was ever hers.

Other people specialize in tracking the cultural and geographical associations of an item. They tell you what part of the world it's from. This could possibly be a subcategory of clairvoyance, "clear seeing," since technically the information is not floating around in the conscious minds of living people. That doesn't tell you something is as advertised, but it can rule out fakes. They can tell you if something ever was in Troy.

Another group of these validators specializes in detecting the associations of objects with other objects. While I think this may be a spin off of the immediate category above – the place-checkers – it's not as valuable as you might think with really obscure old objects. Sometimes there isn't any other item from its known source left to associate it with. As for how this type of reading works, though, that makes more sense to me than the logic behind either of the above techniques.

*Source* runs strongly through some of these artifacts and totems. It emanates from and through the most powerful. When one strong one has been kept near another, even an item that's simply receptive, there's a signature on one or both. And we know that the potentates of the pre-industrial world, of any ruler or any culture that has believed in magic, often have their treasure-chests and chambers. They have their altars and temples where many of these items have stood on display. The items would have been in constant contact with each other, sometimes for long periods of time, centuries or even millennia if they were taken from the same tomb, monument, or treasury. Almost like prehistoric DNA sampling, a reader of this type can tell you if a touch ever happened between power-items and maybe even when.

My employer Jaap Simon works with some very gifted psychics whose talents are receptive and perceptive – as opposed to mine which, except for the quirky one I've mentioned briefly, "the Chimies," are material and assertive. A common term inside and outside the College for people who have or claim psychic gifts is "reader." Jaap Simon works only with the best – and the most honorable – readers.

Most of the readers in the world aren't official members of the College who strongly channel what we call *Source* within them or through them. We work with some like that. They don't get the privilege of the super-long lives and the full suspension of the aging process. It's depressing to some of them to watch themselves decline and note that other people they work with never change. The good news about that is that those candidates usually "age out," as it were, before they make problems. They'll even joke with others that they never age, mean it as a compliment, and about the time they get the picture they're off the planet. They are usually the ones who had a late start in the College anyway, so their chances to put everything together are slimmer.

Other Collegians of this type, the ones we nickname "Transcript Checkers," really do fit into our College. Quite a few channel a lot of *Source*, and they are powerful and long-lived.

Some items, of course, are so energetic that they just about prove themselves. Go back to the kryptonite motif. An idiot could tell by the touch that Excalibur had some kind of mojo. The Ark would probably kill you if you didn't approach it with the right attitude. The Iroquoian Medicine Masks are legends for acting up in most of the museums that house them. Most of them are only a century or two old, and there's no way any museum has any of the most powerful. But most items are mute to most people. The ones my employer tends to deal with are important – and the sums changing hands are vast.

You have to be wondering why anyone would take the word of anyone else enough to pay titanic sums that cannot be legally ensured for ancient items that cannot by any practical means be verified. The answer is that the best verifiers are considered for all measures infallible. A broker like Jaap Simon needs them. His reputation rides on it.

Some of his Transcript Checkers/TC's have proved their worth many a time. How does anybody know if they are really good? The answer is, *easy*.

You can test these people. Get any artifact whose history you know. Give it to one of them to intuit. Try it with a handful of items. You will find that the good ones are seldom wrong.

You can't walk them around a strange town and point to objects and buildings and spots on the earth and ask them to deliver like an ad lib comic. That's a very unfair test of any reader. Good ones know better than to toy with their skills. Pro boxers don't fight in the street just to show how tough they are, for God's sake! Good Transcript Checkers also need time, preparation, and planning. They aren't infallible, because no human is. But the best of the TC's are the final word in our world.

You have to be asking yourself some serious questions at this point. You have to be wondering by what steps anyone verifies the identification of an artifact that's not supposed to exist, that's not only supposed to have been lost in antiquity but that's also so old that it would be hard to preserve by any means.

Dana Lambert's specialty is sensing and tracking an item's human connections. If a famous person was known to have handled and used the object, she can read something if she gets hold of something else that person owned and even visits sites associated with him or her. Usually that exposure comes first so it's all fresh with her. Then, if you can get her to the object in question, she can let you know if there was ever a connection between it and the alleged owners. It helps her to handle it, but it's not utterly vital. She does have to be near it. That's one source of information about the past of an object. That's not all she does, of course. She tries as hard as she can to be exposed to information on all levels, including mainstream history, archaeology, art, and anthropology. Everything helps. That was how I met her: She was prepping at one of Mt. Holyoke's visiting collections for the validation of a very high profile item from the Near East. I never found out too much about it.

With our mutual colleague Nadia Whitney-Hadel, an African-American lady I'll profile soon, the connection is more to place. If you suspect that an item came from a certain region or culture, she will get over there and get familiar with the spaces still available for visiting. You would be surprised how easy it is to be definite about things like that. The Grail came from Jerusalem. The Four Treasures of the Sidhe would have some connection to Tara, today's Dublin, and for sure the Plain of Moytura, the legendary battlefield. She will also get familiar with a lot of other objects thought to have been associated with the one in question.

You still have to be surprised that people believe these two enough to wager vast sums based on little more than their collective assessment. Part of my reaction to that is to say that people like these two are tested often, and usually from the moment of contact with the item to the point of sale.

I've seen people trick my two friends with small and energetically weak items, things that have almost no *Source* within them. I've never seen them dramatically wrong with important ones, especially when they work together and have time for preparation. When these two women known to have great talent say the same thing about an item, it's taken to be as good as it gets. The item they vouch for will keep its value.

These two – and my employer's whole team – are valued for integrity. The profile that keeps us all doing well is based on Jaap's reputation, which is unmatched. If one part of the system ever flopped, he would have to make up the difference. His reputation might take centuries to recover.

3

The College has a very informal network of both Transcript Checkers and Linebackers (also nicknamed CT's, TG's, or CTG's, all short for Campus Tour Guides). I've met a bunch of them at pow-wows and deals, as well as parties. Most of them are freelancers who have numerous occasional employers. I think every part of the world, at least the West and Near East, has these general associations. I don't know what to call them. They don't run so much in cliques, but there isn't anything organized about them, either. Maybe "social spheres" is a better description.

While of course they are all world travelers, they tend to specialize in general regions like Western Europe, the Mediterranean, the Middle East, or the American Southwest. The Transcript Checkers get familiar with the region's history, which makes them better at their jobs of sizing up the artifacts that turn up. The Tour Guides get to know the languages and cultures, which makes them better at navigating their way around – which can really be important if things break down, which they sometimes do. My turf, as you see, is almost exclusively Western Europe and the Atlantic Coast of the U.S.

I don't know how many TC/TG teams like us Jaap Simon has in the stable or who's forming any particular crew – we often nickname them "Frats" or "Houses" – but I suspect he has a couple. He's had to. I've only been with him for fifty years. "The Ghost," Sia Lund, his other Linebacker whom I work with a lot, has been with him or, let's say, his enterprise, for maybe 150.

Many elite Muggles have Collegians working for them, though there's no way most of them get the full picture of the College, no matter how many questions they ask. The richest, hippest Muggles are fascinated by Collegians. Even the Junkies can wangle in with them. In fact, most of the ones who do get the rep of gurus to the stars are low-renters in our College.

As a businessman, Jaap will work with anybody who has a deal to make. Many of the buyers and sellers who approach Jaap about an item have their own crews of TC's and Linebackers. For his own work, Jaap Simon likes his own teams. And most of the people who work for him don't work for anybody else. Why would we? He pays us great. He's as farsighted and as trustworthy as anybody could be, and you have to trust they guy or gal who sends you into deals. Some of them turn into real situations.

Jaap really cares about his people. He likes keeping people together who work well with each other. We have to get along with each other. We often travel together. We also have to trust each other. Sometimes we need to back each other up.

The commerce we engage in is so high-stakes and so deep-cover that potential trouble is ever close at hand. Sometimes people try to head an item off before or even after the deal is made. That's why Linebackers like me and the guy we call *The Ghost with the Bronze Hands* are around. Like a good bike lock, we "keep the honest people honest." And there are temper tantrums in many of our exchanges. Sometimes people get mad at the TC's when they get told that their item isn't what they think it is, and that's another reason for people like me to be there. I'm there to deflect trouble so the TC's can say what they think. They help me, too. They tell me when trouble's coming. The more we work together the better we get at it.

You already know how close I am with Dana Lambert. My other lady colleague, the transcript-checker Nadia Whitney-Hadel, has become a trusted friend. While I may be the "muscle" in our partnership, me and The Ghost (or "The Shadow," a shortening of one of his other so-briquets), neither one of us has the intuition of these ladies. I've always felt a lot safer on any sort of adventure when one of them is around. They can size up a group or a situation and let you know when the trouble may be coming. They can also give you a warning about people. They can usually tell you who's on your side and who isn't.

109

4

You have to be wondering why we keep everything so in-house, down to our very involvement with the College. You might think it's because of the witch-trials. We were never worried about those. They just hauled in the wannabes, anyway, plus a few social undesirables. You couldn't get many real Collegians like that, showing up with the torches and pitchforks. Today we worry about other things. Like notoriety.

For people who live life in terms of centuries, recognition is a problem. Fame is a nightmare. This is the first time in history we've had to deal with it so seriously. Twentieth century film and photography was trouble enough. But in the era of the internet, facial recognition technology, retinal scanning, DNA-tech, and other biometric identifications... Hell, the cell phone camera!... You can't fade back out of the picture once you're in it. If you've looked thirty for ninety years, somebody's going to start wondering, especially if you keep letting on about magic.

But the big reason most of us try to keep such low profiles is related to our economy. Some of us are fabulously wealthy, and we need to protect our wealth. We have no idea how long we might need it. We thrive on slipping under the radar of the Townie/Muggle system of taxation. We'd lose so much of our wealth that it would actually change lifestyles for many of us.

Most Collegians do not age naturally. I'll talk a bit more about that process later. But for now, think of the Highlander of the famous film, except that you'll get busted long before that opening-scene sword-fight in a parking garage. You can't leave your money to yourself if you fake your death, either.

The way most of them preserve wealth while ducking the system is by relocating, which so many Collegians despise, or by leaving the declared property, including houses and estates, to themselves. They create aliases for their children or cousins, declare a percentage of the wealth they really have, pay the inheritance taxes every eighty years or so, leave

110

the apparent bulk to themselves, and coast. The College has some pretty good accountants who can handle all that. The problems, though, of new identities have compounded so much in the 21st century that almost every one of us tries to duck the limelight as much as possible.

Just the way there are craftspersons, musicians, and writers of great talent who never become hits, there are dingbats winning awards today in literature or art. They just get themselves hip somehow and people love to say they like them. It's that way with our College.

There have been wizards famous in literature and legend who were nothing but showboats. There are others who ducked the folklore and storytelling and who have become some of the most powerful people in our College. I bet a lot of those have never even officially entered the College, at least the working arrangement of it. They just go about their business. A long time.

Not everyone who's in our College was known as an occultist in his or her own day. I think some of them were famous, but for other disciplines.

In the Elizabethan period, the age of Shakespeare, science and magic – like astronomy and astrology, or chemistry and alchemy – were just about the same thing. The whole practice of alchemy and its underlying ideas about "the Great Chain of Being" and the Four Elements is basically magic.

Half the best poems of the British Metaphysicals (John Donne and his crew) could be taken to be magic spells, as well as with French Symbolists like Baudelaire and Rimbaud. German Romantics like Novalis and Heine were word-enchanters. Some of Ben Jonson's lyrics are virtual prayers, like about half of Rilke's.

The Romantic Age had a flair for occultism. No Muggle scholar believes Byron or Shelley could have been wizards (though I've heard some talk of them and other "Dark" Romantics as vampires). To me, either one sounds like a great candidate for our College. They could have used their power to become great wordsmiths and ducked out of the limelight when it seemed time. They both died young, and before the age of photography. Nobody knows exactly what either one of them looked like. I'd be dying to meet either one of them. Shelley's death in particular – drowning in the Mediterranean – would have been easy to fake.

Go back to the Asian disciplines of meditation and martial arts. Their very practice is mind over matter, of will over the insensate world. It's very little exaggeration to think that some of their stars could still be around. I bet you Musashi Miyamoto and The Buddha are still around. Nobody knows exactly what they looked like anyway. They'd have to fake a death and make it stick for no more than a generation. Then they'd be in the clear.

I keep thinking we might see Jesus one of these days. He was surely an Ascended Master. He came back from the tomb, or at least He was reported to. Where did He go after that? He could still be around. There was no photo ID in the day, unless you count the Shroud of Turin. He could have gone anywhere.

I keep thinking I'm going to run into other famous, mysterious figures from the past like François Villon: people who've had an aura of mystery about them in their lives and something ambiguous about their deaths. Any of those people would make good Collegians.

I know I'm going to run into Giordano Bruno someday. No way the Inquisition got *him*. That would have been a homunculus they burned, something that looked just like him. I wonder if the guards noticed it wasn't answering questions on the way to the stake. I truly hope I could meet Sappho, though that was a long time ago. She'd probably be really short. She'd probably make herself a brilliant rock star like Kate Bush, then duck out again.

With all the posers in our College – we are a vain lot – I often think about holding a "Come as You Say You Were" party. We'd have Tristan and Iseult frenching on the couch and Nathan Hale spouting forth with his famous line on demand. We could get a rousing Hannibal still frothing about the Romans… Or a raging Cato the Censor cutting loose with his signature signoff to every speech he made to the Senate, no matter what the speech was about: *Carthago delenda est.* Man, talk about two guys you don't want at the same party.

5

You see why wealth the world doesn't know you have is a very valuable commodity in our College. It's become dramatically more vital as the world changes, too. It's not so easy to just drop out of a society that keeps track of drivers' licenses and social security numbers. It's gotten to the point that life isn't as much fun as it ought to be if you're constantly trying to work around those types of things. You have to plan decades in advance.

Back in the old days it was not only easier to hide valuables and identities, but it was easier to spook the public. You could live in the same tower for centuries. Get the reputation of a dangerous enchanter and people would leave you alone – because in some ages, most everybody believes in dangerous enchanters. You can leave your goodies in your abode for unlikely periods of time if you buffalo the community around you. Of course there are people in any age who find magic a tough sell, so you might have to booby trap the place to give it the reputation of being haunted, if not dangerous. You might have to make a major statement every generation that backs everybody off. I think some of the fabled disaster zones in the world like Mexico's Zone of Silence or the Tayos Caves in the Andes or the Dyatlov Pass in Russia may be places where some reclusive Collegians have hangouts and just don't want to be bothered.

But it's all different now in our more material, more developed age. I have to give you an example: the dear, precious, exasperating Bella. You may remember me meeting her and several other Collegians unbeknownst at my introduction to the world of the College at that arty party in Saratoga Springs in the middle 1970s where I also met Jaap Simon. The guest of Dana Lambert, you remember, I was still a student in my Muggle college. I wasn't sure I would ever like Bella, but she's become one of my trusted friends. She is a little pompous, but she has a truly good heart. She loves people and animals, particularly her cats.

In our world, great age is a pedigree. Unlike the vain Muggles who take decades from their true age, vain Collegians add centuries to theirs. Nobody knows how old Bella really is, but it's sure to be in the hundreds.

Bella is portly, stylish, and middle-sized. She has shoulder-length brown hair that she often wears up and occasionally allows to go grey. *Source* came late to her in life, but I know it's strong within her. She has never claimed to be a famous person of the past, but all of us feel like she could have been somebody prominent enough to be mentioned somewhere in the accounts. She's immensely sophisticated. We deduce that she had advantages with education and the arts in her youth, which she surely spent in one of the European capitals. All we know for sure about Bella is that she was a dancer, and that she may once have been a great teacher of dance. I think Europe – the turbulence, the clashes, the revolutions – got too noisy for her, and she came to the Colonies. I think the Thirty Years' War was what really did it for her.

Nobody knows what Bella can really do, but everybody thinks it's plenty. Maybe her gift is just information. Possibly because of her vast and diverse friendships, she knows everybody and everything, at least of relevance to our world. Nobody dares make an enemy of her.

For me and all my circle, it's delightful to spend time with Bella – once a month. One of the most urbane individuals we have, she's every-one's super-cool, high-maintenance great aunt. She has decades-long friendships with people she's met all over the world. You'd think they'd all be hipsters and former students and Collegians like her, but there you're dead wrong. Bella has the gift of making friends among all classes and types of people and can fall into instant, merry conversations with virtually anyone. She is, though, a cultural diehard who remembers the world as she thinks it ought it ought to stay. She likes things to be just right, too, and she can be crotchety when things don't go her way. This combination gets her into trouble.

Bella's had the same New York City apartment since the Civil War.

She had been attached, I am told, to a certain neighborhood in which she'd lived since the Revolution. She was strong enough and basically good-natured enough to preserve her lifestyle across all the societal changes. I could see her striding confidently through the riots of the 1860s, though maybe that was the event that spurred the move to the digs she has now. I've heard even that was an upheaval. I had also heard that she maintained a long friendship with a little neighborhood girl who became the matriarch of a very powerful New York Mafia family, and that they had all looked up to her and looked out for her — like she needed it. Her old friend is decades gone to join the spirits and the family are in a different business now, but people say Bella could go to them for help with just about anything to this day.

You'd wonder why 20th-century trouble could have taken so long to catch up to Bella, but, you see, the world has very little accommodation for people who are 500 years old. It never really has, but it's a lot harder to hide now. Some of us have been around since the picture of society developed. Most of us at least learn to fake it to avoid potential problems. It's a bother, but it's possible if you stay out of trouble.

Bella never drove a car so she never needed a license. She never had a Muggle job so she never needed a social security number. Her political sentiments lean definitively liberal, but she hasn't voted since the days of Susan B. Anthony, and I don't know what name she would have used then.

Bella kept refusing to deal with the modern world of credit cards and social security numbers. By the 1980s she started having run-ins with the legal community, mostly based on her lack of documentation. Then somebody started worrying about her tax situation. They'd tell her to show up for a court appointment and it would coincide with her teatime, or her happy hour, or her long dinner hour, or somebody would just come to town and make her a better offer. ("It's Tuesday, and Vincent is at the bar at Maxwell's. He makes a perfect Cosmo. And Clothilde is in from Brussels, and she hasn't been to New York in a year...")

So she just wouldn't show up. Then they'd give her another date and she'd duck that. You don't need to be psychic to see that that situation isn't going to improve.

Bella is, fundamentally, a good-natured individual, and no matter how flustered she was she was always gentle with the law enforcement people who came to pick her up. She knew they were just doing their jobs. She kept going to court, bickering with the judges, getting thrown into jail, and just... getting out. Once she even ducked out of the trial. Just disappeared. All of a sudden everybody seemed to be looking in a different direction at the same time, then when they looked back, Bella wasn't there. After that, she kept peacefully going to jail and then vanishing, expecting them to give up. They didn't believe they couldn't hold her, and they kept after her. Her problems escalated every time, too, and it didn't register with her until it started to impact her enjoyment of life.

They kept interrupting her at meals in her favorite haunts. This just shows you how far out of the century Bella was. She thought she could maintain her lifestyle in one part of her world while she was fucking it up in another. That was how they always got her. At her own place, it was easy to make it look like she wasn't home. It wasn't so easy anywhere else.

They knew where to find her every time she made a break: by five at one of the same five Lower Manhattan restaurants. She'd go in with an entourage for a sprawling, several-drink dinner and the marshals would show up. After awhile they were there waiting. She is that predictable. She got to be great friends with a couple of the officers. There was actually a little core of them that would gather outside her cell just to talk to her. She spent extra time in it just for the late hour conversations. Then she'd... get home.

Bella can't admit it when she's licked. She is also pretty vain. Before long her favorite haunts were turning her away because of the scene she brought in. She was offended. Betrayed. She'd come to think of the staff and management as personal friends. She got to find the cycle too embarrassing, and that's when it started to change.

Life anywhere in the U.S. got so inconvenient for Bella that she had to scoot down to one of the resort areas of Mexico. It wasn't tough for her to pull off the move, even with her caravan of belongings. Some members of her Muggle entourage actually came with her. It was quite the grand tour, I hear. Enough others came for long visits to keep her quite entertained. The tough part for her was adapting to the environment. She gave it a year or two, but she hated the Yucatan coast. Nothing against Cancun, but Bella's a Northeasterner by nature: early winters, joyful springs, gaudy summers, and moody autumns. She's also an urbanite. She likes the fact that trees and woods are there for other people; she doesn't need them much herself.

I thought she'd wait the situation out a few decades until she could make a reappearance in New York at a point at which nobody could presume it's still her. But she seemed to have decided to make peace in her own way. I don't know how she managed it. I don't know how anyone would. I could see her meeting the presiding judge unexpectedly in his own bedroom and starting out by saying, "Now, listen to this, dear boy…" I honestly think that could have happened.

She probably both impressed him and terrified him. They came to understand each other and agreed to let the thing drop on both ends – with a few concessions. Bella probably paid a fine that seemed significant to the powers of the state but that was a dewdrop in her world. They probably sent someone to help her fill out all her paperwork and get her up to date, and she's probably still friends with that individual. She consented to give the Big Apple a break for a few decades and they agreed to drop the matter otherwise. That explains her elaborate crash pad in Saratoga Springs, actually a carriage house behind one of the finest mansions on North Broadway. Her lawn parties during race season are legendary. Those *True Blood* Sundays were decadent.

I know Bella still visits the City now and then. I think she has a monthly dinner night for the cops and detectives she got to be friends with during her ordeal. Pretty sure it's first Tuesday of every month. But she's taken up residence in my region, at least for as much of the year as she stays anyplace. I'll tell you more about her later.

I hope when the coast is finally clear for Bella she will still recognize the Big Apple she loved, but I guarantee you she wishes she had done things differently before they blew up. What's wealth and power and long life if you can't live the way you want? Nobody else I know wants it to go that far. Most everybody has learned from her example.

So you see from all this that it's highly serviceable to have some items around, often inconspicuous and easily hidden, that are worth something. You sell one off whenever you need some more money and… there you go.

But I'm not in trouble. I have my thing figured out.

Chapter 6

# The Tower

1

For the last forty years I've lived in a farmhouse just outside Saratoga Springs, NY. My parcel was carved out of a horsey estate edging the village limits, all that was left of a farm that dated to the early 1800s. There's a good bit of undeveloped land around me, and a lot of visual intrigue. I'm close enough to the village to walk if I really feel like it but just far enough outside the core to have no close neighbors but my "landlord" downstairs.

I put "landlord" in quotes because I really own the whole spread. Though I appear to be renting on all the tax records, I bought it off of him a long time ago with a large cash payment and a special agreement. I pay him rent so it shows up on his taxes. He lives here as long as he cares to. Should you wonder why he would go for that, the answer is that I made him a very handsome offer, and that he trusts me – plus we have a secret contract in each of our safety deposit boxes. We don't hang out a lot, but we are quite comfortable with each other, and we look out for each other. His name is Clinton Saturday. Nobody calls him anything other than Clint. More on him later.

I started out in a two-floor apartment in his converted barn. I had the tower and a big attic, basically the converted hayloft. Clint had the whole first and second floors. The tower, which was surely once a silo, I mostly used for storage. We've expanded since, and the configuration of my digs has changed a bit. Now I've got four levels: the garage at the base of the tower, the whole second floor, which is my living and kitchen space, the converted attic, and the tower itself, on whose top floor I do yoga and sometimes sleep. Clint and whoever he has with him at the time have the spacious first level. Since his kids have all moved out, that's all he needs. This is a wonderful lifestyle for me.

I got to love Saratoga Springs on my first visit when I was a college student. I was fascinated by the architecture, the parks, and the sense of history and sheer latent energy about the town. Saratoga Springs is actually where I came of age, as it is, into my life and lifestyle as an Arts Major in our College.

The village is always entertaining. You could walk there every night of the week and never get bored of the houses or streets. The people are eclectic and often high-rolling, and the cast of human characters is ever-changing. Half the world comes to Saratoga in the month of August, and I'd swear the other half passes through during the rest of the year. I love the change of seasons, as well as my woods-and-mountains sports. The upper Hudson Valley gets a serious winter.

In short, I have a groove here. I have my adventures when they happen. I have a very secure lifestyle, my friends all know where to find me, and I am happy. This is another reason for my secrecy, at least about being a wizard: I just like things the way they are. I don't think I'd be happy if I had to pull up stakes in a hurry.

I also have a cover: I have a little touring company in Saratoga Springs and a few other villages around here. I lead ghost walks. I come at it more from a historic point of view. I'm not trying to speak for the spirits. I'm trying to educate people on history, architecture, and folklore. The walking tour business combined with other things like bus tours and the occasional lecture or conference really do well as a part-time thing, but not as well as the evidence of my lifestyle. I travel a good bit, and there's no way to explain to anyone what I do for Jaap Simon.

I have to have a cover. Since almost nobody overstates what they make to the IRS, the Feds never suspect that I might be doing it. In 2018 I told them I made $100-120K, which I probably could in 2020 dollars (once this damned Covid epidemic cools off) if I worked hard enough, and how do they know? It's enough to explain the trackable parts of my lifestyle. The one obvious luxury I give myself is a nice car, a late-model, high-end SUV. It's slick to look at, big enough to hold my bike or my skis, and great on the snowy roads. I will always enjoy a comfort like that.

Saratoga Springs doesn't really have cowboys, and I don't know that it ever did. But my landlord Clint Saturday fits the part. He grew up in Texas, after all, and he does wear the occasional subdued cowboy hat. He came back here and took over this old farmhouse because his domestic partner at the time was from nearby Washington County. I think it might once have been in her family.

Clint Saturday is a medium-sized, aquiline-featured man with light skin, reddish brown hair, and small brown eyes. He's light-bodied, though he has wide shoulders and gives the sense of authority. He's never without facial hair, most commonly a mustache, but I've seen all sorts of goatees and short beards. He talks little, and says almost nothing about himself. He's not evasive. He's just completely devoid of ego and totally uninterested in old news.

In an idle moment I did a search on his family history based on the few details I've gotten out of him and was astonished to find that his first name comes from a family connection to Dewitt Clinton, one of New York's most important early governors. Clint could quite well be in the direct line, like a triple-great-grandson. I couldn't prove that in the quick search I did, but most people would have been trumping up that connection. He did have family in the Hudson Valley and he'd spent time here as a kid, so the region was familiar to him.

For twenty-seven years Clint was the owner of one of Saratoga

Springs' most beloved pubs. It was a legend for its happy hours, as well as its remarkable collection of artifacts and curios based on the theme of Victorian London.

I met Clint a year after I'd decided to move to Saratoga Springs. He had more space than he was using in his converted barn, and I got tired of living so far out on the lake. I answered an ad for a studio apartment, which turned out to be a bedroom off Clint's tower. This was right about the time Clint opened his theme restaurant and made himself a local, if self-effacing, celebrity.

Clint had planned carefully for his special place. He was constantly on the lookout for items that would help put across the visual theme he had in mind. He scoured estate sales and antique dealers in the Hudson Valley. Almost all of his stuff came dirt cheap, but the mass of it created enormous atmosphere.

One of Clint's display cases featured an old riding crop whose handle was made from an apparent chess piece, a rude carved ivory horse's head. I'd been living in Clint's barn for a year when I heard about that item becoming the focus of a situation. Now and then someone in Clint's restaurant-pub took an interest in the piece. Though a number of people offered him something for it, the price – thirteen bucks – never changed. Not only was it queer that a series of strangers would have the same taste and evaluation skills, but Clint was fairly sure that that unlucky figure was what he had paid for the item years before.

It would have left a hole in his display case to sell the thing, and Clint wasn't charmed by the way these people asked. They had a swagger. Still, despite his theme-marketing savvy, Clint's a businessman. All they had to do was up the offer. Instead, they started pressuring him – and he started thinking there was more to the matter.

Clint has never known completely what I do for Jaap Simon, and he knows nothing about the College. He knew from the beginning about my little walking tour company. He knows I always have my ears open e story. One Friday evening in early September as I was sip-ping a cold one at his burnished bar he came out of the office to brief me on the situation. Then he walked me to the display case and asked me if I could tell him anything.

I'd passed the device many a time. His pub was one of my hangouts in my first years in Saratoga. I was in my 20s, don't forget, and still occasionally doing the bar thing. The whole piece may indeed have belonged to a person of the era Clint was trying to represent, but I could tell by looking at it that the chess piece itself was way older. I could tell him now that that wasn't the only item in his displays that had a little "file," as we sometimes say in the College: a bit of psychic baggage. Then, I just told him to keep me posted. Whenever there was a new development afterward he'd come and talk to me about it.

More strange people started showing up at his place and making trouble. Some complained about meals and service. Some just ordered things like herb tea and water, taking up space and staring at menus like they would memorize them. They were arrogant.

When I pressed Clint on the general "look" of these individuals who were displaying this interest, he said they all looked "like they knew something." You can expect a lot of things out of Clint, but one of them will never be elaboration. I asked enough other questions about their dress and appearance to deduce that these queriers were artsy-types or New Agers. I wondered if they could be College, or working for a Collegian. The disciples of some of our Collegians do look like that. Yes, some of us have our vanities. Entourages. I think it's a bad idea, but some do it.

Clint's the wrong guy to hassle. It makes him toughen up. Reflexively. He started wearing his six-gun under a blazer. Yes, a six-gun. He's a legal owner, and this was the 1980s. If that sounds anachronistic to you, those revolvers are among the least likely handguns in the world to jam. They work under pressure, which is the only time that counts. The holster was also hidden under the flap of whatever jacket Clint wore at the time, and he's always liked that look, the jacket over the jeans. Almost nobody ever noticed. Plus, crews of Clint's hunting and biker friends did regular shifts, backing him at the pub. They walked him to his car every night when he closed.

People stopped bugging him where he worked. Things escalated otherwise.

His staff and patrons started thinking his building was haunted. (It was haunted anyway. It's still haunted.)

Clint's sleep was troubled. He started having hallucinations during the day. He described them as seeing distant objects he mistook for people morph into stumps and mailboxes – or like seeing birds land in a yard, turn into cats, and run off. So many of these happened when he was driving that he started to worry about his functioning.

Now, pitching apparitions like these, even into someone's sleep, is entry-level College stuff. Freshman. It was almost laughable. But some of the toughest people on this planet – people who fear virtually nothing natural – have an almost psychotic dread of anything supernatural. I've seen it over and over again. By the time the spookery started following Clint home and troubling his partner, her kids, his dogs, and his tenants at other properties, he was looking for ideas.

It came to a head one March night during a wee-hours sojourn to the loo at the end of Clint's long second floor hallway. On his return, Clint passed an old oval mirror in which he was used to seeing his sleepy self. Something else was looking back at him from it. It rattled him to his slippers.

I heard about it probably a minute later, if that's as long as it took him to get into his robe and come knocking on my door at the foot of the hallway landing. At first I was more worried about a fire than some-one else's midnight sighting. I got a few lights on in the kitchen, set him down, and started water for the tea. It took a few minutes to get the busi-ness out of him. His hand shook so much when he took his Constant

Comment that the spoon rattled against the rim of the mug, and he looked at the source of the unexpected sound with at first horror-filled eyes as if even this might be a sign of magical torment.

I had to ask a lot of questions to get an impression of what he'd seen in the glass. The picture I got of it was of a life-sized, living statue of a slender, adult human being inside an armless, seamless ivory leather suit. He could see it all from the waist up as if it was standing in his place. There were irregular cutouts about the shape of a human eye socket through which living brown eyes peered, and, most menacingly to Clint, banana-sized rabbit ears made of the same skin, holding the only stitching he saw. He wondered if this was the most direct sign yet that he was being stalked by a demon at the behest of the Devil himself.

I calmed him down. "Clint, can you think of anything you have done in your entire life to be getting the Devil after you?"

I agree that his vision would have been alarming to anyone who had only one sinister possibility for it in mind. It also could have been a nightmare. That was the tactic I took: It was a half-waking dream. I didn't mention that the hare has long been one of the traditional animal-symbols of the Devil in Europe. I also know that symbols of the Devil are very popular as projections of people who want to make you think you are being pursued by the Devil.

Apparition-sightings I often liken to dreams, another situation in which the perceiver's impressions can hold hidden clues. I asked a few more questions about the qualities of light and shade of the thing he saw. *I just saw it in the mirror,* was all I could get about that. But it didn't seem like the form he'd seen was suffering. It looked alive, too. The eyes glistened. It was someone inside a funny suit looking at him as if to make a wordless statement, probably a challenge.

I was sure it had something to do with that riding-crop all the goonies were after. I didn't tell Clint that. I just said I would check into it.

I was a very new Collegian at that point. I was in my twenties and had just returned from my first big adventure in Europe. I had a long way to go, as I do still. A shakedown situation from a blunt, petty operator like these incidents seemed to reveal didn't scare me. Maybe it should have. Things are so often not what they appear to be in our world.

Lucky for me, this one was that simple. I had a long afternoon happy hour with Bella and Albert Frontiere. Albert especially has a lot of Muggle contacts, and mostly through him I was able to get the story on the troubling parties. They were a crew of aspiring Science Majors, probably none of whom were ever going to be College. They were trying to put together an entire set of Medieval-era chessmen, and the last missing piece was a knight. They had decided that the handle on this riding crop was it.

It wasn't. It was a lot more recent than that. It could have been hand-carved by an old Hudson Valley farmer. The knight isn't even made like a horse's head by any of the cultures they thought it could have come from! Nevertheless, they were bent on getting it. They had put together a series of rituals that were augmenting the natural energy of all of Clint's establishments: his pub, his home, and his properties. If it surprises you that a chess set might interest someone in or around the College, let it not.

On my first foray for Jaap Simon I toured the British National Museum and, on a lark, asked one of the guards if the place had any ghost stories. He wasn't too sure about the ghosts, but he told me about two exhibits with spooky reputations. The guard dogs wouldn't go near them on their rounds. They had to be dragged past.

One was the smoky obsidian glass disc that has become famous throughout Europe as "Montezuma's Mirror." It's got a real occult history. The other display past which the dogs feared to tread is called "The Lewis Chessmen," a set of 84 walrus-ivory chess pieces thought to have been made in Scandinavia, probably Norway, in the 12th century. They were found in 1831 on Lewis Island in the Hebrides (an island chain in

Northern Scotland). A Scot named Malcolm "Sprot" McLeod spotted a stone kist or storage-structure inside a sand dune that been exposed by the high tide. He and his trusty spade decided to see what was in it. When he set eyes on his first couple of chessmen, he thought he'd found a nest of sleeping Little People and tore off running. Sager heads – like his wife's – realized they were more likely to be pricey than perilous.

Also called "The Uig Chessmen" for the bay by which they were found, they may have been hidden during a raid or battle for safekeeping. Some think they might have been stored there by a trader who never returned for them.

Why would a set of simple gaming pieces get this kind of reputation? In reality, I have no answer for you. Some things start to channel and store *Source* and nobody seems to know why. In terms of folklore, I can say at least something. There is a pattern. Games, gaming, riddling, and wagers are all the subjects of many a magical fable, and chess was after all "the Game of Kings." For Celtic societies, chess was a game often played between Fairies and mortals as a form of a wager. Speaking like a Spiritualist, now, maybe someone's life was won or lost over a game with those pieces, and a bit of after-life mojo went with them. If the Bergman film *The Seventh Seal* happened to be a true story, that board and set with which the Crusader duels with Death would surely have some psychic afterglow.

To get back to Clint… The folks who had showed up to cause trouble at his Saratoga business were local amateurs, Muggles/Townies from the same Troy, NY, outfit. They were excited by the game they were playing but not at all fully aware of it – and they weren't hard to find. The owner of the New Age shop on Broadway knew them all. They'd been holding monthly meetings there till they started being a pain about it. I gather that they were leaving messes and not paying the full fee arranged for the rental of the space. One visit to one of their meetings at a head shop in Ballston Spa was all it took for me to back them off, at least the ones

I found there. They started out pompous and arrogant, but they seem to have heard about me and didn't want to start anything. They were following the lead of their guru, the prime spellcaster plaguing Clint.

He wasn't hard to find, either. I've honestly forgotten what he called himself then, but this was "the Touch," as they say in my day of a heavy. If he'd been College we might have called him a Linebacker, but as it is, he was a Junkie: Adjunct Faculty. He was a self-proclaimed wizard. He had other words for it, but that's what he meant. He or whoever he was working for had just enough clout to cause minor-league trouble like what Clint was going through. You don't have to be College to do some of this stuff.

I went to visit him at his Albany apartment and tried to talk him out of the long-range juju. I found the Touch to be a big, very strongly-bodied man. Virtually bald, he had blunt features and a beard with no mustache. I'd seen him before around and about Saratoga. He was a hippie. Everything was "Far out," and, "Oh, wow!" at least when he was happy, which was most of the time. Otherwise, he was a bully, which to me seemed a contradiction. When I started to explain to him why he really had to back off, he shot me a right. I met it with a palm, my left, the Beam-hand, which was just starting to develop. It gave him a bit of a shock, which was all it took. He sat back and listened.

Through my own broker I had found a reasonable price for the item they wanted. I told him to offer it to Clint. He of course never followed through. I could see right from the start that this was a battle of egos and attitudes. It was $13 or nothing.

As for the chess set that crew of Muggles were trying to assemble: That dog wasn't going to hunt. Just a look at the piece Clint owned was enough to settle that for Dana Lambert, one of the best verifiers in our College. The complete set, could they ever put it together, would be much more energetic than anything short of it but no one's occult secret weapon. If a non-imaginative person was living in the house with the full set, once every ten years he or she might witness something weird: a flicker of light over the game, a piece on the board spontaneously trembling, or a hum from the closet in which the set is kept. It might cause them to think the house was haunted. The odds of that would be good anywhere in the Hudson Valley, demon-chess sets or not. But it was not going to be like the Lewis Chessmen. They're the real deal. I don't think you'd get a night's sleep with those in the house.

As for Mr. Touch…. I'm not petty enough to pick on him unless I hear of him starting trouble for other undeserving people. I am petty enough to be curious about him, and I've kept my ears open for news on him through the years.

His Capital District posse got fed up with him and all his talk, especially when he drew me in and couldn't keep me off them. He moved to Woodstock, then I hear New Paltz. He figured out a way to get himself on government disability payments, so he can survive, though it's not a great living. He turned up at a few New Age conferences and tried to get in with the Onondaga Nation by showing up at rallies and loudly supporting some of their causes. Most of the Onondaga were fed up with him by the late 1990s, and he split the Hudson Valley and ended up in a major city in the Southeast. He gave up pretending to have magic, but he stayed in the general business and found new takers. It took twenty years, but he actually got himself fairly famous for awhile on "reality" ghost-TV in the 1990s as a paranormal investigator and exorcist. He's not College and he's never going to be, but he traveled like a rock star while the craze lasted. He led seminars, headlined conferences, consulted for celebrities… I can recommend him, too. He has a unique knack for getting things wrong. Do exactly the opposite of what he tells you and you'll be OK.

At any rate, the trouble stopped for Clint. He never knew all the way why, but he has been eternally grateful to me. He got to keep his piece, too. His respect for me went up. At this point it borders on something almost religious, at least in any matter bordering on the metaphysical.

Since then Clint's become a true friend and a trusted counsel for local matters. He's one of the very few Townies who has any idea what I do. He knows just enough to know that it's something he doesn't want to know too much about. But the relationship has benefited me immeasurably. I can truck out of my digs on short notice and unpredictable ventures, make one phone call, and count on my stuff being OK and my cats being taken care of. I should tell you about them. They're big parts of my life.

2

I love where I live. The environment around me is that intriguing balance of minimally-landscaped pastures and orchards, Classical-style human constructions – gazebos, pagodas, statuary – and fully-wild spaces: woods, ravines, and ponds. They have a name for this mix; they call it "the Romantic Landscape," pastoral style. Three of Saratoga's most iconic parks – Congress, SPAC, and a retreat today called *Yaddo*, the former estate of financier Spencer Trask – fit this bill, though on a far grander scale.

The nights here are particularly mysterious. They can be challenging, too. I've had a number of surprises. This one goes back to a tender August evening in the 1980s, shortly after I took up living here.

It was probably 3 AM. Funny noises outside were coming through the screens of my then-second-level bedroom. They seemed fairly distant, fifty feet or so, among the trees past the split-rail fence. They were bizarre. I presumed without much question that the maker was an animal native to the Northeast, just one whose call I'd never heard before. I'm no naturalist, and I never underestimate the capacity of the animal world to surprise me. I fell back to sleep.

The calls came back late the night after, and they were closer to my screened window. I studied them. They came in spells, a few seconds apart. Hissy, screechy, percussive cough-cackles, they were utterly indescribable in letters. I was fairly sure that the producer of them was animal (as opposed to vegetable or mineral), but they were so utterly wacky that I couldn't decide on the general class of the critter producing them. There was something comical about them, too, and I chuckled at some of my impressions. I was envisioning amorous tree-toads, basso crickets, or gravel-voiced owls.

They were also eerie, and deceptive. They came from a variety of heights and positions in the yard, from, I'd say, six to twenty feet in the air, and always near trees or stumps or other likely perches. They moved several times in an hour, lending support to the idea that the emanator might be a flying critter, perching and hiding on the other side of an obstacle, though the sound itself was still an X-factor. I couldn't fancy the sounds coming from a bird. They didn't tune up till deep in the night.

By the third night I doubted that the calls were coming from a hostile source. No attacker would announce itself before the first stroke. If the calls represented a warning or a message, well, they could call at another time. I was really tired. I set up my "psychic alarm," something that protects me while I sleep – one secret I won't tell you about – and drifted back to dreamland.

The possibility that the calls were the manifestation of something in my world, the College, did linger with me, though. A messenger like them could well be important, if not sinister. I also considered the chance that there was Native medicine at work, as if some Mohawk witch or elder had decided to send me a message, if not one of their shapeshifting assassins who was just warming up for the real deal. I called some Native friends the next morning and asked them to shake the boughs and see if I was in any hot water. All of them replied that the odds were slim. We were going through a peaceable period, and my stock was still high with everyone they knew.

On the fourth night, a steamy, still one, the calls were close enough to the house to be loud – and tantalizing. I crept all through my quarters, sneaking from window to window on the north side of my broad house, peering one-eyed out the corners till I tired of it. I never caught a glimpse of whatever was making the sounds.

The morning and afternoon of the next day I made some calls to naturalists and woodsmen. Not even Ed Montour, Danny's author-speaker father, knew what was making the noises.

I called a friend, a blonde lady wildlife-rescuer, a former server at Clint's restaurant. We went a couple funny rounds over the phone in which I tried to imitate the sounds I was hearing and she duplicated the high-pitched calls of various animals she knew. "What you got there's a raccoon," she decided at the end.

I wasn't sold. The critter climbed high, into slender branches, I observed.

"Did you think it might be a baby?" she said.

It changed its position suspiciously quickly. I pointed that out.

"Did you ever think there might be *two* of them?" she said with just a hint of triumph. Still struggling with the idea that the matter might include even one raccoon, I had to admit that she had me. I had never considered that it might be a duet, if not a cub-chorus.

It was on the fifth night that the mystery was solved. Dana Lambert was relaxing on my deck with a pinot noir, conversing through the screen, overlooking the yard and enjoying the mood of the blissful end-of-summer night. I was in the kitchen at work on one of my classic vegetarian stir-fries. The light I had came from above me and didn't spill much out onto the deck, but my space must have been a glowing beacon to anyone or anything outside within a hundred yards.

I was just about to call Dana in when I heard her laugh. "Oh, look, Rick!" she called out. She is the only person who still occasionally calls me that. A tiny grey and white kitten had climbed the deck and leaped into her lap. I could barely see it in the dimness.

I presumed it would be parched, famished, and vermin-ridden. For the last reason, I didn't want it in my house. I called Dana to set her new friend down and come to dinner. It was hard keeping the little thing from rushing in. I had to put a hand down and gently press its golf-ball forehead back as the screen closed.

The only thing I knew about cats at that point in time was that I didn't want one. But I am a compassionate being, at least I think of myself that way. While I looked for a pair of sauce-dishes to put out water and milk – as I said, I didn't know much about cats – the critter cut loose with the cackle-call I had been hearing for the last few nights. This had been the source.

The scene following was actually comical, though it would have been pathetic had it not had a happy ending. This fist-sized pack of wool and attitude actually tried to fight its way in. It tested the screen a few times, jumping up and clinging until it fell back. Then it jumped up onto a window sill, stood up into the light, and tried to hold on. The glass panes stymied its baby-claws, but I met its eyes as it turned its head sideways and tried to clamp its teeth onto one of the vertical pieces – I have since found that they call those grilles, glazing bars, or even *muntins* – and fell back again. Its expression was determined, intent… But not angry. It was puckish. That was the last I saw of it that night. I don't know where it went.

The image of that focused little brow as it held to an uncertain perch – fighting for entry into a world of light, maybe for its own life – made an impression on me. I resolved that if the creature made it through the night, we would be off to the vets for an exam and some de-toxing. Then I'd find it a good home.

The next morning I checked the deck and walked around the house a few times, announcing myself with loud and hearty rounds of "Hey, Kitty!" to no response. *Maybe it's found a home*, I thought with some relief. I ran a load of laundry to the basement – it opened with a trap-door in the garage floor – and found the critter waiting for me at the top of the stairs. I shouldn't have been surprised. The fieldstone foundations of the Revolutionary-era house surely had gaps big enough to fit more than a kitten. I also spotted a few milky-looking splats here and there with tiny, bug-eyed, evil-looking caterpillar-heads sprouting or sprawling out of them. Yes, milk isn't good for cats, at least cow's milk, even though they like it. Goes right through them. Now I know that. The hard way.

Clint's dog-owning ex-girlfriend had left us a carrier crate, and it was little trouble to get the critter in. It was seemingly dying for a warm touch. The vets would discover that this cat had no fleas. I could have told them that it had worms. It would turn out that it would be a little girl, too, which truly surprised me. I associated the spunk I'd seen with the character of males – life-lesson number one. She was found to weigh a single pound and guessed to be six weeks old, too young to be separated from her mother. I was advised to give her a bath in some specific kind of dish detergent. That was lesson number two, and it turned into a disaster. I had prepped the kitchen sink with comfortably warm water, but the cat still thought I was trying to drown her. That was the last half-bath she's ever had.

I started looking for a good home for her. I found it, all right. That grey tux has been with me since. It's been an adventure in a lot of ways. She's always testing me, the smoke-and-cotton, putty-nosed creature, but I've come to love her past words. We've have had many adventures. She's been a mouser, a joker, a house-companion, and a sentinel – I think she can see Spirit, as the Spiritualists call it. She's never lost that impulse to prank me and everyone. Because of the perils of the broad undeveloped block in which I live (hawks, owls, foxes, eagles, coons, coyotes) I try to keep her an indoor cat, but good luck with that. I knew from the beginning that the name I gave her would have to be a key to her character and the remarkable journey she had to enter my life. She really did come to me out of the night, and her nature has always been maddeningly mysterious. In a few days I named her after the generic Southwestern figure of the Trickster, Coyote, hero of a great many tales. I spell it *Yodie* so the vets will know how to pronounce it.

To you this probably looks all too cliched. They say all witches get their familiars, their little servant-animal with a demon inside it. But I'm not a witch, and I had been a Collegian for years before Yodie came to me. She's a remarkable little being.

She was compact and fist-sized for only a very short period. In a week and a half I noticed her lengthening in form. She seemed to grow fastest at the torso. Six months later during one of our nocturnal adventures in my bedroom, I was trying to haul her out from under a chair where she had taken refuge and was impressed by her unfolding length. (She wouldn't let me sleep because I hadn't figured out the trick I will mention in the next paragraph.) I kept trying to de-attach her claws from the upholstery at one end and keep hold of her center of gravity. I tugged gently and she kept stretching. She was also purring, all during the ordeal. She enjoyed that, the little punk!

Yodie lives with two legacies of her former outcast state. One is that she still has food-anxieties. It's been a lot of years, and the minute that bowl, no matter what its size, gets a bit under three-quarters-full, Yodie will start begging for more. If it happens at night, good luck trying to sleep. And when she bugs you, you don't get a minute's peace, not until you figure out what she wants or until there's a door between the two of you. It was the source of a number of dramas in our first year together. When in doubt, check the bowl. When you're going to bed, fill the bowl. All the way. Always. I always put out two bowls and she always eats from only one, and then starts it up.

Also, Yodie no longer has a normal cat-voice. I know enough about cats by now to know that there is no single 'normal' for their vocalizations, but Yodie's expressions are cramped, hissy, and unique even for cats. It's like she has no ring, no music, to her voice any more. She lacks the capacity to meow. I think it was due to those several days straight making distress-calls for that mother who would never come. Yodie's vocal chords – like those of too many 70s metal-rockers – never survived those sustained bouts of juvenile screaming.

Yodie's become a trusted companion. She also loves to get my goat. Wherever I don't want her, that's where she wants to be. She's a chronic furniture-scratcher and rug-puker. She's an indoor-stalker and an out-side-sneaker. But she clearly loves me. And she's an odd mix of a simple little animal and… something beyond us.

As you'll see in the coming pages, Yodie's got some gifts that seem to transcend those of the typical *Felis catus*, which have always been regarded as ominous enough on their own. Yodie's a fine sentinel. She spots things the human eye can't see. She senses disruptions in the tones and tenors of the home environment. She "comes and tells me" when something is up.

I don't feel at all feminine, but I think I have become her mother-figure. At one vital stage of her life when the perceptible universe was either ignoring her or trying to eat her, I was the provider of warmth, shelter, sustenance, and kindness. She's attached to me, as much as she daunts me, as tough as she tries to act. She follows me from room to room like a dog. She got so miserable every time I left the house that I had to get her a companion. Which brings us to Savvin.

3

Years into my tenure with Yodie, a Muggle psychic and cat-rescuer in my yoga class mentioned that she was hoping to find a home for one of two kittens she'd found in her barn. On an overcast Halloween afternoon we met in the parking lot of a Starbucks right off the Northway in Glens Falls. She opened the trunk of her Subaru wagon to reveal a crate that could have held a German shepherd. I peered in, trying to spot a cat among some blankets at the back.

"You sure it's in there?" I said.

"She's just being shy," said my friend, reaching in and hauling out what appeared to be the quivering pelt of a juvenile skunk. This she transferred tenderly into the smaller crate in my back seat.

"You sure it's OK?"

"Oh, she'll come around."

On the half-hour drive, most of it highway, there was barely a sound from the back seat. I wasn't sure this was going to work. I wasn't even sure the critter was healthy.

I had been advised that it was good for animals to get used to each other distantly and gradually, possibly even for weeks. My by-then three-level living space held quite a few rooms. It wasn't difficult to keep Yodie and the newcomer separate, though it was much to the discomfort of Yodie, who hates being left out of anything. Yodie got the whole house, and the newbie, with crate, litter, food, and water, got my bedroom. I opened the crate door when I left the room to take a shower, and when I came back the device was empty. I made a thorough search of the obvious hiding-places for a three-pound, eleven-week old kitten and came up with nothing. Then I heard a tiny sound, a despairing little "Ick." It seemed to be coming from behind an old wooden dresser. I came to it, craned around, and realized that my slinky new friend had, apparently dreading a tornado, compressed her mass almost completely into a palm-sized space between the wall and one of the broad feet supporting the dresser. "Suit yourself," I said inwardly as I dressed. I did hear a few more rounds of the grieving call, paced to about once every two minutes.

I came home late, a little the worse for wear. It was Halloween, don't forget. I'd been at some lively festivities in Saratoga Springs. The one I enjoyed the most had been the glam party of Albert Frontiere. His coteries tend to be half-Collegians and half high-rolling Townies, many of them gorgeous. It had been fun trying to figure who was who under the costumes. The earlier-mentioned Bella had been in attendance as Marie Antoinette, with several of her younger friends as courtiers.

I got so hammered and stoned that I decided to leave my car at Albert's and hike/Glide over the Skidmore Campus and then back into the city, sticking as close to treelines as I could. That was a trip! And on Halloween. Marvelous.

I found my original fur-friend Yodie waiting by the door of the deck, seemingly irritated with me for keeping a secret from her. I had no idea how she was going to handle another kitty in the house. I wasn't sure how I would. The early signs hadn't been encouraging.

When I entered my bedroom – careful not to let any low-lying furries get by me either way – my new housemate was not in her first hideout. I scoured the room and found her in a similar position to the one I'd remembered, just behind a different piece of old wood furniture. *Suit yourself again*, I thought, and got into bed. If the new cat kept acting that warped, she might be looking for a new rescuer. There was one improvement: That little sound it had been making like clockwork – *Ick* – every two minutes seemed down to one in fifteen. At least I could sleep with that.

One thing I had trouble sleeping through was Yodie's carrying-on. She obviously could sense our new friend and was dying to check her out. She was also indignant at being shut out of my bedroom, which hasn't been necessary since those bouts from her kitten-days. She set up such a power of scratching and huffing that it was hard to fall asleep. Sometime between three and four Yodie gave up, but by then I had a new worry. Someone-as-yet-to-be-named was up on the bed, eagerly perching on the blanket on the right side of my chest. That someone was over her stagefright and in the mood to play.

I stuck my right forearm up like the periscope of a submarine and arced the hand over like the bill of a duck. The warm squirmie snaked herself under it, sort of an auto-petting routine, as long as I could stay awake. At one point in, probably three minutes, I fell back asleep. The next thing I knew, little miss you-know-who had pounced on my chest. Her expectant little face peered at me over the covers. *Enough of this*, I said to myself. I'd been through six months of this stage – nocturnal frisking – with Yodie and was resolved not to have to go through any of it that night. I lifted my unsuspecting friend by her midsection and transported her to the spare bedroom just across the hall. There was little in it but a bed, a closet, a night-table, a lamp, and a few items of clothing and pillows – ideal for kitty-snuggling. By the time I had also transferred the litter, food, and water, miss Yodie was back and curious. At least I could leave my bedroom door open, and that part of our night was back to normal.

I slept hard but unevenly. I half-woke a few times to hear our new friend making high noises from her own room. *Now that she's come out of her shell*, I figured, *she's in the mood for company. Too late.*

At some point later in the night I thought I heard a distinct escalation in the reedy yowling. I semi-dreamed of a cartoonish Felix-the-Cat style feline, the solo-flyer on a roller-coaster, rising and dropping to the sound of one of those slide-whistles tonically imitating the high-to-low-to-high-to-low course. I presumed it was either entirely a dream or just the newbie not liking to be alone. I couldn't imagine any kind of trouble she could get herself into. I'd kitten-proofed that small spare room beyond the level of my housekeeping elsewhere.

In the morning as I was brushing my teeth I ducked in to check on our new guest. I was surprised to find her nowhere, at least not out in the open. Her orca coloring should have been easy to spot against anything else in the room. I had expected her to make a rush for the door and was sure she hadn't made it by me. This was quite the curiosity.

I shut the door again, finished brushing my teeth, and took a walk through the downstairs. No new kitty was to be observed. Yodie had been napping on a window sill, and she joined me in the kitchen as I refreshed her food and water bowls. This alone convinced me that our guest was not out of her room. Yodie would have been right on her.

In fifteen minutes I was back in the guest room, going through every imaginable space of it that could possibly conceal a three-pounder. I upended clothes-piles, turned over pillows, went through the closet... Nothing. Then the old, cast-iron radiator clanked in the corner by the window. There was a tiny bit of space between it and the wall, but it was fiery hot. Surely I didn't need to check there. Nothing would go near it for long, at least not willingly... I got sideways, pressed my temple against the wall, and peered down into the accordion-like folds. My heart skipped! Something white, black, and furry was wedged in at the bottom. I couldn't see a head, legs, or tail.

The last time I felt a pang like that had been the last time anything attacked me. The tiny creature had been exploring her room, wedged herself lengthwise between the wall and the heating unit, got stuck over a broad pipe beneath the metal bellows, howled for help – legs dangling at each end – until she passed out, and likely died a terrible death.

My goal was to get a hand under her belly and haul her straight up, but the space was too tight. I had to extend my fingers and could just touch her on the back. She was soft and still warm, but that wasn't all encouraging. I had not been worried about her freezing to death.

I was 1% dreading what I would say to her rescuer about her overnight passing in my care and 99% frenzied with concern for the little critter herself. I had to figure out if there was enough life left in her to be saved. I went through my mental rolodex of emergency vets.

I managed to bring my extended palms in from the sides of the radiator and got a few fingers on the right under her upper chest, her limp chin on my index knuckle. I worked the left over gently and got under her lower quarters. From there I craned her straight up, knuckles against the wall. She felt a lot warmer than Yodie usually feels when I pick her up.

Cradling her like a priceless artifact, I set her on the bed as softly as I could. I was shocked to see her perk her head up and look at me without expression. I shut the door, sped to the kitchen, came back with a cup of the coldest water that could come out of my faucet, and offered her a sip. She seemed happy lying on the bed, looking about. That was my first eighteen hours with her, and we haven't had any emergencies like it since.

My friend had been calling the little thing "Rosie." She did have a curious, carnation-bud of a nose – and pink paw-pads – but *Rosie* wasn't doing it for me. I usually like to get to know an animal and get the impression of a personality before giving it any kind of name. This one's comes from one pronunciation of the Celtic name for the day she came to me: *Samhain*.

Savvin started out as a major league cuddler, at least with humans. She had no fear of us, even strangers. My guests could walk in on her and she'd just look at them brightly from the bed or the couch. She hungered and thirsted to be on my lap or chest. She was a plucky critter, too. She had uncountable play-fights and chases with the eleven-pound Yodie.

At six months Savvin got her spaying and turned immediately into such a shy bird that it shocked me. I've never heard of a personality transplant that dramatic due to an operation, but people have told me since that it may not be so revolutionary. I mean, if you think about it, a spaying could seem like a UFO-abduction experience to a cat right down to the lights and genital probing. The idea that Daddy would turn her over for such a thing would cut into her native trust for the world.

The interactions between these two feline personalities have been delightful to watch unfold. There's a little rivalry, but overall they get on very well. They don't like me to see them sleeping together on those cold nights, but I know they do it.

You might think that if ever a companion animal would have magic, it would be a cat that came to you at Halloween. I haven't seen it with Savvin. Yodie's the one with the serious mojo. Whoever sent her to me I may never know.

All cats, though, have their mysteries. It's an undercurrent among the Native Elders I know that all cats can see *Spirit* but that dogs need to be trained. If an Elder ever offers you a puppy, you might be sure to take it and treat it well, because it may look out for you in senses you cannot anticipate.

These two are like my antennae, my lookouts, my sentries, my bellwethers, my emotional comforters, and my spiritual guardians. When something comes to me in my domestic space – not that unusual in the dynamic activities of my world – they are the ones, particularly Yodie, who spot it first. They are my protectors and my detectors. I've had at least one close call at the tower that I will tell you about someday. Without them, I don't think I'd have made it as far as I have.

I've spent so much time developing the story of my cats because you can't understand my life and some of the adventures that come to me without knowing my home environment, and you can't get the picture of that without knowing about them.

But back to our war… First I have to tell you some more about our College and my entry into it. My *matriculation*. I have to tell you something about witches.

146

# Chapter 7

# Something About Witches

1

I told you this might be a disorganized book. It's my memoirs. My mind isn't that organized. You shouldn't expect any more out of me.

I want to get back to a few things about the College before I get on to my own powers and that war I keep telling you I'll tell you about. I've been referring to my community I jokingly call *wizards* as "the College" for awhile now. Yes, almost certainly as in, "the Invisible College." I should tell you more about us and our slang.

Most human communities have their in-jokes, their evolving lingo of names and terms. I would bet that some of these motifs we use have been going around for centuries. It's useful to have this kind of code-language and terminology just in case the very wrong person could be listening when we talk in public. Yes, we hang out with each other, at least when enough of us are together in the same city. We hang out in restaurants and pubs. We go to concerts and conferences and do just about everything else Muggle/Townie people do. Most of us have Muggle/Townie friends. Some of them know about us, most don't. The odds of running into the wrong eavesdropper is actually high, at least when a batch of us are out roistering in some hotel bar or wising off at a movie. So we have our code-language. And then we spin like crazy off from it.

The difference between our jive and that of anyone else might be that ours in the College changes only very slowly. Just for my own kicks and giggles I've tried to get some general information about the wizard-slang before my time and haven't come up with much. We don't chronicle a lot, but even people in our outfit don't remember much that nobody ever wrote down. This bit about the College for sure goes way back.

In the specific sense, "The Invisible College" is the term used to refer to a bunch of British scholars and questers who used to meet and associate to discuss matters – generally philosophy – that would have been outside the academic mainstream of the day, generally the 1640s. They were taking things further than the establishment was inclined to go. The Man, the Establishment, whatever you call the PC police of the day, were already starting to shade toward the materialist/physicalist outlook on things. It was an improvement in its day, because most of the age was way too far toward the magico-spiritualist.

Some scholars call these guys "natural philosophers." Knowing the centuries that gave us alchemy, the Rosicrucians, the Metaphysical Poets, and "the Great Chain of Being," this means that they would have been into magic. I don't have any faith that it really worked for them since I think I know how "magic" – I still hate the term – really does work. I think they were on the wrong track, at least the ones I've heard about. The way they thought you could do "magic" was what I would have said was a noble try.

But they really believed in it. They seem to me to have been filled with passion for their pursuits. They met and talked with each other because nobody else could get what they were so into. In my take on the matter, they weren't doing this to gain personal power or to take over their nation or the world. They were hoping to reform the world, to elevate humanity, and to look out for all life in ways that were not possible in their day. That's why it was such a passionate quest for them, because they believed in the perfectibility of human society and life on the planet. They thought they were questing scientifically in a way that might change the world for the better. Their science looks mostly like magic to us. Hell, real magic would have been right up their alley.

Some of the scholars think this Invisible College may start with the circle around Robert Boyle (1627-1691), an Anglo-Irish philosopher, inventor, and experimenter. But to me there are very clear signs of the thing up to a century before Boyle. I have my own suspicions that even the name "the Invisible College" is older. Shakespeare's buddy Ben Jonson used the phrase in one of his plays before Boyle was even born. And I don't think Jonson invented it. Jonson was just the most famous early user of it, which is why people think it started with him. The term and the real thing behind it was there way before him.

I honestly think one reason for the secrecy and privacy of the 17th century version of that College was because the Church was still going through bouts of intolerance. There was quite a bit of religious tension, don't forget, that preceded and followed the Protestant Reformation. Whenever there's stress like this on a culture, extreme reactions – like the Inquisition or the witch trials – seem to follow, and not just with Christians. The unusual, apparently sacrificial burials found around the Sutton Hoo ship have been interpreted as extreme measures taken by a pagan, island society in dread of the mysterious, urbanized, totalitarian Christianity taking shape on the Continent.

But I think another major reason for the original College to be underground is that the rest of the academic community was starting to move in a way that we would have thought of as scientific. And the reason they disliked that direction was because they at least believed they were getting results their way. They wouldn't have been so passionate about it otherwise.

In fact, a lot of the things forecasted by the alchemists and Rosicrucians of the day, including extended lifespan and vitality and limited "magical" powers, are what I observe among my fellow Collegians. I can't help myself quoting any form of that word "magic" because it's so misleading to the 21st century reader. I just don't have a better one.

The phrase "The Invisible College" is also used in a general sense to refer to the line of underground spiritual teachers and questers that sprouted out of the tradition of Boyle and the original 17th century

Anglo-Irish crew that's been outed to history. They all hail out of the Western mystical system often called "the Hermetic-Cabalist tradition," incorporating Egyptian, Judaic, and Greek mystical elements and ritual forms. A few Cabalists and Hermeticists have indeed ended up in the College we are always talking about, and so many of our puns and wisecracks come from this original source that it's only fair to tell you about it, at least if you are going to keep reading my memoirs.

2

If we Collegians were easy to spot, you wouldn't need convincing that we are around. All of the Collegians I hang out with have that look about them that they are "in the know." We look a little sly.

Some of us are surely arrogant and flamboyant. Some of us love to give the air that we belong to an in-group – and that we don't need anything from anybody else. But we aren't the only people who give that aura of hipness, and I think our secret about ourselves is safe on that score.

The best of us make ourselves look innocuous, like Jaap Simon, the Suit/FAO I work for, or even simple-minded, like that one very large, very dangerous fellow you met near the start of this book. You can't tell a group of us at all unless you get close, infiltrate, and catch some of the jokes and references.

So how would you pick us out out of a crowd? In my observation, we Collegians tend toward the artsy look, whatever that may be for the day. When we're hanging out in any public place, we probably look like a batch of art dealers, authors, college professors, or artists. But then, artists look like what they are, too, and most of them aren't wizards.

There are ways you can at least rule out many people as "College": Almost none of us look truly young, like under 30. So few of us gain our power even that early in our lives so that the repeated channelling of *Source* starts to affect the natural processes of aging and healing. The reason I look the way I do is because I did find *Source* early. I'm one of the rare ones. I'm the youngest-looking Collegian I know. Most of us who do look fairly young are like me, "the naturals," the Arts Majors. My type of power is from within. More on that to come, too.

Another key to spotting us could be, though, that the ones of us who look old don't move around like most other old people. We have a vigor and ease of movement that almost no senior has. That's *Source* in us, sometimes "the Force." Yes, wisecracking on the *Star Wars* motif. More on that to come, too.

I'm going to give you another little tip in spotting the real oldsters: Most of the truly old ones, like centuries old, are short. Yes. This is a big key. Most world societies have gained a lot of height in the last century or two.

If someone comes up to you claiming to be a truly famous person like Lord Byron, one of my favorite British "Dark" Romantic poets — FYI, a very popular figure to be impersonated — well, his height was well known. It was boasted about in Byron's day that he was a lordly 5'9," which is not a height to be impressed with now. Not only can you judge the look of the person trying to persuade you he is Byron, but you also know if the size is off. Otherwise, truly tall people tend to make rare wizards, at least old ones.

I honestly think the height and even the body proportions relative to the height are key observations, at least for people who claim to be a few centuries old. Short people in my own time appear to be blockier than taller ones. No seven footer is proportionally as broad as a stocky five-footer. So look for relatively short people who have relatively light builds.

Check the accent, too. You almost never hear a straight American accent out of these people. There will always be a giveaway, some odd tone, phrase, or intonation. This is not as strange as it looks. Almost every really old Collegian was born on another continent, don't forget. The U.S. is only two and a half centuries old, and we've had our current accents for less than that. Even for wizards, no matter how much time they have, it is surprisingly hard to learn to speak a second language without an accent. Even losing one of the accents within their own birth-language is quite hard for most people without constant professional training, which almost no one in the College would bother with. So there will always be a giveaway, some odd tone, phrase, or intonation, in almost every contemporary language any Collegian speaks. I can only catch them when they try English.

3

The single big trick with us Collegians is that most of us stop aging at the point at which *Source* starts flowing within us. If you could detect and then prove something like that, *Flow* or *Source*, we have more than one name for it, you'd be on to us. But why would you? The single big trick with all you Townies is that you don't live long enough to really notice someone else failing to age, unless they are indiscreet enough to develop close Townie relationships, stay put in one community, and let themselves be seen or photographed enough times to prove something. Otherwise, the agelessness may seem unusual but hardly remarkable. Then you are gone. You move someplace else – or they do – or you leave the planet. Or they do. The mortality rate due to turf wars with other Collegians is not negligible. I'm not sure we truly replace our ranks any more.

But I do need to give you an impression of what a crew of us at a party or bar might look like. We don't tend to be large people. Really large Collegians are extremely rare. We don't tend to be obese, but almost none of us are svelte athletes like MMA artists or power-gurus like lifters. We aren't young, either. The very youngest of us look like me – around 25 – and that's rare. It's envied greatly in the College, finding your power, your Admission, early in your original physical life. They nickname that "Freshman Orientation," or FO, when *Source* starts to really work in you.

We Collegians are evenly spread between male and female. The macho, Linebacker-types tend more to be male. The intuitive, knowledge-specialists tend more to be female. But that's just an average. There are some lady Collegians – Arts Majors – who can really mess you up. They're right up there with the top male Linebackers, just a bit rarer. They're also slyer, in my perhaps un-PC estimate. Some of the males are absolute goons.

Some of us Collegians don't participate much in the life of the College – the commerce – and all the intrigues and situations that entails. I can't calculate how many like that there may be out there, but it wouldn't shock me if a lot of the little villages in rural areas or rent-controlled old apartments in the cities have that one shy bird who goes about his or her business quietly for a suspicious number of decades, should anyone notice. They love their cats, their afternoon tea, their Sunday dinners out – and they may be the holder of hidden powers or aptitudes.

But we humans are a social species, and most of us have a need to associate with our own kind. And Collegians do informally congregate for social events or business arrangements. It's never the identical list of us, and some of the businesspeople like Jaap Simon have absolutely no interest in making any kind of scene. But there is a crowd of us that ebbs and flows to occasional gatherings like the foppish British aristocrats in Pope's "Rape of the Lock," drifting from place to ever-so-chic place, only ours are all over the world. And some of the events are in desperate places like craggy castles and remote islands, at least when the business is sensitive. I swear that some Collegians live for those hangouts, at least for the fun ones. Saratoga Springs during race season (August) is one of them. They love Mardi Gras in New Orleans, and they've started to really like the Spoletto Festival in Charleston and in Spoletto, Italy, where it started. The Sundance Film Festival and Burning Man are fairly new hangouts. Burning Man is a trip.

I'll give you one free tip on how to spot a group of Collegians in action: Go to the first-night, late-night showing of a flick about magic or fantasy in some urban area. Harry Potter, *Star Wars*, LOTR... They just die at pop misconceptions about magic. They're fiends for old fantasies like *The 7th Voyage of Sinbad* and *The Wizard of Oz*. In fact, if you see a bunch of senior citizens anywhere going loudly and hysterically through routines about "Tim the Enchanter" and the attack rabbit or anything else from Python's "Grail," you can bet they're College. It's been half a century and they aren't tired of it yet.

They love asking for trouble, too, at least when they're together showing off. If you see a dozen people who look old but are acting like kids, maybe even in partial costumes like witch-hats... Frisking, laughing, shrieking, just waiting for someone to mess with them... particularly at a big-screen theater at a mall or in a tough neighborhood... Odds are good that they're Collegians. And they won't need security to walk them back to their cars. Mess at your peril.

4

I've been thinking of formats that would give you an idea what a group of Collegians might look like if you spotted them together. I first thought of eclectic gatherings like, say, a cocktail party of artsy college faculty and grad students. That might accomplish the dress and the range of ages. A few of us do look young, but none of us look *too* young. I've never seen a Collegian that I could have mistaken for a high schooler. But I think a better motif might be one that might surprise you: horror-writers.

One year in recent memory, the World Fantasy Conference was held in Saratoga Springs. The local organizers knew about my village ghost walk, and they approached me to lead a tour and even speak on a panel about local folklore. They had no clue about my status in the College, and I of course never let anything of it out. I actually started to get to be popular in the horror/fantasy community as a speaker on ghostly subjects, and I got invited to many conferences about the nation. I got to hang out a good bit with the authors, and I got to know the look of them pretty well.

Go to a horror/sci-fi/fantasy conference yourself. They call them "cons," and just about every weekend they have one in some American capital. Check out the authors. You have to do more than just walk around. If that's all you do, you'll get the authors mixed up with the attendees, some of whom come dressed like Chewbacca and Spock and, more recently, Daenerys Stormborn, Breaker of Shackles, Mother of Dragons, The Prince That Was Promised, Khaleesi of the Great Grass Sea...

Go to the hotel hosting that con before it opens to the public, typically on the Thursday night. Most of the authors, plus occasional publishers and agents, will be there, and almost no one else, so they'll be easy to spot. Even better, go to the hotel pub around ten o'clock that same night. The horror writers will be there, most of them hanging together. They love the dark corners of the bar. You'll see lots of black T-shirts, though an occasional few look like authors are stereotyped to look – blazers and mock-Ts. Some are in their 20s, though that's rare, and some are in their 70s, and that's rare. The women tend to dress a lot better.

You'll spot men without a lot of physical pretense, ones who look like they were nerds or geeks in high school. Others look like they would have been the thugs or hoods. The women look like they were shy girls or tough girls or smart girls in adolescence. Just about all of them look like outsiders who glory in it.

They drink heavily, some of them. They laugh outrageously, they make jokes nobody outside their corner of the bar might get, and they seem to have no vanities about their appearances. Except for that last part, they sound like Collegians. They also retire to shifting room parties in the hotel when the bar closes and do more drugs, almost always of the 70s kind, and stay up half the night.

Here's the feature about horror authors that catches the College best: Most of them don't have any real friends where they live. They either do their day jobs and then write, or they just write. And since the only people they really love hanging out with are other horror writers, the only time they have any real fun is when they travel to these conferences. They see their best friends only every few weeks for a weekend at a time. That means they need to make it good.

You also have to separate the horror people from the science fiction and fantasy authors. They may all end up at the same cons, but they separate themselves, not always voluntarily.

Science fiction has the glory of seeming informed. Some of its authors are doctors, academics, and scientists.

Fantasy glows with the sense of being imaginative. A lot of its authors are former history or lit majors if not also dreamy poetic types hankering for the idealized past.

The best sci-fi and fantasy is considered nothing better than escape-literature in academic and artsy circles, and both genres tend to be snubbed when time comes round to give the respect of serious awards. At least they can both pee on horror, which, despite its vast number of devotees, is stereotyped, like pornography, to have no big point but titillation.

Horror takes on a lurid, almost obscene aura in the general imagination, at least among people who don't know it, as if people who write books and stories about horrible things may really want to do horrible things. At the best, it makes horror seem a low-rent discipline among the other genres. The horror authors, all but the most successful, feel like an oppressed group. Even a Stephen King or a Dean Koontz wouldn't feign to be a stylist. I know that. I've met them both. I admire them for it, too. Pretense in anyone is silly and vain. Show it with the walk, not the talk.

While some of the authors refuse to admit that they write horror books and tales – classifying their work in one of the other fantastic genres – others revel in the grungy associations. Horror itself has sub-genres, including Gothic, Dark Fantasy, Paranormal, Splatter, and even something they call *Steampunk*.

I really liked the horror authors I got to know. I found most of them to be very bright and capable people with impressive bodies of knowledge about many fields, including history and science. They looked to me like they had at least the capabilities of most of today's college professors who have picked trendy but conceptually and stylistically light genres to focus on. The horror writers were generalists, though, not specialists. I also found them to be very gentle individuals, which probably shocks most of you. It's as if the reason they write about horrible events and circumstances is because they are such sensitive souls. The horror of the world impresses them so much more than it does the rest of us that they can't let it go. They heal or cope by venting about it in text.

The other reason I got to know the horror community so well is because I had an on and off affair with one of the agents I met at that first conference. I was in my 40s at the time and still having affairs with the occasional Muggle. I'd have taken a run at this one yesterday. She really meant something to me. She was also very attractive. She reminded me and everyone of Sophia Loren, one of the most glorious stars the screen has ever seen. She had the aquiline nose, the full, sensuous lips, the feline, "wiser-than-my-years" eyes... She was of Italian ancestry like Loren, too. She was just compressed, a shorter, wider-bodied version. She was certainly the sensual hit of that conference. She had a set of breasts that would have attracted comment even were they not topped with such a winsome face. Those breasts were forces of nature.

I used to coordinate with her to see which of the horror cons she was going to. Then I'd try to get on as a speaker, which always worked if I made the pitch in time. Otherwise I went as an attendee. We had some glorious weekends.

I couldn't get any closer to her because she was married, which I didn't know for awhile. She wouldn't leave the marriage. I can't keep getting it on with a woman I know to be married, anyway. Then I met another woman. It seemed to crush my agent-friend when I told her. I still can't figure that one out. Since then she's folded her agency and almost completely dropped out of everything. I can't even find her. I don't know what's become of her.

5

I doubt that the original Invisible College of British occultists led directly to what we have now. I think for sure our College is way older, and that some of their people just joined ours and brought in their influences. There are other traditions in our College, too, besides the mainstream Euro, especially in the States. A lot of Africans and Caribbeans and near-Easterners bring their own traditions along with them. Many individuals in my sphere of our College have social and professional relations with many Native American Elders, particularly of the Northeast. I do notice that at least the American/European circles I run in don't have too many Asians. I don't think that has anything to do with discrimination. I think it's because the Asians have their own College, if not several. I think they feel like they don't need us.

But as I have said, I'm only 70. I do see it as a possibility that a wave of the original Hermetic/Cabalist power-people have survived into the present moment to perpetuate their teaching – a line of direct descent from the Egyptians through the Greeks, the Cabalists, the Knights Templar, the Rosicrucians, the Freemasons… There are people in our network who like to let on that they are at least that old. Now, whether they're all just vain fakers or whether some of them are really on to something, not all of us are sure. But I put some trust into the "old-timer" theory. Some of them have sold me.

A lot of the old-timers have probably gotten knocked off by now, too, usually in wars with other Collegians. Surely some just retire and go dark. Just about everybody is allowed to do that if they really want to. Like with the Mafia, they can drop out and chill out, as long as they stay completely out of College intrigues and don't start anything new. This means not even taking sides in a dispute by giving advice, because that would be considered re-entering.

They usually have to wait for a peaceful time to do that, though – a "Recess," or "a Summer Break." They can't just give somebody a quick shot like an attack or steal something and then call time-out. Fortunately for them I've never heard of anyone trying that. I think they know it would be worse that way. People have to pay the dues for whatever cycle they start. Whoever they riled up would just pretend to accept the truce, then pick the most vulnerable moment and take a shot back. Things are better when they're out in the open.

6

Most of the public thinks of anything supernatural – ghosts, ESP, UFOs, Bigfoot, fairies, magic – as all one big mishmash. Even mysterious things fall into tidier categories than that. You may not believe in magic, but it may help you understand and enjoy these reflections if you understand how things are classified. There is a logic to the way they shake out.

You see where we get our flexible, ever-evolving, jocular slang, the running theme of "the College." I've told you that in the professional side of our interchanges we have different functions: people who arrange deals, people who validate the deals being made, and people who deliver the items beings dealt. It really doesn't talk about the root of their power, their use of *Source*.

We have two general styles for "magic," the use of *Source*. They overlap the above professional roles in our College. We have nicknames for them, too, in our loose slang. We split ourselves into "Science Majors" and "Arts Majors."

As he does so often, the great Seneca scholar Arthur Parker hits the matter on the head in his discussions of the witches of his own people. Parker notes that they come in two styles, distinguished by their methods.

Some witches work their will through objects and spells. This is a general style of magic found all over the world and often classified as *sorcery*. In some parts of the world it's basically all they have. Though I've never heard any of my Native friends use this word – they call it all *witched* or *medicine* or sometimes, *work* – this is what sorcery is: magic done with spells and implements. This is what most of us would do if we decided to try to do magic. We'd approach it like baking: Get the ingredients and follow a recipe. Among the Six Nations of the Iroquois, this is considered the younger kind of witchcraft/magic. These, for Parker, are the "new" witches.

With his other category of witches, the power, the "magic," is innate.

This is the old form. Born/natural witches are the original black magicians, using the power of "malefic mental suggestion," which seems to be mostly psychic. Like me, they channel *Source* without the use of other items. They can bling you with a thought or a gesture. They may be helped by training, but they don't need it to work wizardry. They can take features if not the outright forms of animals, or at least the Native peoples have always believed this. The world's first witch/wizard, the original, the Ur-Shaman, was surely of this type. I wonder if he/she is still around.

Almost everything either type of witch does in Arthur Parker's analysis can be done by the other. It's all how you get there. Same with our College, too. One type is not better/stronger than the other. The trick is simply that the witch/wizard using the implements goes through a lot more training, and needs a bit of preparation for the work being done. Some of the natural witches don't go through much training at all.

7

The above divisions noticed by Parker and a wave of ethnologists before him hold up in our somewhat flexible College-slang, typically in the two divisions we call "Arts Majors" and "Science Majors."

Some of us get the power we have from scholarship, study, focused intent, and implements. Those implements are seldom the wands, rings, books, or staves your movie stereotype would have, but there's some carry-over. We nickname those people, "Science Majors." Their work is all based on what they learn, develop, and acquire through time, practice, and tutoring. Shakespeare's Prospero or J. K. Rowling's Harry Potter are examples of these man-made types – sorcerers. Prospero needs his book and staff to get anything going, and Potter needs his wand. People like these are some of the best customers for the type of articles I chaperone, because they use them.

The Science Majors take the longest time to develop. Almost none of this type are ever the young-looking Collegians. Science Majors tend to be the planners. They are almost all quite intelligent. They develop subtlety and craft.

Then we have the Arts Majors, the type that for Arthur Parker was the natural/innate witch/wizard. Samantha on the old TV series *Bewitched* was one of these natural witches, an Arts Major like me, with innate powers. She wiggles her lovely button nose and things just happen. Her powers were a Hell of a lot greater than mine. I, though, happen to be real.

In an echo of the old attitudes, you can see one reason why we in the College like the secrecy: In his book about the Templars (*The Murdered Magicians*), Peter Partner sums it up pretty well. The sorcerer is a less dangerous figure in the long run than the natural witch, according to Partner. If the sorcerer decides to be destructive, society has a couple of options. Keeping a sorcerer away from the magical tools and techniques is the most peaceable of them. Take those away and he or she goes back to being a Townie, though a knowledgeable and connected one. A Muggle.

The innate witch/wizard like me is the blunter type. The natural witches like me have their weapons on them at all times. Ones like that can just up and zap you, at least to the extent of the abilities they have. They are permanent threats to the society, at least if they decide to be. Society is only truly safe from one of this kind of witch when they are under the ground. Fini. *Morte*. Dead.

So, in short, life is easier with secrecy. You see how well it works. How many people really believe in us anymore?

8

Now, within that general format of sorcery – tool-and-spell magic, the Potter/Prospero type – there are two styles as well. One is often called by some of the Euros "Natural Magic," as in, using the powers and formulas and reactions of the natural world. The other is sometimes called "Angel Magic," or "Enochian Magic" after the system of Dr. John Dee. They may also call this *conjuring* or *necromancy*. The terms, as you see, are not inflexible.

The first form is a lot less predictable than the second. It's also a lot less dangerous, and there's a lot less "Intramural" (College) suspicion of it. I'll give you a couple of examples that might help you keep them separated.

Suppose your main goal is to get your fields watered. Let's say you want the rain to come, or maybe you wish a creek would reroute its course just enough to help you cut some channels for irrigation. In the first style of magic, the "Natural" kind, it's like a recipe, a formula. It's like cooking or chemistry. You get the right ingredients, use them right, at the right time and in the right place, and *Voila!* Water. The sky cries or the creek leaks. The magic is just a short cut for digging a canal or waiting for nature to take its course.

You have to be as specific as you can, of course. Whatever force makes some of these things happen doesn't read your mind, and embarrassments happen frequently with spellcasters who don't focus properly. ("Life sure has a sick sense of humor, doesn't it?" says the ill-fated Bodhi at the end of *Point Break.*) It's almost better that magic is so hard to do, because there would be a lot of absurdities out there going on due to missed terminology.

In the second style of bell, book, and candle magic, though, the more ambiguous one, you do everything like you did above, but this time you use the ritual to call on a spook, a disembodied being, to do the job for you. *It* makes rain or reroutes the stream.

How a witch/wizard of my style, the Natural kind, would go about watering the fields in the above analogy, I can't tell you. Maybe this isn't the kind of witch/wizard you go to for that sort of stuff. I wouldn't be able to reroute that stream, at least not more efficiently than a couple non-Collegians with bulldozers or a team of horses and a plow. I don't have the foggiest idea how I'd call rain. But a couple points need to be made.

One of them is that if you get a spook to do the work for you, the spook is going to want something back. That's why this "Angel Magic" is the more ambiguous and the more mistrusted. The price upon the world and ultimately you is sometimes going to be fearful. The ultimate payback can only be held off so long.

Now, I don't deal with these critters, these disembodied beings, spirits, angels, demons, or whatever. I don't even know for sure they're out there. My abilities don't let me look that far. As I've told you, my psychic/informational talents are low-rollers. We Collegians are in very different categories. But the big picture of what I've just told you holds together. Take Voodoo.

I know some people stereotype Voodoo as a primitive faith of uneducated people. Stereotyping is its own problem, I've found. Voodoo, however you spell it, (*Vodun, Voudoun*) has some very interesting theories about this appeal to spirits/gods and what they might want back from a human being. Maybe someday I will talk about that in more depth. I have my issues with some of the practices, but there's nothing wrong with the logic. The religion and its practice is actually quite well thought out.

Maybe that first wizard, the Ur-Shaman, the oldest natural witch, is one of the ones they appeal to. I am sure they answer to many names, seldom giving away the real one, a point of power against them, FYI.

9

There are other people in our College, though, besides the Arts and Science Majors, and they are neither students nor faculty in our running banter. I've told you a little already about the Information People. They are the ones who keep the business of our College going, and they keep our social networks together, though indirectly. They are basically brokers. They are a combination of record-keepers, auctioneers, appraisers, auditors, payroll agents, and a delivery service.

These are the ones we nickname "Administrators," sometimes "the Board." We also call them "Development," "Guidance Counselors," "Financial Aid Officers" ("FAOs"), Alums, and a few other things I've heard. I would say most often we call them "the Suits." It's the shortest.

The Suits are almost always former Science Majors, at least the Suits that are in our College. The ones I know don't outwardly seem to have power within them, and they don't seem to practice it through rituals. You might think everybody would walk all over them, but it's not that way at all. Almost all of the ones I know are respected, if not always liked, in our College. They are valuable because of their information. They make everything work for everybody else. Besides, the important ones have some pretty powerful Arts Majors – Linebackers – looking out for them. The Linebackers come with them to negotiations, and they usually aren't far away when there's signs of a stressful time coming.

This pursuit – being a broker of priceless, contraband, and often metaphysically powerful objects – is surely passed along in families and organizations. It would be only logical. Not all the FAOs/brokers are Collegians, and these deals can take way past the length of a single natural human life to be made. But many of these Suits have been in business for a mighty long time. It seems certain to me that some of them have acquired extended life-spans. I think Jaap Simon may be one of them. Possibly because he says so little about himself, and that so self-effacingly, it's natural to wonder about him.

I fancy that he's been in Schenectady since the settler-era. I bet he's had an office or residence in this same area, the bounds of the former stockade and trading post, since the 1660s. Imagining him in a Davy Crockett-style coonskin cap always gives me a laugh, and my evidence for this Colonial-era connection is nonexistent. I just lean to thinking so poetically about it based on the nature of some of the Collegians whose backgrounds I do know, plus one clue: Jaap's nickname, a virtual give-away of Dutch ancestry.

The Dutch were the first Euro settlers of the Hudson Valley, and even though they were displaced and absorbed by the English-speakers, they left a lot of cultural influence in the region, including many place-names. Years after my first meeting I asked Jaap about his nickname and he simply said that it was a traditional one in his family. His grandfather and many male relations before had been called it. His family alternated first names for their first born sons. His grandfather was a Jacob. His dad had been a Benjamin. His son was Ben. He talked now and then about Ben.

At this point you have to be curious about some of the items we escort between parties, most of them Collegians. Since many of them are ob-scure, I'll use one you've probably never heard of as an example. I'm pretty sure I was involved with its sale and transport.

Raedwald of East Anglia was one of the most powerful kings in Eng-land in the dim period we often call, "the Heptarchy," the time after the Roman pullout when the Germanic tribes were still holding together in their own seven kingdoms. What's known in our College as Raedwald's Runestone was a powerful totem given to the king to use in life, and it guided him through his many triumphs. I'm sure he had a great *skald* (poet) or *Gothi* (sort of a Nordic Druid) by his side during most of his cri-sis-points, too, or else he wouldn't have interpreted the device so well. I'm sure the Townie world has never heard of such a thing, but it's quite logical to think that a Saxon king would have a token like it. That world had a lot of faith in an Other-world.

Once the venerable king was laid to his rest, most likely, in the famed Sutton Hoo ship burial, the incised amber lozenge could have been too valuable to leave where all else of Raedwald lay. Let's say the stone was taken back by stealth – even substituted for a fake – at the time of the interment or sometime after by the *Gothi* who had given it to Raedwald, and from there it drifted around College circles in Europe. Maybe it was even taken at the opening of the site in 1939. I do believe it ended up in Germany at some point before I may have picked it up in the 1980s.

I'm not saying all this for sure happened. I bet it did, because it pulls some threads together, but I'm using it to make a point. Let's keep rolling with it. Let's say the Runestone ended up being owned by a powerful Muggle family for generations, fully knowing what it was. Say that the family finally decided it would rather have money – a LOT of money – and was willing to part with the item. They could hardly advertise it or take it to Sotheby's. No one would believe what it was anyway, at least not in the Muggle world. There would have to be a contact-person for something like this. There would have to be special verification.

Everything has to be underground, too. Someone with a lot of discretion has to keep records of who has these items and who may be interested in buying them when they shake loose – customarily for centuries. A business like that would be an earner and preserver of vast wealth for the family of the brokers, too, Collegians or not. That's what the College's third rail, its administrators/Suits, do.

Now this analysis is putting it broadly. I put things into categories because they are easier to talk about in broad strokes. I don't see what's wrong with that. I've always found that I learned the best when I had clear, visualizable categories to handle.

I've told you that the Suits are the deal-makers. They don't get involved in any action. If there's a war going on in the College, it's usually fought through surrogates. But I don't think all the Suits are Muggles.

You can't convince me that a lot of them, especially the really rich and legendary ones, don't have something extra about them, something they are not supposed to have, even something that would overlap into the realm of the Arts Majors. They let everybody think they're one kind of Collegian and keep a few cards in the sleeve for when they need them. I say that because I do it. We all try to cover up at least something, some ability, we have. No one wants everyone to know what their strengths are, because then people can start plotting for their weaknesses.

I think most of the Suits put on the guise of being natural-born Muggles, just very well-informed and well-connected ones. And besides, some of them live a really long time. They have a lot of those tricks. The old ones, those who look the weakest, are probably the most dangerous.

While we're on this, I suspect there's quite a bit of blurring that goes on everywhere in the College, especially between Arts and Science majors. I think most of the one have trace abilities of the other in them. They all like to hold something back. I'll use myself as an example.

I'm "the natural witch" Arthur Parker talked about. My gifts are almost exclusively physical, which a parapsychologist would classify as *psychokinesis*, and abbreviate it **PK**. A parapsychologist would find me a more reliable – and weaponized – version of the great Victorian performance medium D. D. Home. (I've heard they say it, "hoom" or even "hume.") Home's gifts, his real ones, were almost entirely physical, and concerning the levitation of his body and even the apparent stretching of his limbs.

Like Home, my information talents are faint. I do, though, have one particularly strange power – a totally receptive one – that I can tell you about. I've alluded to it before. I call it "the Chimies" – those little voices that have been with me since my childhood. I'll get to that when I tell you about my powers.

Chapter 8

# The Two Byrons

1

There are actually quite a few Townies/Muggles who hang out in our circles. Sometimes we call the ones who make a habit out of it "Adjunct Faculty," or just "Junkies." I suppose for them, hanging out with people who are vastly wealthy, metaphysically powerful, and intriguingly sinister is the ultimate social trip, even if they can't brag about it on Facebook. They're basic groupies, and some of them know it. The term *Adjunct Faculty* applies to them relatively well.

Some young holders of a doctorate or master's degree hitch on as underpaid adjuncts at colleges and universities, hoping they will end up as tenured faculty, full professors, if they are good. They basically work on semester-long contracts. People of their class may end up doing 80% of the teaching, making 10% of the faculty payroll, and gaining none of the respect. Their one advantage may be that they are doing something they love – and, for some of them, that they can tell their friends that they are college professors. Then younger people who have better credentials or sell themselves better – or who simply never fell for the trap – get hired over them.

I don't meant to disrespect all adjunct faculty in Muggle colleges. Many if not most people who teach like this do it for the love. They hope to give something back to the world based on the skills they have. But if you leave them out and account for the fact that we don't do any direct teaching in our College, the motif holds together. Our adjuncts hang on to our College in the hope that they may someday be of it. As with Muggle colleges, I've never seen it work that way. And they put up with a lot.

Sometimes they get mocked, exploited, and even humiliated, and they can't do a damn thing about it. It's no fun when that happens, and most Collegians can't stand to watch it. It's the low-ranking Collegians who would do a thing like that to them. Usually.

These Adjuncts also talk, because what's the fun of hanging out with gloriously rich and powerful people if you can't show it off? I know they often get their own cults of Townies: people who don't know any of us but admire them. That's probably why they're in it: the status. Outside the College they can let on that they are pretty big people. Just a few of them hitch on with little cults of their own, sometimes even involving some pretty elite Muggles. I could mention some names from the last 40 years that many of you would know.

Their status with us is pretty low, of course. Almost all of them start to age out before long, which is a sign that *Source* isn't really with them. I'd imagine with that comes a bit of maturity and wisdom, too, and they rethink their lives and decide to do something else. Some of them do get emotional when they finally realize they aren't what they think they are to us, and they threaten to bring the whole thing down with a call to the tip line of the IRS, which wouldn't be pretty for anybody if the IRS bought it. But, yeah, try telling someone at the IRS about ageless magicians with caves full of treasure and see how far you get.

Some of them do a pretty good job faking that they may be Collegians, which is where it can start to get interesting. If you're wondering how anyone could infiltrate College events, pretend to be a Collegian, refuse to prove their abilities, and last for ten minutes without having someone turn their shorts into, say, a pair of ferrets undergoing a marital dispute... The answer is, *easy*. We're not a club that has discreet passwords or one of the old Masonic lodges that has meticulously developed philosophy. We may even be the reverse of that.

Old Collegians have their acknowledged talents and specialties, there's no doubt about that. That's how we get known for what we do and capitalize in our underground economy. But almost no Collegian will ever reveal his or her abilities, at least on demand. I've never seen one of them get drunk enough to start doing it, at least not with their significant abilities. I've seen one or two get crazy and do minor miracles like levitating small objects, if that's within their skill sets, but it's fairly taboo – and stupid.

Collegians will almost always try to conceal their abilities. Anything anyone of us can do might come in handy in a life-or-death situation. The more people know about us, the better they can plan the trap. And when it snaps, as I can tell you from personal experience, it snaps quick. So the long and the short of it is that people with no abilities to show will not be expected to show them. They'll look more convincing if they politely but confidently refuse. Most Junkies have mastered that move, at least around Collegians.

If you're wondering why we'd tolerate these ticking time bombs, these frail and gossipy hot potatoes, there are two answers. One is that you can't always be sure who people are. You hesitate to run a risk by calling them out. The other is that these people can be very helpful to us. They're people just like Collegians, merely younger than most of us. They have the gifts and skills and wit of the age, and some of us who are older and have other priorities just don't get the period we live in. You think we spend time watching TV and getting hip? The internet is a new one for just about all of us, and some of these Adjuncts are right up on it. Plus, some of them are entertaining. To us, they're what the court jesters must have been to the Medieval kings.

Think about something else: Just because someone isn't the Collegian they claim to be, at least after a couple cocktails, it doesn't at all mean that he or she isn't a Collegian of some sort. And he or she might have a friend, a patron, that nobody wants to mess with. You have to be careful not to piss off the wrong person.

My younger and more arrogant self made a lot of mistakes when I was getting used to the College. Jaap Simon used to talk to me about it in the most patient way. Ah, maturity is something seldom gifted to the young.

On separate occasions I called out both the Byrons – two guys who claimed to be Lord Byron, the British Romantic poet – to no particular consequences except being thought to be a dick by the handful of people in earshot; but in general terms that was pretty lucky. People have hidden powers. What they really have… Comes out when it has to.

2

I bring up this Lord Byron thing because it and the whole situation of College impersonators is more relevant than you might guess. In the College, we're used to posers. There are people who infiltrate the College who aren't really of it. Some of them are popular, too, at least until they blow it. Some of them are popular even after, at least if they're fun at parties.

Some Collegians like the allure of having been someone famous in history. Some of them doubtless were, and it's fun trying to figure out who might have been who. Some, if not most, probably weren't anyone memorable from the past.

Many figures from history seem like they would make good Collegians, and it's also fun to speculate which of them might have made it to our day. As far as alter-egos go, the era of the Gothic novel has been very popular with our College. The only reason Mary Shelley and the Brontë sisters haven't been taken up more often as personae is that the truly vain lady Collegians among us don't want to be only 200 years old.

The second wave of the major British Romantic poets stands out. Byron, Shelley, and Keats had metaphysical cachets during their lives, plus early deaths. They may or may not have left beautiful corpses, if there is such a thing, but they left memorable last portraits and have remained figures of fascination. Their admirers regarded them as if they were wizards. Some stodgy literary purists took them with the dread of outright Satanists.

When I first hit the College in the later 1970s there were two good-looking guys hanging around College events who were supposed to be Lord Byron, each having survived the apparent 1824 death in Greece and gone underground, eventually becoming Collegians. I ran into them separately at "Mixers" – one of our nicknames for those occasional, globe-trotting College events – the first in Paris and the second at one of Albert Frontiere's gigs in Key West. Both were middle-sized, dark-haired, and cleft-chinned. Both answered to different public names by then, which is no surprise. I've told you about notoriety in our College. Even people who want attention learn how to fake not wanting it.

The Byron-thing wasn't something they made a big deal about, and certainly not in public around unconnected Muggles. Neither of them pranced around bars reciting cantos from "Don Juan" no matter how wasted he ever got. It was sort of an Intramural – College – thing, and each of them liked alluding, not parading. Each loved those small late-night afterglows at which esteemed Collegians whispered to elite Muggles and nodded in their direction. Each loved the aura of the Byronic hero and being drawn to concede – with reluctance and understatement – his sins and adventures as though living down a Cain-like curse. Then he'd let on, usually in the presence of sexual prospects of whichever gender interested him that night, that George Gordon, the 6th Baron Byron, might once have been as he was known.

The original "wicked lord" is one of my favorite figures from history. I didn't love him as a poet, but he was one of the all-time characters in world literature. He was flamboyant, norm-defying, wacky, mysterious… Just a comet, a starburst, a shooting star of a human being. There was so much both to admire and to empathize with in Byron that he was one of the old-timers I really wish had gone into the College. I would be dying to meet him if he did, and any chance that he had was worth taking.

So when somebody told me who each one of the twin Byrons was supposed to be, I made a point of chatting them up on separate occasions. Each one was certainly arrogant enough to have been the real Byron. That they had down really well.

The Italian Byron said he liked living in Europe because of its liberal attitudes, but he managed to say that without dissing the U.S., which I appreciated. I never saw him stateside, though I hear he visited now and then. The American one lived somewhere, if anywhere, on the Eastern

Seaboard of the U.S. I got to know him a bit better.

I came across Byron #2, the American one, for the first time at one of Albert Frontiere's bashes, this one in New Orleans. I never saw the American one anywhere but at a ritzy party. He was short on details about himself and his pursuits. Whenever I pressed him about anything, he pretended to lose focus, hear himself called, spot an old friend, and cut through a crowd to visit with a small group thirty feet away, all of whom had more money than he presumed I had. Of course, that made me want to chase him down and call him out, but I resisted.

I gathered that he spent time drifting between the estate of one vastly wealthy Collegian to that of another. Most of the old Collegians are so well off that hanger-ons are no burden to them at all. They're actually appreciated if, like the American Byron, they're characters. It was hysterical to watch the American Byron operate when he was trying to score. When I was a new punk in the College I used to actually try to cut in on his action, at least when the apparent target was a woman.

There aren't any photographs of the real Byron, and people said his portraits didn't do him justice, so you couldn't rule either of these guys out by appearance. Both looked about 35, which was close enough to Byron's death-age. One was a little too tan, I think, for Byron. The other was too dark-eyed. They did both look close enough that I could see why they'd pick Byron as an alter ego. They had the face-shape and the coloring. They had, or had mastered, the 'tude.

Neither one sold me, though. The Italian didn't have a clue about the clubfoot the original Byron had the first time I talked to him in Bruges, and I don't know how you miss that if you study up on Byron. He was better off with it the second time I ran into him, I think in Strasbourg.

The American Byron knew about the foot and claimed that the joys of 20th century surgery had freed him from the issue by 1944. But the Italian one had a lot better theory of how he faked his death in 1824 and got out of his first grave at Missolonghi. The American one sounded like he was winging it when I put the question to him.

*So what did they bring back to England,* I asked, *when they relocated what they thought was your body?*

*One of my first victims,* said the American Byron, making eye contact in a way surely meant to be imposing. Then he reached across a hot red-head in a low-cut dress for another Prosecco, leaving me to try to remember if I had ever seen him during the day. One of the first vampire tales to be popular in Europe was indeed written by Byron's friend, Dr. Polidori – Byron called him "Polly-Golly" – on that legendary night of ghost-story writing that involved several still-famous people.

The Italian Byron made a lot more sense about his College entry. He said that the spirits he met in the real-life encounter that inspired his poem "Manfred" had given him the powers that launched him on his study. But then I asked him if they were in cahoots with the same spirits Shelley met on Mont Blanc and he looked at me like I was an insolent peasant. It sounded like I knew more about his alleged good friend than he did.

I did ask each Byron to show me some of his new work. It took a lot of prodding with the American one. He should just have said that he was rusty on his English from having spoken French, Italian, and Greek for so many years in the Continent. He eventually showed me something in free verse, which the real Byron would probably have turned to by 1930. It had nothing to it. It was just bad enough to win an award in 2020 if written by a person with the right connections. The Italian one I called out over the dinner table at a party in southern France, and he composed and recited something on the spot. It wasn't too bad. Everybody laughed and clapped. He ignored me from then on like I was another form of insolent peasant.

I don't think either one of them was a bad guy or I'd have made more out of their attitudes. I think they were both nervous trying to keep up this facade that you'd need to be both a great student of the period and a decent actor to pull off. Besides, I don't need to overreact if somebody thinks I'm a peasant. A peasant compared to what? What would it matter anyway? As for insolent… That I can't argue with. It was my 20s.

3

So let's say your Byron isn't really Byron. That doesn't mean he isn't somebody special. Maybe he's Cagliostro. Or Christopher Marlowe. Or somebody you've never heard of, and with something you don't want to mess with without a better reason than getting pissed off by his act at a party. That's our world.

As for the two Byrons: In the 1990s, I happened to be at an auction at Sotheby's in New York escorting one of my lower-priority items when a portrait of the real Byron came up for sale and got me reflecting that I hadn't seen either of the two Dark Swans in years. I was sitting at the time behind a couple seasoned Collegians trying to pay attention to the bidding, and I had to ask a lot of questions to piece the story together as they remembered it.

It seems that the American Byron was in Louisville for the Kentucky Derby in the late 1980s, which was likely enough. He always loved making the scene. That year, the Italian one showed up as part of some Collegian's entourage. The pair could have easily avoided each other, and I think they would have been delighted to.

But like Pete Townsend tracking Jeff Beck all over London that night in 1966 to tell him about the then-unknown Jimi Hendrix copping his chops at Bag o' Nails, somebody came up to one of the Byrons in a highly public circumstance and told him about the other. From that point, the die was cast. The two had to stay in character. They ran into each other at brunch at the Paddock Grill of the Churchill Downs and went into full frontal umbrage. The duel was arranged for the next morning. Nobody saw it, though. Nobody's heard anything of either of them since.

If you're wondering why the dueling Byrons wouldn't be front page news in our College, well, we're used to drama. A pair of somebodies strutting and fretting and then dropping out doesn't represent drama to us.

After that chat at the auction I started getting even more curious about the Byrons and asked around a bit more. I was surprised to find out how many people had liked them. The general consensus was that neither had ever sold them all the way as Byron, but that both were "just a real hoot" to hang around with. They were both noted conquistadors, too. The American one was said to be bi. The Italian one was at the least bi-curious.

Maybe they met for the duel and died mutually of their wounds. But I doubt it. I think they both ducked the duel, split the Derby as quick as they could, and dropped out of the Junkie-scene for fear of ever running into each other again. Whichever one knew he wasn't the original Byron – which, for me, was both of them – would have been terrified of the other. In his day, the author of *The Corsair* was dreaded as a duelist, with sword or pistol.

I can think of another reason for them to drop out. I'm sure they were both Muggles, sure to lose their looks twenty years after I met them. Even early-succeeding Muggles have a short window in which they have both fame and beauty. We often call that "the Hollywood problem." If I ran into either Byron today I doubt I would recognize him.

If they really did duel, my vote was for the Italian. He was a better poet in three languages than the American was in English. Not good, but just better. For even calling himself a poet the American deserved to get a scare, though I think death would have been a little harsh. But the odds are that they both went into reality TV, which is the quickest way anyone knows for untalented people to become stars.

# Chapter 9

# Beam, Gleam, Glow, and Glide

1

There weren't any magical fireworks on my first mission for Jaap Simon – no beastie-fights – but it was transformative in many ways. I'll tell you about it someday. Let's just say, I evolved, in ways that didn't necessarily lead to this, but that were massively significant to me.

The missions evolved, too, becoming trickier and higher-value. I got a number of surprises, usually, I think, depending on the importance of the item. Most of the time I never knew what I was transporting. A lot of those incidents will come up in these recollections. But since I've told you how I got started in the College and a bit about the life of it, I had better tell you about the powers I have that have kept me in the College and made me a very wealthy man. I'm retiring, so I have nothing to hide.

In the College, it's not unusual for people's powers to be quirky. It's actually the rule with the Arts Majors, though there are general patterns. Among the Linebackers, almost all of them relate to projecting personal psychic/"magical" force certain distances from their bodies. These powers are pretty tame compared to most of what you have read about wizards in books or seen in films, but these and others I'll be telling you about are surely what gave rise to the world's legends and traditions about magic. And compared to the material world you live in and what you almost certainly believe to be possible, what people like me can do is damned significant.

Of course in parapsychology they call powers like these *psychokinesis* or sometimes *telekinesis*: "mind moving matter." Because of the way I've developed it, I see parallels with some of the martial-arts mythology of the channeling and projection of ch'i, which may just be their word for *Source*. The difference may be that the Asians have a system for developing and training people, as well as the philosophy that goes with it. In other parts of the world, at least the developed West, people develop as freaky geniuses.

You see all that with the artists, you realize. In the West, the utter greats are often rebels, and greatly innovative – sometimes they absolutely push the consciousness of their day – but sometimes slack in craft. Their greatest works are often accidents, inspiration meeting rare precision. In the East, the greats are the absolute masters of technique. Innovation is something meticulously built upon earlier models.

Except for the genius part, that was me – the Western type. I have a couple of quirky aptitudes that come in real handy – and one major offensive punch.

You can't take this power away from me, you can't detect that I even have it, and I've never seen it fail. It's also what makes me what I am – one of the most dangerous people on the planet, at least at close range. You have seen it before. It's a sort of a psychic force that I project through each of my hands. It's powerful close to my body-core. If you are anywhere within six feet of me I can take you out. Or just about anything.

My right, as you've seen, is the stubbier, more concentrated force. Sometimes I call it the Axe-Hand or the Laser-Axe. Most of the time I call it the Gleam. I extend my hand like I'm going to do a karate-chop and just energize it. The feeling is not unpleasant – a little tingle. Then a glow comes over it that I can see in dim conditions. No one else seems to be able to see it under any circumstances.

The Gleam didn't start instantaneously. There was a growth curve and then an apparent kickoff that took me by complete surprise. I didn't even have a name for its first subdued effects. After awhile I started calling it "the Hammer Hand."

For the longest time it was just an accentuation of the strength of my hand and especially its hardness. It was basically like turning the material of my hand and the first few inches of my wrist into a sort of amplified hunk of steel. I couldn't see anything different about it, but when I hit something with it, usually when I got jumped by people or critters, it landed like a crowbar and stung like a cattle prod. With a bit of concentration I could punch my extended fingers through a wall. I had a grip like Beowulf. I could make a fist out of it, too, but it hit with so much more force when I opened the hand and kept all the fingers pointing in the same direction. It really was a fearful weapon. It also had a painful shocking effect on any living thing I even touched with it. I discovered all that by accident, of course, one step at a time.

This Hammer Hand made me a very dangerous person, especially to people and things unprepared for it. Still, it was no major weapon. I'll talk more later about its development into the force I have today. For now, I can tell you that the Gleam seems to have hit its peak on one traumatic experience on one of my missions for Jaap Simon. At the time of a crisis – a life or death situation, actually – I was bearing something on me that I suspect to have been a very powerful totem. Jaap had no idea how important it was going to be to someone whose identity we still don't know. That clash was probably what kicked off the full potential of the Gleam. It's possible, of course, that the Gleam was always building in me. It's also possible that my continued association with the power-totems I have escorted – channelers of *Source* – set my natural psychokinetic abilities onto a growth curve. It's also possible that that one important item itself plus the tension of the moment was all it took to spike me to another level.

If it sounds irrational to you to suggest that a single incident might have a lasting developmental effect, I have to tell you that many of the famous poltergeist – RSPK, "Recurring Spontaneous Psycho-Kinesis" – cases in the literature have had traceable single events that seem to have set off the cycle. Typically they're natural electrical events like some kinds of storms, but they can also appear to be due to long association with other electrical/geomantic power sources like springs or wells. The Fox Sisters' famous cottage in Hydesville, NY, was notoriously built atop a remarkable blind spring. The young Fox girls lived on top of it at the start of their manifestations.

By now I can do the Gleam reflexively. I test it all the time on my own, and its range is very little longer than my open hand. It's utterly devastating to anything material. I can drive it right through any substance I've ever encountered. Walls, steel, living critters… When I spread my fingers and try to clutch something, the force weakens somewhat, but then each finger is a laser-claw. I can wrench just about anything away from whatever's holding it. Chains, doorknobs, ribs. I can rip or punch bricks right out of a wall. I had to be careful in the early going not to punch my whole arm through something because the rest of the arm wasn't completely protected. I didn't want to bring a pile of bricks down on me. I don't punch with it much anymore. I've developed an instinctive slashing technique. That's the first move when something jumps me. I can fire that sucker up at the blink of an eye.

I've never been able to figure out whether its effect is of heat, cold, radiation, or molecular destabilization. But if you can imagine one of the *Star Wars* Jedi lightsabers that takes the outline of somebody's hand, that's it.

I can't moderate this force too much. If I'm real careful I can keep it super-low and just amplify my grip strength – quite a bit, like Superman – which is how the thing started to develop in me. But there isn't much after that except the full-go. I'm like that Navy SEAL who walked off from a bar brawl because he didn't know how to fight any more. "I only know how to kill," he said.

When I crank the Gleam, the Axe-Hand, up, anything I hit or stick with it is a goner, at lease in a vital spot. Going to lose blood and tissue, that's for sure. There are a couple drawbacks with that, though: I have cooked up by that same DNA lab-with-a-*Star Trek*-"Beam me up, Scottie!"-transporter that had sent the Troll after me early on in this book. (You remember the hunt for those witches.) Sometimes we call the little flying ones *Gremlins*. That or *Bogies*.

They were really ugly critters. They looked like grey, leathery bats that weighed about half a pound each, but they had un-batlike heads, hornlike ears that could have been antennae, and bony four-inch stingers like big mosquitoes. The first one of them scraped my denimed right thigh with its nozzle and left a scratch that burned like fire and absolutely infuriated me with the insensate things. A straight shot from one of those doohickeys would fill you with enough jism to kill a hippo, probably quickly. I let out a roar that just let the others in on where I was, and the little flock took turns dive-bombing in from all directions.

I backed against an old brick wall and got my Hammer Hand going, slapping them out of the air, but it was tough tracking them in the dimness. This was going to be a hard game to win, at least without taking a deadly wound. Most natural animals would have backed off with fear for their lives by then, at least after I swatted down the first handful. There had to have been a dozen left. But the mindless critters weren't natural, even if they were killable. They had single missions for which they had been programmed by whoever made them, and they were just smart enough to get them done. In my experience of these things, they were going to drop dead or go into some form of hibernation back in the realm that sent them soon after their missions were done, anyway. They could have had three-hour life spans. There was nothing for them to gain by backing off.

I actually think my outrage worked in my favor, because otherwise I doubt I would ever have thought of trying to coat my whole being with the same barely-visible gleam that coated my energized right hand. I remember at the moment being inspired by films and literature of protective force-fields, and started envisioning the gleam of each hand creeping up each arm and coating my upper body.

I could actually see it. By the time I swatted one of them down with just an elbow as it made a pass toward my torso, I knew it was working. I reflexively slapped one nasty little kamikaze that fluttered and buzzed my neck and eyes, but otherwise I stood tall and let the full flock dive-bomb into me. It was satisfying to watch them, one after the other, stick, squeak, and drop.

under a tree-shadow on a fall night…

Imagine me, who has more power than you do, but who sees these things and knows how they might come in and strike. Imagine me, who is often a target, shining for them in the darkness. Like bugs to the porch lamp, they can find me. I'd love to go out and get hammered, get stoned, forget it all once in a awhile… There are times of the year that I never rest – only around a bunch of other trusted Collegians – because if at any point I drop my guard, whatever I should be afraid of may be coming. It will hit by surprise because that is the time you hit any foe. So I am seldom off alert.

Why should I be? When I'm running in the woods and I think I see a scarecrow-like human form along my trail only to see it, at second glance, lapse back into a small tree… Is it a visual effect of the foliage and the fading light? Is it one more potential foe keeping up the scouting?

6

The abilities I have are so so implausible that I've spent a lot of time wondering about their development. I've gone back over my life and looked hard at my earliest memories. You see that the first signs of my Gleam, the Axe-hand, might have been that peculiar grip I observed in my youth. I see now that it was probably due to an innate channeling of psychic ability or *Source* amplifying the natural strength of the hand like a psychokinetic extra gear. From there, I worked at the gift, and it just got better.

The Gleam has been a handy tool and weapon, but I was little more dangerous than a good knife-fighter until I developed my defensive Glow. I remember the first time it might have hinted at itself. I say "might have" since it's a memory from a long way back, and it made no sense to me at the time. It came near the end of the summer before my senior year in high school. I remember the evening crazily well.

It started at sunset. My best friend and I had a couple hits from a hash pipe under a shelter in the orchard behind my parents' house. Rain started and ended as abruptly as a burst of tears. Beads on the leaves and branches about us were licked with tangerine from some source we could barely see. Everything stilled as the sun dipped, and we stepped out to find the open sky at a testy peace. Coal-factory clouds packed the western horizon. A peachy middle-ground gave way to the ridges to our east and the thickening blue of the drawing dark. We set out walking.

That town is full of visual intrigue: old farms, historic homes, classic churches, and a couple impressive vistas of the ridges about the Connecticut River Valley. It has patches of undeveloped and surprisingly rugged ground.

# Chapter 10
# The Chimies

1

You can tell I'm retiring. I've told you about my powers, my "magic" skills. They are fundamentally and personally physical: fighting, protecting myself, and levitating my form. I bet they are not what you were expecting out of a wizard. You were expecting vast wisdom and perhaps a steady dialogue with spirits and supernatural beings. You were expecting me to hold enchanted artifacts and use them to cast powerful spells. But in an overview, this picture I have presented of my abilities is fairly consistent within the College, at least what we can observe of each other.

We Collegians, in a broad stroke, work virtually exclusively with knowledge/information *or* power. We know things or we can do them. That actually makes sense in the light of my theory that all "magic" is an enhancement of human psychic abilities. This is the way good parapsychologists classify psychic talents. ESP (extrasensory perception) is informational. PK (psycho-kinesis) is physical. They have some very logical ways of explaining it.

Now, sometimes, I hear, they think the two, ESP and PK, may barely be related, other than the fact that they are both psychic forces. Others begin to call them "Micro-PK" and "Macro-PK." This means, basically, "Little Psychic Force" and "Big Psychic Force." The reason they may do it like that is because the amount of physical energy needed to move any object in the material world should be a Hell of a lot greater than that to receive or transmit a simple thought.

And indeed the type of physical force that any tested individual could exert using PK has typically been very small. This is what made the Cold

211

War-era Russians give up trying to weaponize PK: too weak, too moody. This was why the U.S. tended to focus on information/ESP talents, especially remote viewing.

I think the testers' problem was that they left the psychological components of mood and necessity out of their calculations, testing their subjects in the sterile and controlled conditions of the lab. Other than wanting to pass a test, there was no real motive for their subjects to do anything. They over-tested their subjects, too, working them till they were exhausted. They didn't get the best of the candidates, anyway. No one trained and employed in the College – and no Elder in one of the world's traditional systems – would have any incentive to sign up for that kind of prodding. They were getting beginners and Junkies.

I have one aptitude left to tell you about, and it's the strangest of them all in the light of all the above observations, since I really shouldn't have it. I won't call a power since it's more of a gift. It's the one informational talent I have, the only receptive power in my limited set of "extra" aptitudes. It may be a personal quirk as well, and one that has nothing to do with my life in the College. It's the gift that surprises me the most. At the direst risk of echoing the line from *The Sixth Sense*, I have to confess: *I hear dead people.*

2

The reason I dread parodying a phrase from a popular film, even if it's true, is that film and TV so far is so poor a teacher about the ghostly. Sometimes some program or other might say something accurate, but to even suggest that one minute of it is right is to give people the idea that the other 99% might be right, too, which is a disservice. The public doesn't read the fine print. But I have to affirm it: I hear "the little voices." You've seen me mention this before.

In almost every indoor space – and many outdoor ones – at which people have lived, gathered, or died, I hear voices behind the veil of reality. "The Chimies," I call them. These voices are not coherent. I can't talk to them. They don't talk to me. If I ever hear a recognizable word out of them, I consider it an accident.

The "spirits" I hear, if spirits they are, are site-based. They pertain to buildings, usually with dense or long human habitation or dramatic activity. They cling to spaces on the landscape like monuments and battlefields.

I often call them "the little voices" since almost all of them are faint and high. They impress me with a childlike quality. They don't communicate; they emote. They don't speak; they feel. Because of the musical quality to their tones, I think of them almost like *vocalise* (VO-ca-LEEZ), that musical style in which the human voice is used as an instrument, usually in the background, without forming any words. One of my favorite jazz musicians, Pat Metheny, features the voices of several people doing vocalise on one of his popular songs, "Last Train Home."

But the Chimies are a long way from distant spirits in another realm continuing to express themselves with song like birds in the meadows. They aren't just the echoes of ancient voices, either, at least not completely. The Chimies react to situations in their immediate environment, in the moment. Maybe they read people's minds (telepathy). Maybe they anticipate the future (clairvoyance). Maybe they detect the emotions, even the pheromones, in the living persons in the space. Whatever the means, they sense the intentions of living people better than some of the people around them. They know when trouble is coming. If you can detect this buzz, it's a real advantage in a crisis. The Chimies are often my first clue in a negotiation that things could be heading south. I always try to schedule my touchy encounters for places in which there are likely to be Chimies.

The Chimies are only semi-conscious. They have an emotional sense of intelligence that I would put at about the level of young children or even companion animals like dogs and cats. They know what keeps them comfortable. They know what freaks them.

There can be dozens of these voices, even, seemingly, hundreds, in really old, powerful places. They seem all ages and strengths, these Chimies. That, or "the Cheepies." I call them that a lot, too, because when they get really excited – usually a trouble sign – they go up even higher in pitch and lose most of their musicality. They go from open-mouthed hums to shrieks and eeks and eeeeee-hs. It's truly quite eerie when they hit that stage. It's a real distraction, too.

I'd seriously use the old "Sixth Sense" line, "I see dead people," substituting *hear* for the verb, except that I don't think they are dead people. I don't think they're really spirits, at least what most of us think of when we use the word. I think this for a couple of reasons.

For one, I don't believe that, once the coil has slipped, the higher form of us has much attraction to the physical spaces of the earth. Whatever's lasting of the human dead has left their graves. Even their former homes are no longer theirs. I know the TV psychics make a big deal out of "unfinished business" for human apparitions (ghosts) and psychic displays at haunted sites, but these displays look pretty paltry to be from the evolved and parted soul/spirit of the most intelligent organism on the planet. And the displays the ghosthunters catch look like accidents or pranks, not attempts to express something. And the ghosthunters stalk them like they're wildlife in a rain forest. You think they don't hear you coming? You and your eighty pounds of gear? I don't think the human dead have a physical place, at least not the highest forms of us. No, the Chimies are something else.

3

You've probably heard of "white noise." The ghosthunters make such a big deal out of the swishy sounds they get when they leave the amped-up mikes on all night in an allegedly haunted site. They think that if they can manufacture words or phrases out of it, it's an attempt of "the spirits" to communicate. Think whatever you like. I think it's all an amalgam of faint or distant natural sounds.

But have you heard of "pink noise"? Pink noise is the static clutter you heard between stations in the old days on your car radio when you did the tuning by turning a knob. Pink noise has all the industrial fuzz of white noise, but it's also got a trace of a hum, a faint jangle of musical tones and instruments.

The Chimies are like that, if you can imagine them just as voices. They are clearly pink. Sometimes they're even red. They have a musical tone. They're as confusing as if they had the hiss, but they're like loads of humans humming at the same time, and most of them far away.

Most of the time when I enter sites, the Chimies are merry to encounter me, chirping like happy children. It's like it entertains them when someone who can perceive them comes along – or else they're like that all the time, in a semi-conscious state of existence. They do not make what you would call works of tonal art unless you can joyfully listen to the exertions of Philip Glass. It's like children's voices at varying tempos and pitches making attempts to yodel in chorus.

They could be partly the echoes of conversations that had once gone on in those places, and to some extent I think that could be involved – reliving old dramas – but that's not the whole explanation. The Chimies react as situations evolve and change. They like things calm and peaceful. They like new people. It's like we're all a sort of TV docudrama for them, and they look in on us like we're a fishbowl for them. They dislike suspense. They hate pain and violence. If someone they don't trust enters the space, they react. When something scares or irritates them, their voices start to lose their music.

Imagine a hundred merry conversations in a crowded restaurant with poor acoustics. You have trouble enough following your friends at your own table. You can't understand anything around you, but the tone is consistent. Then… a child falls out of a high seat, a woman gets up and starts stripping, or Godzilla plonks down a columnar leg outside the storefront. Without even seeing whatever it was, you could tell that something happened in all three of those situations from the sudden near-silences, then the altered tones. That's what it's like for me when I'm in a place that hosts the Chimies and something is about to change in the living situation around me.

Some of the times that I have been invited somewhere with the goal of dispatching me, the voices were often my first clue that I was not among friends. That doesn't help me as much as you would think. Just because the Chimies don't like someone doesn't mean I can't work with them. I've had to deal with some pretty desperate characters in my decades in this role. People don't have to be friends to be allies.

The Chimies have a sense of justice about them, too. I have been at sites at which there was trauma – murder-houses – and here the voices are not so happy. The voices were absolutely cheering when Danny Montour and I put an end to that batch of child-killers.

I have never met anyone who has claimed to hear something precisely like the Chimies. It's no wonder that no one has said so, at least in the College. That's the last community you want knowing your secrets.

I tell no one about these Chimies. There's no advantage in it. A Townie would think you're crazy. In the College, well, they'd probably believe it, but then it would get into the gossip-wagon. Even a friend might get loose and talk to someone who isn't a friend – or one who is then and isn't later. If any of my someday-to-be-opponents gleaned that I have this informational power, I'd lose an edge. They would be trying to figure out ways around it.

4

The capacity to hear the Chimies is my only perceptive power. It's the hardest for me to figure out.

The reason it seems so odd to me to be able to have an extrasensory – informational – gift in addition to what I presume are my psychokinetic ("magic") powers is that, based on what I've seen of the College, what I've read of the great psychics and mediums of the past, and what I know of parapsychology, people using their psychic faculties can either know things or do them. There's often a little overlap, as you'd expect, because life isn't so tidy. I guess that's my overlap. I'm not saying it makes sense, but it's consistent with a pattern.

Just look to the past, the Victorian Era, the heyday of Spiritualism. The performance mediums who could produce or evoke material effects didn't tend to be very good psychic readers. People of one bent tried to claim they worked in the other because the public expected to see both of them at all events, but it was usually an afterthought, and often a flop. Case in point, the marvelous levitation-medium D. D. Home, who was not much of a speaker to spirits. The still-controversial Davenport Brothers never claimed to speak for the spirits at all; they just got up on stage and did wonky things. The good psychic readers who promised to produce the physical effects were often the ones busted faking them.

While I think the famous Fox Sisters, founders of Spiritualism, were probably good mediums, they may not have been directly responsible for the effects of rapping and other things that went with them in their early years. To me the situation seems fairly simple: One of them was the "focus," as they call it, of poltergeist phenomena, what we often call, RSPK, "Recurring Spontaneous Psycho-Kinesis," which basically means, "Crazy stuff keeps happening and nobody knows who does it."

RSPK is thought to be an involuntary response of the unconscious mind of a human being, typically young and under stress. It is, I think, an uncontrolled venting of *Source*, the same force I think all Collegians use. The reason the Foxes got busted faking it later in their careers is because poltergeist phenomena is temporary. The outbreaks almost never last longer than a cycle of eighteen months. The cycle timed out. The effects almost never happen to adults, either. Whichever sister was at the root of it all aged out.

I remember from my earliest years that I could hear these things, these wordless, toneful voices I call the Chimies. I told my mother about them when I was really little and she didn't buy in. I figured only kids could hear them. Then I told my siblings and a few of the kids at school about them. That was the point at which I figured I'd better give it all a rest. I learned from an early age that other people didn't hear the Chimies. I just figured it was one of my peculiarities.

When I entered the homes of my school friends I could tell how active – and how happy – some of their homes had been. I could hear tension, sometimes, too.

I've been in negotiations that I didn't think were dangerous but that were setups. I've been in places that would have been dangerous to anyone. I've been with strangers who were simple murderers, and on that site, sometimes in the very room. In that sense, my attempted offing would have been nothing personal or professional. I've been alerted by the tone, or the change in tone, of the Chimies.

5

You have to be wondering how I can ever feel alone, how I can ever have any privacy, feeling accompanied every moment of my life. I have a couple of reactions to that.

One is that the Chimies aren't everywhere. I can't hear them everywhere, anyway. In the air, on the water, or in natural space that never had heavy human habitation, I don't hear much of anything. When I drive on paved routes that seem dead to me, like stretches of the I-90 in New York or the lots of most of our strip malls, I sense no voices even when I stop to listen for them. When I speed sometimes over power-tracks like the leys in Europe or old Native trails anywhere, I sense that there might be voices, but they're behind me when I should have heard them. The next may be ahead, but not for long, and they're by me before I catch them. Too fast, too faint.

It reminds me of the tale about the Australian aboriginals and their "songlines" all through the outback. Their whole culture had based an aspect of its spirituality on the proper songs to be sung as people walked by certain places on the landscape. These songs were elaborate and measured. Musical, rhythmic, they were easier to remember across the generations, and they helped preserve many of the culture's legends and site-traditions. The buildup, the crescendo, and the wind-down were meant to be delivered at a walking pace. One day some anthropologists gave a ride to a couple aboriginals and noticed them in the back of the jeep singing at high rates, attempting to deliver the traditional songs as they rode by the traditional sites – at about five times the walking speed. They just about hyperventilated. Finally, they gave up.

My Chimies sing like that all the time.

So many of the indoor spaces I frequent have them. When I go into someone's house, say a young family home, I may hear nothing, or very little. In the forty years of its existence only ten people could have lived there, thirty slept there, and only a hundred may have ever even entered.

Only a small number of them could have any emotional connection to the site above so many others they could have loved or dreaded in life. If they happen to be focused on that place, they might be active there after life, and I might hear them. They have the optimism and the anxiety of children. But they are just buzzing, dreaming, almost raving – though they are very seldom agitated. They are just active. They chatter in half-sentences the way babies make their babble. They are unfocused.

When I go into a grand building like an old family home, a historic inn, or a church, now this is different. There are more voices. They are louder. I hear them more clearly and individually, too. American buildings may have a lot of life per year in them – human history is a lot speeded-up in this country – but very few of them go any farther back than two centuries. When you compare this with some of the indoor spaces in Europe… I don't think I could focus on much else in those scenarios. If I were in Chartres Cathedral, I think I would have trouble taking a knife-fight seriously because of all the Chimies I'd hear – at least if I didn't have a way to tune them out. Fortunately, I have. Just the way I've learned to avoid talking about them, I have learned how to stop listening to them in most normal conditions.

You tune things out, too. I'll go back to my analogy about the crowded café or pub. Think about your last experience in one. You remember conversations with your friends. The ones around you fade right out. You took little or no note of them, at least enough to be memorable now. The only thing you might have noticed would have been something truly loud or outrageous, or aimed at you, which would mean that it became part of your conversation. That's like my reaction to the Chimies. I tune them out until I decide to check in on them.

6

So what do I think they are, these Chimies? Are they ghosts? Nature-spirits? Devas? My own intuition?

I think the Chimies could be the lowest forms of the human psyche that are left behind on earth. I think they are the immaterial essences that stay at places that were significant to people before they died. I do not think they are complete human spirits. I think they are the "low" parts of the soul.

I am not alone in thinking that we may have several aspects to our immaterial, inner selves. Many world societies have believed that there may be more than one component to the soul. The philosophies are so numerous and intricate that I think I should only suggest the matter with an example or two.

The Hawaiian power-people, the Kahunas, are regarded in many circles as some of the most powerful indigenous elders in the world, as a class second to absolutely none. The Kahunas have a very solid theory about the three components of the human psyche. Only one of them is the aspect that ascends, what we would recognize as "the spirit/soul." The other two are more likely to stay earthbound, and one of them – but for being immaterial – is pretty brutish.

The upstate Iroquoian Nations including the Mohawk have their own informal division among the ghosts and spirits of their own, or at least their ancestral storytelling seems to say so. One less-coherent and less-conscious element of the psyche is that responsible for most of the ghosts people talk about seeing in most of the Longhouse tales. Another – the highest element of the human essence – is that that rises up, if it is worthy, to be with the Great Spirit. It may be this that comes back and communicates directly with living loved ones when it's absolutely needed. And again, there may be a middle-soul in between them, as with the Kahunas, and this may be the crisis-apparition.

Parapsychology seems to agree with the general picture. Ghosts (apparitions) and spirits (personal essences) are not presumed to be one in the same. When you interview a serious eyewitness, it's usually easy to figure out which sort of thing they report experiencing. One is a site-bound apparition, your typical haunted house. The other is a reach-back from a late or soon-to-be-late loved one. Usually one of you is in a jam. They're about to die or you're in trouble.

Now, do I think the people behind the voices of these Chimies died on the spots they seem to occupy? I do not. In many of the places in which I have heard the Chimies, few people if any have ever died. Has anyone died in your house? Your apartment? If so, how many? Enough to make a chorus?

No, I think the Chimies may even be semi-migratory, though I have no basis for this other than my intuition. I think they unconsciously drift to just a handful of places that were significant to them in their human lives: churches, family homes, schools, and, yes, places that haunted them, such as their death-sites. Like moths to porch lights, they flock, I think, to human action. They to go to spaces that comforted them in life or that obsess them after.

Because almost everything given enough time has served as one or the other to someone, in really old cities like London or Venice it's hard for me to find any building in which I do not hear them. Even new buildings are atop the sites of older ones, and that to me seems to be the variable: the site itself. In many places in the U.S., the Chimies are pretty faint. I do find that in communities people have really loved, the Chimies are more common. Saratoga Springs is full of them.

# Chapter 11

# The Magickal Battle of Britain

## 1

We all need someone to cuddle with now and then, even wizards. We're still human, and humans are a social species. We need someone to talk to – that way, at least most of us. We also get horny. It's different in my case from being a Muggle 17-year-old, but it's definitely still an urge.

As I've told you, Dana Lambert and I are intermittent lovers. We affect the transactions without a lot of drama. When she's passing through the upper Hudson Valley she often gives me a call and stays over. She even likes my healthy but fairly bland vegetarian cooking. Sometimes we have interludes when we travel together on missions for our mutual employer. We may not see each other for months afterward. It's wonderful for each of us to have someone like the other.

Neither one of us knows anyone in the College we might be interested in. Most Collegians, even the few who do not look pretty old, are jaded. Something like real love is an outgrown emotion for them. The capacity for attachment truly can change rapidly and dramatically once someone begins channeling *Source*. If you got a few decades out of your generation, saw the years take their effects on everyone else, and saw all your old connections fade away, you might get a little jaded yourself. I still remember that conversation I had with Nadia Whitney-Hadel, my dear friend and fellow member of what we sometimes call 'Team Jaap.'

Nadia's a pleasant-looking African-American lady fond of gypsy-style dresses and scarves. She's at least 200 years old. I think her first name at birth might have been Magnalia and she went to the version we all use in the early 1900s. Her last name comes from the two names of the Louisiana plantation on which she was raised. She could have called herself anything at the Emancipation, but what she picked was a means of distancing herself from and yet reminding herself of those roots. Nadia taught me a lot of what I know about Hoodoo and Voodoo. Yes, they're different. She's one of Jaap's verifiers and also best friends with Dana Lambert. She's had seven children, all of them in her pre-College life, the mid-1800s, and none of them went College. She took an interest in them throughout their lives and looked out for them wherever they went. Things got awkward when some of them started to look older than she did. She started thinking she had to detach herself to protect her own heart. After that she cut ties with her grandchildren to keep them out of the College's turmoil, letting them fly to their own fates as if she had lived a natural span and disappeared like she had died.

I know she didn't stay uninterested. It all came out when a crew of us were on one of Jaap's errands. We were all trying to sleep one night in a fine Edinburgh hotel and somebody got to wondering where Nadia was. We found her in the hotel lobby at 4 AM taking in a Falcons game on cable. At first she just said she couldn't sleep, but at one point in the second quarter a player got hurt and she gasped in a way that had to be personal. She was in such a state when they carted him off on the stretcher that we got her to talk, and we saw what she'd been holding in. One of her great-grandsons had turned into a killer linebacker who played for a couple of NFL teams, and even on the job she tried to catch his games. I think she's tried to keep long-range touch with them all like that. The number of them could be in the hundreds by now, and the triumphs and tragedies have to be mounting by the day.

I don't know if full Collegians can still have kids. I would think so, but I can't think of any right now who do, at least not ones born after *Source* really started working in them. I know Nadia wouldn't be interested. "Because I can't stand to watch any more of them die," is what she said when I asked. I still remember the look in her eyes.

Most Collegians love their animals more than other people. Some of the animals that hang out so closely with the workers of *Source* develop long lifespans themselves. That old stereotype of the witch and her familiar has to come from somewhere. One of my cats hasn't changed since she hit ten pounds. It's at the point that the vets are getting suspicious. Time for new vets.

It's hard for evolved – compassionate – Collegians to have decent love affairs with Muggles. Most of them are children to us, at least to the really old Collegians. I'm not at that point yet. I still have a fairly young heart. But I've grown into myself the way I am, and I couldn't touch any but the most evolved, successful Muggle. It would be too damaging for her. She has to be so secure that losing me won't hurt her – and that she can cut me loose when I fall short of expectations, as I always will. My work, my moods, my travel... I go places no one not of the College can go. I also have secrets.

I've had affairs with some seemingly-secure Muggles, some of which I've mentioned to you. I've been with heiresses and artists and one actress whose name you would know. I had some kind of affair with a lady singer and guitar player who made a big splash among the other artists but never really hit with the public, largely because of her drug issues. She could do without me, that's for sure. She dumped me – or else it was the drug that dumped me, because I was always trying to straighten her out. She was the subject of a popular song of the 1990s, titled with her first name. I won't give you any other clues. She's passed on by now.

You might wonder how I ever crossed paths with some of these glamorati, but that's not such a miracle. Some Collegians really are in the higher rungs of society. Some of them like Albert Frontiere like to grandstand, and you're likely to meet anyone at their parties. Muggle celebrities are at the top of their own world, but they tend to be fascinated by people who don't need them, as well as people who seem to know things they don't. Very few of the Muggle stars ever get the picture of who the old Collegians are; they think of them as artsy eccentrics and spiritual gurus, but there is a definite allure about them. I think it was the droll Adam

Carolla who said, "Age is instant cool."

What really might get you wondering is how I ever connected with any of these women to whom I've alluded. It makes me wonder. Normally a man who isn't famous or conspicuously wealthy wouldn't be in the game with them no matter how composed he looked. Something about my "act" or whatever you call it impressed them. It didn't impress me about myself. Age, again, is instant cool, at least to a certain point. I was twenty to thirty years older than they were, all but for the singer, and I still looked like the boy-toy. There's a certain charm in that mix.

I admit that I do project absolute physical confidence. I have since my late 20s when *Source* really started to flow through me. Like an MMA fighter or a Special Forces operator, I fear no bully and no likely human situation, and the very thought of doing so never even comes to me. I understand that that can be an intoxicant to many women, at least ones within your league.

I remember one incident in LA with one of those "out-of-my-league" girlfriends – yes, the 80s/90s actress you would remember – when we were leaving an edgy cafe around twilight and had to pass through a dozen tough-looking inner city guys, apparently gang-bangers, to get back to her car. I could feel the tension in her hand on my arm, and I could sense her feel the calmness I radiated. I threw an arm around her, headed right down the sidewalk into the core of them, and smiled with assurance. They yielded to us, and we passed right through them. I was ready to gut the first one who made a hostile move.

The trick with the College/Townie connection is that most Townies of whatever status are going to want things to progress after the initial love-buzz drops off. Marriage, children, shared lives… That's about the point at which the Collegian cuts and runs, sometimes with a laugh. Plus, the Townies aren't going to look 30 very long. A lot of Collegians of either gender will drop them heartlessly when they age out. In short, the affair is almost always devastating to the non-Collegian.

That still doesn't stop many Collegians from having their affairs with Muggles, some of them promiscuously. It's frowned upon. It's even dangerous. It's a good way to shorten your life. You let your guard down, sleeping by a lover, and trouble could be coming if you let him or her feel exploited.

We've lost some famous Collegians in domestic knifings or shootings. I honestly think that's what happened to Jean-Paul Marat in 1793. I think he was a lot older than he was presumed to be, and that he was working for some dark players in the College. We all think there was more going on between him and Charlotte Corday than meets the eye. You see the result, don't you? She bled him out in his tub and was guillotined four days later. Two deaths. Easily avoided. Marat got what he deserved anyway. Many of us think the skin disease that beleaguered him was a lashback from some other Collegians for his deviltry with the Jacobins. I see no excuses for the Reign of Terror.

Most of the lost Muggle-lovers have been male. The lady Collegians tend to be better by a mile at seeing trouble coming. They seem less likely to display their conquests to make points about their prominence or desirability. They're less arrogant, plus less likely to be chivalrously protective till it's too late. They also pick better. The gay male wizards take the biggest chances of all, in my experience. Men are more impulsively violent than women, whatever their choice in sexual partners may be.

And so many of us who have developed long life spans get pretty shy about running any inessential risks. You'd think that, with our powers, we'd be bolder than anyone, but that isn't the case at all, at least in my observation. Not all of us are Arts Majors who can call our abilities up without preparation. Once people get into the groove of long life and great wealth, many of them get real precious about themselves. They see how long and how well they could live and they dread the loss of all that. We're like the *Sidhe*, the fairy-folk of Gaelic legend: We can get killed in combat, but otherwise age, sickness, and other factors of normal mortality don't affect us. We have more to lose than most people.

The old-time Muggles took risks for power and glory that seem utterly mad today. Some historians conjectured that the short lifespans of the ancient world had to be a factor in their choices. If you feel like you've only got ten or twenty years ahead of you anyway, why not put it all on one throw? Die king or die trying?

2

Since it was Dana Lambert who brought me into the College, it might surprise you that I have never told you about her "matriculation" – her own route in. One night so long ago that I can't remember the year, I asked her about it. It started in 1939. She was a girl of 19 hoping to contribute to the war effort and being groomed for work in espionage. And England was in big trouble. It stood alone.

The Axis Powers had knocked down all their foes in the continent. As far as anyone knew, it was the end of Britain – if the Germans could invade. If Hitler took England, he'd have easily taken, if uneasily owned, Ireland. With the Isles in Hitler's grasp, the Americans would have had no landing-stage to amass troops and war materials. There'd have been no D-Day. Without having to fight a two-front war, Hitler could have shifted forces to the Eastern Front against the Russians, which would almost surely have proved decisive. World War II could have turned. The world would be very different now. He was planning on coming for the United States in one generation. He had a hand-painted globe that suggested that.

Fortunately for Britain, the Germans had to cross the North Sea to get at her. To do that, they had to be sure their transport ships wouldn't get blasted out of the water. To do that, they had to knock out the British air defenses. The momentous clash the Germans called *Die Luftschlacht* ("the Air Battle") *um England* was the first major military campaign in history waged almost entirely in the air. It was a desperate moment, so desperate that the British were willing to accept help from any quarter, no matter how unlikely. Enter one of the oddest military ventures in history, "the Magickal Battle of Britain."

The list of Hitler's wacko notions includes more than theories about race. His relationship with occultism is ambivalent at best. While the Nazis were known for scourging most of the German occult groups into subsidence, they were also remarkable for almost magical concepts of

230

history, prehistory, and destiny that drove national policy and military decisions. Hitler sparked a global search for occult artifacts and mystery civilizations. His elite SS divisions were initiated in some neopagan rituals that turned them into fanatics. They could be bastards, but they were probably the best troops of the war. It might be said that the only occultism Hitler liked was his own.

Hitler implemented his mystical theories in the conduct of the war, and it hastened the demise of the Third Reich – all while repressing witches and Freemasons in his own turf. And as with the Jews, a lot of the people Hitler repressed had not thought of themselves as other than loyal Germans before, and they could have helped Germany in its war effort. It could have used its witches. Whether it knew it or not, The Third Reich was in a duel arcane.

You don't stereotype occultists as devout patriots, but when you are in a clash against the force that created the Holocaust, the normal boundaries come down. It seems as though the British people down to the village idiot were united in defense of their homeland. A handful of the most prominent British occultists came to the British war department offering to unite the others of their kind in nothing less than a magical campaign against Hitler, even hoping to be advised on the optimal timing for their ceremonial efforts. Something about their offer caught official attention.

It's still a mystery why an espionage organization would even bother. By 1939 most of the Western world had lost its faith in the power of magic to do anything at all. It had also gotten over its stereotypes that all witches were malicious Satanists. "It couldn't hurt," seems to have been the attitude from the top with this offbeat episode. After all, one of Britain's grandest traditions is that of its witches. Oddest of all might be the handler MI6 would send the British team: Ian Fleming, the literary father of James Bond, the swank, gritty Agent 007.

How do witches get an audience with the war department in the first place? The initial touch might have come through the notorious author/black magician Aleister Crowley, considered a wannabe in most parts of our College. Crowley had personal connections to a bisexual aristocrat, Lord Tregedar, working in MI5 of the British Secret Service. Crowley had written some pro-German articles in World War I, but that global conflict was a lot easier to be confused about. World War I was not a war of national and cultural survival for the British, and it held no Auschwitz. Crowley was always a trickster, anyway. Whether or not the articles were meant to be a blind, they were the perfect cover for Crowley's World War II work with the British Secret Service. He helped structure the occult effort against Hitler.

In October of 1939, British author/occultist Dion Fortune (Violet Wirth) – no witch of any type – set out to establish, train, and coordinate a psychic home-defense force through a series of letters to her mystical followers. She began with timed, group meditations based on the practices of the famous Hermetic Order of the Golden Dawn founded by a trio of British Freemasons.

On July 31, Lughnasa eve, 1940, in the thick of the actual air campaign, the founder of modern Wicca, Gerald Gardner, called covens all over southern England into an astral gang-attack on the German war effort in the Channel. The energy spent was said to have been so intense that five of the psychic soldiers died shortly after. Some have claimed that all knew this could happen and that those who died gave their lives willingly in defense of England. In that sense, the rite was almost sacrificial.

Whether or not the Magickal Battle of Britain turned the tide, *Unternehmen Seelöwe*, Operation Sea Lion, died on the drawing board. By 1945, the Reich collapsed. Hitler took his own life on May Eve, the German Walpurgisnacht, another night of ritual significance.

Here's another thing people forget: It was in 1939, shortly before the war started, that a certain very famous archaeological discovery was made, the ship burial at Sutton Hoo. Sutton Hoo, the name of the nearby village, is presumed to mean "South Village Hill" in Anglo-Saxon, often called "Old English." Sutton Hoo is in East Anglia, a part of England still named for the Angles, one of the original Germanic tribes. I know so much about it because I researched it. I still believe I was involved in escorting an item from it, that Runestone.

The ship burial at Sutton Hoo opened a whole new light on one major group of ancestors of the modern English, the Germanic tribes called the Anglo-Saxons. There were more tribes in England than just those two, but they were all entrepreneurial imperialists filling the power-vacuum left by the retreating Roman Empire. By the 600s they were morphing as tribes but still living in seven tidy if scrappy kingdoms, that murky, four-century period called the Heptarchy.

One of the greatest of the Angle rulers was Raedwald (sometimes Redwald) of East Anglia, today's Norfolk and Suffolk. His name means, "Strong Counselor," and he lived up to it. He made a series of bold, correct decisions, reputedly with the aid of an artifact etched with a runic spell. I think I transported Raedwald's Runestone. I sure transported something that looked like it ought to have looked, an incised lozenge, probably amber. It would have been next to my heart for weeks, at least through its packaging. It nearly cost me my life. That I will tell you about later.

The stone was was buried with Raedwald at Sutton Hoo, possibly just to get it out of circulation but possibly as sort of protective totem against an invasion of his former turf from the sea. There are others like it around England, and people had better leave the rest of them there. Once the tomb was breached, Hitler's occultists had a better line on things. At least that's one interpretation for the way things worked out. German agents were at least rumored to have snuck this item out of the dig and brought it back to Berlin. For Raedwald the item did pretty well, but it was a poison pill for Hitler, filling him with anticipatory confidence. His generals couldn't get him to see sense. When you look at the moves he made in that war, it's like something was giving him the worst advice possible and getting him to take it. Like MacBeth, Hitler should have made surer of the angels he chose to trust.

Dana Lambert had been assigned to this operation, the Magickal Battle of Britain, from the start. She worked with Ian Fleming as a note-taker, secretary, liaison, and gal Friday. She had more contact with the latter-day witches than he did. She knew Aleister Crowley. She knew Fortune and Gardner and other spellcasters, including William Seabrook and Florence Birdseye of the Voodoo-like American anti-Hitler rite even covered by *Life Magazine.* She knew the esoteric artist Katherine Emma Maltwood and thought her the best bet of the whole bunch to be a true Collegian, then or still.

That was Dana's introduction to the College. She came into the matter with no belief or interest in magical subjects, and surely none of either in the prospect of any abilities of her own, but that's how it started. She handled objects, including ancient power-totems, sometimes for hours a day. She started to feel things from some of them. It grew overwhelming. One day she told someone, and the game was on. It was discovered that she had an aptitude for telling the pasts of objects, typically the human pasts, the experiences of the holders and handlers. She was tested constantly during the war years.

Dana was challenged at first by her own gifts. They upset her Anglican attitudes, yet the evidence of them was more certain to her than the religion in which she'd been raised. Ah, there I'm with her. God, if She/He's there, plays damn hard to get.

She worked for the department for a few years after the war. Don't forget that was the Cold War era. Each side knew the other was working to weaponize ESP and other human psychic abilities. From perspectives of both the military and its espionage wing, Dana was an object of fascination. She saw that rather quickly. She liked having a decent job but had no desire for a career being studied like a lab rat and used like a tool. At one point she started faking failure in their tests. That's something they'd have seen through if they'd had more experience with parapsychology – or statistics. Being wrong too much is a phenomenon in itself.

MI5 started thinking she had lost her gifts or even that her successes had been coincidental from the start. She left the service in the year of my birth.

Because of her connections to the public occultists in the Magickal Battle, she had met people in our College who are not so public. From there it was a short hop into life as an Arts Major.

Dana hates talking about herself, and it's beyond the caution I've already told you about that's innate to our College. She rambled a bit when I got her going, but she did say quite a few more interesting things about herself.

She had been born in Salisbury, England, in 1920. Her constant exposure to the power-totems, she figures, and her channeling of *Source* is what's kept her looking like a trim 35-year-old for the last six decades. She has lived long enough in the U.S. to have lost most traces of her West Country accent. Most people think she may be Canadian, to which she is happy enough to answer.

Dana Lambert is clairsentient and claircognizant. "If you categorize people as AV equipment," she says, "I'm a receiver." She can hear people think. She is so sensitive to the pangs of others that she avoids certain parties, most bars, and anywhere else people overdo drugs and alcohol. That explains her standoffish pose in the climate of the 1970s Five Colleges when I first met her. Half the people around her were abusing at that stage of their lives. She was stepping back.

She has dramatic recollections of past lives and suspects that one of her former selves could have been one of the "sin eaters," that odd figure in many world societies who heals others by taking on the guilt of their transgressions. In her current life she has, strangely, almost no memories from before the age of seven.

Dana is a private and devoted mystic, but in no discipline that has a name. She does not consider herself a modern-day shaman, but she loves learning from shamanic practice. She has done ayahuasca. She is devoted to yoga. She is into plant medicine and something she calls "Evolutionary Herbalism." She is consistent, even religious, about her healing practices and diet. She believes that *frequency* – whatever she means by that – could be the future of medicine. She loves thinking about life from the perspective of the Four Elements, which she finds to be a marvelous system of insight into virtually anything earthly. I agree with her on that.

Dana's been a dancer her whole life. She may have been quite celebrated as a girl. She has a mirror in her studio by which she practices every day she is home. She refuses to let anyone see her dance anymore, though. It's almost a phobia. "I came to a place where I understood that I was using dance as a way of controlling my life," she said, "rather than expressing my self." Whatever that means, it's a loss for the rest of us. I've been in many parts of the world with her and seen her sway to music in many environments, at least until she realizes someone could be watching. Her subdued movements display a wonderful, almost African sense of rhythm.

She likes privacy more than most attractive women. ("Any noise I didn't choose is a problem," she once said to me about living conditions.) She lives part of the year downstate in a cabin in the middle of a private forest. She wonders how much society would be improved if more introverts were in charge.

It was as we lay by each other in the candlelight that she told me all this. I presume that her path into the College – her "matriculation" – had been like mine, through an outwardly casual meeting with Jaap Simon, probably brokered by another Collegian who spotted the right mix of talent and temperament. Jaap Simon could have have heard of her through any of her acquaintances in the Muggle occult community and her keen work in British intelligence. He really does move in those circles, and he has his feelers out for good people.

Once the pair crossed paths, well… I think a lot of folks could have detected *Source* running through Dana Lambert. But precisely how she connected with my employer as a Transcript Checker and became my eventual colleague, I don't know, because that's where she nodded off, and I haven't been able to get her back on the subject since.

I found out later from a mutual acquaintance that Dana may have been a close friend of the British antiquarian, dowser, and occultist T. C. Lethbridge (1901-1971), once Keeper of Anglo-Saxon Antiquities for the Museum of Anthropology and Archaeology at Cambridge. I always wondered if the connection to Sutton Hoo and Raedwald's trinket – and possibly Jaap Simon – might have come that way.

Tom Lethbridge could have been at least one of the models for Dr. Indiana Jones. He was a big man in British occult circles, and it would have been more miraculous if he and some of the other people I've mentioned hadn't come into contact, particularly during the war years. I do know that Lethbridge was in Iceland in the summer of 1939 on a venture with the public and historic explanation of being a mission of military reconnaissance, but that most of what he did was archaeological investigation of his own sort, doubtless using dowsing. I also know that he had some sort of falling out – at least publicly – with the military and the mainstream archaeologists after. Now, whether that was because of something connected to his work in Iceland, at Cambridge, or something else, I don't know, and I haven't been able to find out. Maybe it was all a front anyway. Maybe people decided he could do his best work publicly distanced from any kind of establishment. Why Dana wouldn't have told me all that on the night of the big expose was another mystery.

Dana was already snoozing beside me when I remembered something else I'd been meaning to ask her about, and of a personal nature, for the longest time. Years before that moment I'd been researching something else on microfilm and passed my eyes across a front-page *Paris Soir* story about a scandal involving an Olympic diver. The paparazzi – not sure they called them that then – had staked out his digs in the Olympic Village and come up with a picture of him stepping out onto the street. It was a burlesque right out of *The Pink Panther*. The woman pacing right behind him as if she'd been in his room with him was a dead ringer for Dana. Her dress and hair and everything was 60s-style, but even through the distortion of the viewing apparatus I was sure it was her. The resemblance was haunting.

The idea that I could have any certainty about it under the circumstances is silly. A lot of people look like each other at a distance, especially in black and white photos. There is, though, a distinctive feature of Dana's brow and nose from just the right angle, and this shot caught it perfectly. The reporters called her "an unidentified woman" and used words to describe her like *sculpturale* ("statuesque") and *allure Germanique* ("Germanic-looking"), which I guess may apply. Dana can be a remarkable chameleon with her appearance, and it's a great tool to her if she decides to don or doff the glam. I think I have always been put off by the initial "Squaw" guise I told you about at the beginning of our acquaintance. I've never been able to see her as she can appear to others if she feels like it.

Out of curiosity I went to the same paper for the next few editions to see if there was any resolution to the case, including the mystery-woman's identity. Quite a bit of ink was spilled in the effort. The diver was still in trouble, but they never settled on who the woman was or where she got off to in such a hurry.

As a matter of both curiosity and testing my own impressions, I've always wondered what Dana would say about that exotic incident. I have never yet remembered to ask whenever we've met up. I'm pretty sure she'd tell the truth about it. We're allies in every professional sense. We have no strings on each other, especially not over something that took place when I was a little kid. Then again, maybe she has some secrets even from me. I would be disappointed otherwise.

# DÆMONOLOGIE,
# IN FORME
## OF A DIA-
## LOGVE,

*Diuided into three books:*

WRITTEN BY THE HIGH
and mightie Prince, IAMES by the
*grace of God King of* England,
Scotland, France *and* Ireland,
*Defender of the Faith, &c.*

LONDON,
Printed by *Arnold Hatfield* for
*Robert VVald-graue.*
1603

Chapter 12

# Blood Drives

1

The stereotype is out there that all of history's repressed witches, at
least in Europe and post-Contact North America, were matriarchal pa-
gans, violently and tragically repressed by the mainstream society due to
a white-guy patriarchal complex that somehow made it from the individual and personal into the societal. I never got how that works, though,
how preferences and complexes that are individual and probably fairly
private can get whole societies to behave accordingly. I get even less how
that idea got stuck as a fixture of contemporary scholarship. It seems rid-
iculous. Is there any proof that life ever works that way? If there isn't,
why do we think like that?

I argue with the ethnic characterization, too. It's not just because I'm
a white guy. It's because all over the world, some kinds of spirituality and
magical practice – how do you draw the line? – have been repressed by
the mainstream. It wasn't by any means just European societies.

Most world societies of any development have had a mainstream (in-
group) supernaturalism usually called religion or spirituality, and they've
had an out-crowd supernaturalism they call magic or witchcraft. Most
often the supernaturalism they preferred was simply that of the dominant
culture. The supernaturalism they disliked was that of a repressed culture
within it. Most of society's witches have been its downtrodden. Well, *duh*.
Bill Gates doesn't need magic spells that usually don't work to get what
he wants out of life. It's poor people who turn to the shortcuts like magic.
They also buy most of the lottery tickets.

But if we go back for a minute to the matter of the European witch trials – I mean, how does a psychosis like that take over a whole society? – I think there is no single answer, and surely no simple one. British novelist, poet, and scholar Charles Williams (1886-1945) made a much-celebrated study of the matter in his book *Witchcraft* (1941).

A lifelong editor for Oxford University Press, Williams was a fine researcher as well as an occultist, a member of A. E. Waite's Rosicrucian outfit, The Fellowship of the Rosy Cross. He was also one of the celebrated "Inklings," one of those titanic wits in the Oxford circle of J. R. R. Tolkien, C. S. Lewis, and Owen Barfield. For nearly twenty years (1930s-1949), the Inklings were an informal literary club that met on Tuesdays at noon in that Oxford pub, The Eagle and Child. They read drafts of their own work to each other, including Tolkien's "Rings" books and Lewis' novels. They discussed literature, history, and philosophy. They were also irreverent. Many Inklings sessions ended with pint-fueled time-trials, reading aloud from the unspeakably fulsome prose of Amanda McKittrick Ros (1860-1939), widely accounted the worst writer ever published. The winner was the one who could read her passages the longest without breaking into laughter.

In Williams' analysis of the European witch-phenomenon, the victims of the persecution weren't all folk healers, local psychics, or pagan diehards. They weren't all Christian spinoffs like Gnostics or Cathars. Some were truly worshippers of the Evil One.

That sounds so crazy that it begs for clarification. Why would anyone go that route? Who roots for Satan? I think there were reasons in both religion and psychology.

Christianity has many spins, and its presentation of itself has changed a lot in general over the centuries. But it's never suited everybody in any age.

For the Golden Age Greeks who have given Westerners a lot of our fundamental attitudes, the prime religious conflict was not between a God and a Devil. It was between two gods who represented fundamental opposites in principles.

Apollo was the god of civilization, of basically the conscious mind. Apollo was very much an embodiment of self-discipline, sobriety, the urban environment, the clarity of mathematics, and living "the right life" by society.

His opposite, Dionysus, "the Twice-Born," was the god of the woods and basically the unconscious mind. Dionysus stood for intoxication and, among other things, unbridled sexuality.

From early on mainstream Christianity has presented itself as a pretty Apollonian faith, especially sexually, promoting nuclear families, hetero sex, and no sex of any kind outside marriage. That's its public face, anyway. For many people that sort of discipline doesn't work for reasons of simple temperament. For the most extreme among them, the deity partly modeled on Apollo's opposite made a better vent.

This isn't a simple discussion. Almost nothing in life is black and white. There are elements of Jesus and the Devil in both Apollo and Dionysus.

I see why Dionysus would appeal to some people. There are times when I like a little Bacchic revel. But Dionysus is not the Medieval Devil. He's alternate, not evil, and he doesn't bring with him the package of Hell. Why would anyone play such a dead-end game as to go with Satan?

I can think of a few possibilities. One is, of course, that the Devil, if there is one, might not be the being he/she is stereotyped to be. He or She could be the victim of a historic PR campaign. Another might be that he/she is a deceiver, hiding his/her real purpose, plus its end picture. I also think there are some people who truly enjoy being contrary, if not working woe.

2

The case of the Aberdeen witches (1596-7) makes for an interesting study. Some scholars think something exceptional was going on with it, and there may be something to that. For one thing, most of the drama of the British witch trials was in the future at that point. This one couldn't be said to be a copycat panic. For another, most of the material on it is in the city archives and not those of the Church. This trial seems to have been carried out by the witches' fellow citizens. Finally, the coven seems to have been tightly organized into nefarious specialties. A source as mainstream as *Man, Myth and Magic* – a series of Time-Life style books that were popular in the 1970s – noted this.

One Aberdeener, Isobel Cockie, pulled the old fairy-trick of bewitching mills and livestock. Her colleague Margaret Ogg could curse butcher-meat at a distance, presumably causing quick rot and even poisoning. Helen Rogie could sicken or kill her victims by making figures of lead or wax meant to represent them. That's a Voodoo-style technique known around the world. The Victorian mythologist Sir James Frazer would have called it one of his examples of homeopathic (or sympathetic) magic, "like influences like."

Isobel Strachan batted so far out of her league with classy younger men that she became notorious as a worker of love-charms. Isobel Ritchie made a special line of confectionery designed to ease expectant mothers, while Isobel Ogg's forte was the raising of storms like that that nearly settled for Jamie Stuart, King James I, on his way to and from Norway, the second time while ferrying his new bride. The witches had one gift that was common to all, that of causing "the sudden sickness," making their victims lay "one half of the day roasting as if in an oven, with an unquenchable thirst, the other half of the day melting away with an extraordinary cold sweat."

Now, again, I've told you that I firmly believe magic to be no more than the enhancement of human extrasensory abilities. It works in two fashions, channeling *Source* either by means of information/knowledge or by personal aptitude. Re the former, they can go by tools and formulas or they can go by appealing to supernatural beings, none of which I've ever met personally. And I don't think the Aberdeen coven was composed of any real Collegians, at least none who got caught.

But to get back to that coven idea and using the Aberdeen cult as a model, we see that they were remarkably specialized. That makes sense; you focus on one thing, you get better at it. It implies that if the coven wanted to get you, it had a series of options, each done by an expert. It also implies that if you take out any of its people, you take out a component of its strength – and invite a serious and frenzied lashback from multiple quarters.

That's what I thought had happened to me as I recovered after the dust-up in that dim Saratoga Springs parking lot. It was right after cleaning house on those losers in the 'Dacks.

3

So. Where was I? Starting wars? Oh, yeah. Rousting witches and all that. Yes, back on the last night of July, 1993.

I stood under the boughs of a tree, shaded from the overhead light that spattered ivory patterns on somebody's demolished Saab. I called Bella as soon as my head cleared. It was fifteen minutes after midnight.

I got her on her cell phone and told her I needed to talk. She was three blocks away, in midst of a night-long Lughnasa celebration that had started with a clandestine Wiccan ceremony by one of the ponds at the Yaddo, migrated to race-season kickoff parties, and was merging into the afterglow of a birthday celebration for one of Bella's former dance students, by then a woman of 60. I caught up with her an hour later, holding court at the head of a long table in the upstairs salon of one of the fine hotels on Broadway.

Trays of appetizers were cycling in from somewhere, which puzzled me. The courtyard bar had been thriving as I'd entered, but the kitchen was closed. It turns out that the trays were being walked over from a neighboring restaurant. Ah, Bella! She has connections.

Hair down, clad in a voluminous, deep green dress with whorling Celtic patterns and with several dark scarves about her, Bella looked like my image of the Morrigan in her matronal guise. I pulled a chair up to her left with my back to the length of the table.

I was hoping to get a quiet one-on-one with her, but good luck. She assured me that we were the only Collegians among the twenty people present, and the buzz of conversation and laughter seemed to ensure that we'd be able to speak confidentially. I updated her on the events of the preceding twelve hours.

"Well, of course you were going to get something started, Eric. You have to keep from letting that Danny Montour get you into trouble. His father's a good friend of mine, but that boy can be crazy! We've always worried about him."

"Saving a couple kids was something I needed to ask about?" I said with consternation.

"Eric, there are a dozen other ways you could have done it. Besides killing people."

"We had to act fast. The Elders were the ones. They put us on it."

"You can't go around killing people!"

"Bunch of psychos."

"You have no idea who's working for who in this world. And speaking of which, everybody knows you're in with Jaap Simon. Now they think he might be involved. Did you think of that?"

"How did they know it was us?"

"Eric, people know things. You should have seen that coming, too. How many people knew you two were going on that crusade? Do you trust all of them personally?"

I shrugged. I didn't know many of those Elders at all. And this wasn't the reception I was hoping for.

In the lull I looked around the table, observing Bella's merry, artsy, rainbow friends in full party-mode. I realized that because of our slang, somebody not exposed to our exact subject might think we were discussing politics in the Skidmore English department. Bella sure looked the part. "So who did we piss off?" I said.

"Well, that's the problem, isn't it? Usually people think about things like that before they blow something up. Now they know about you and you're the one looking for answers." I settled back and thought about that.

"Now listen, Eric. Every Collegian in the Northeast knows that at least one party like that was operating in the Hudson Valley. We've known that for a hundred years."

"Why hasn't somebody knocked them off by now?"

"Well, maybe it's because we couldn't find them," she said. "They wouldn't exactly be advertising. But maybe somebody, maybe several people, use them for business, Eric. You should have been able to figure that out."

I got it instantly. That explained the Troll. Somebody bigger than they were put them up to what they were doing. Maybe I should have been able to figure it out. "That's a Hell of a way to try to get something done," I said as I processed things.

"Everybody says they hate the blood-drive, but the practice can be effective."

"Didn't help the Aztec much," I said.

"It does work," said Bella. "The Aztec only prove it."

"Empire of millions. Five hundred Spanish peasants take them down."

"The Aztec wouldn't have run their part of the world so long if they hadn't had something propping them up. It took the X-factor of a totally new society from another part of the world to tip them over. The trouble is that blood-work is like credit. The debt keeps growing. Sooner or later the payback is due."

"Deservedly," I said.

"Don't lay it all on the Aztec like that, dear boy," said Bella. "Blood-work is a stage, and most societies go through it. With most of them it was a low-key practice that didn't last that long. In Mesoamerica it was a component of religion. It was all over Mesoamerica at the time of the Contact period."

"I didn't know people were still doing that. Our people. Collegians."

"I don't know any of our people who do the blood-work, but I've heard of people using people who do. I don't know any of them, either. But the blood-drive is typically very good at getting the answers to questions you can't get any other way. It doesn't matter who does the ceremony if it's done right and then you can piggy-back on it from a distance. You don't have to be the one if you can find a stooge. You know, some of us can get the Junkies to do just about anything. The real trick is to get the timing of everything exactly right."

"And stay free of the fallout…"

"That's what you turned upside down," said Bella. "Now people think you or Danny or Jaap are after the same thing they're after."

"How do you know all this?" I said.

"Because it's the only thing that makes sense, dear boy! Besides, we've seen stuff like this before."

"So now what do we do?"

"Well, what does Jaap Simon have to say about it?"

*Ooops.*

4

Something important had clearly shifted. I had sensed it at ten that morning, standing in the open door of my car and looking up to the sky. At first I thought it might be something in the natural world.

Every summer there comes that point at which you get the first hint of the early Northeastern fall. It's not always the same day every year, and it's probably your imagination anyway. I couldn't tell you what gave me the impression that that was the moment for 1993. It could have been a breeze that was not as lush as the day seemed to call for. It might have been a bank of clouds that simply reminded me of autumn. It made me realize that I ought to be enjoying what was left of the golden season. Winters are long in the Northeast.

Danny Montour seemed to be sensing something, too, as we drove, though I can't tell you for sure it was the first stroke of Autumn. We'd taken the less-traveled roads to get to Schenectady, and he seemed to be admiring the sky more than I was. I don't remember us saying much except comparing a few notes from the night before. We had just killed a few people, don't forget, about sixteen hours earlier.

It was noon the same day – Sunday, August 1 – when I realized that the shift I'd felt was in the College. It came as I was seated with eight other people around the long table in Jaap Simon's curio-cluttered meeting room.

When my eyes stray in meetings in Simon's office, I usually look down and focus on discolorations in the surface of the funky old ball-and-claw-legged table, matching the chair that supported me. When my gaze roams the room, I find myself wandering into meditations on the animal/vegetable/mineral curiosities on file-cabinets, mantles, and window sills. But this human cast kept me fascinated.

One was, of course, Jaap Simon, at the middle. The seat left open for me when I arrived was beside him at his right. Danny Montour took the one beside me.

To Jaap's left were our two transcript-checkers, Dana Lambert and Nadia Whitney-Hadel. At the head of the table to my left was Sia Lund, "The Ghost with the Bronze Hands," in his snappy navy Adidas track suit. I was glad to see him here. It had to be important. He really did have a striking resemblance to David Carradine as Kwai Chang Caine in the 60s karate Western *Kung Fu*.

The seventh person at the meeting was Albert Frontiere, seated across from Jaap. What the Hell was he doing here? Albert spends lots of his time in the States, but he is pretty much a west European Registrar, at least when he feels like working: France, Germany, Scandinavia, the British Isles... The eighth and ninth candidates, one on each side of him, nearly got me up and fighting.

One was the Doughboy who had just about killed me the night before. Those blows had come at me like strokes from a machine. It really did seem to me that he had undergone some sort of transformation as we'd fought, becoming something darker and even blunter than his balloony self.

As I studied him – his pig-bristle short hair, his dorky thick glasses, and his massive limbs – I wondered if he could have been someone truly famous in the College, maybe even in the legends of the Muggle world. The Golem. Hercules. Ajax. Surely he was at the very least an impressive assassin who used the look of stupidity as a guise. That's to be expected in these realms. People always have a hook, a blind, a wild card. Anyone who could play dumb and set up the scene the way he did was a master. And a stealth-artist. How did he and his partner track me to that restaurant? It was masterful.

He looked back at me with very little expression, maybe just the hint of a smirk as if thinking he got away with something. My first instinct was to wipe that grin right off him, to lance him under the table with my left and then go over it for the kill with my right.

My second instinct was to realize that this would be a mad, predatory, outrageous thing to do, especially at a conference brokered by my employer. For all I knew this was a peace treaty.

I nearly gasped when I was introduced to the ninth guest: Edmundo Frye. I knew he went by many names, but this one was famous in our circles. To even meet him – and know who he was – was breathtaking.

I'd never seen this guy – that I know of – but he surely matched the description: a slight, medium-sized man. He had weak shoulders, thinning brown hair, and little round wire-rimmed glasses. His T-shirt showed through at the throat of a patterned spread-collar shirt, topped by a cheap-looking brown poplin blazer. *Why does anybody come to a Sunday morning meeting in a suit, especially a cheap one?* I thought to myself. *Where do you get brown poplin, anyway?* He looked like the British musician Joe Jackson (whose work I like, incidentally).

I'd heard all about Frye from some pretty formidable characters, including The Ghost, Sia Lund. I'm not sure he was College. He could have been a Muggle, but with one exquisite talent: He was one of the world's great assassins. He could kill anybody he could get near, and he didn't just work for the College.

Frye didn't look like he weighed more than 150 pounds. He had no mass or muscle development to speak of, though looks can be deceptive. Refer to his blubbery sidekick. He didn't look like someone who should worry me, Danny, or The Ghost, but he could have been more dangerous than any of us, because he looks so innocuous that you would never see him coming. And when we're not expecting trouble, Lund and I are as killable as anyone.

Frye had gotten himself into the international martial arts community, which was surely where he and The Ghost had crossed paths. I

252

don't think he competed on the mats, but he showed up at conferences and competitions and was a routine figure at hotel bars and after-parties. He actually taught knife-techniques now and then, and he was highly respected. Could he demonstrate! Surely he had at least one slender blade on him somewhere. He had other talents he didn't teach.

Frye could sidle up to almost anyone, pick his moment, snake in a shot with an icepick or some other implement, and be off like a shadow. He liked public spaces. Cracks in crowds made easy getaways for a nonchalant slim-body, and the target may not even realize that he or she had been poked. The pain would be slight, if even perceptible. Even if his target's bodyguards spotted the jostle, they would let the inoffensive Frye get away. Out of charity, the victim might even call for it, suggesting it just a tap – a pulled muscle, a pinched nerve, or even a digestive complaint.

Before too long – Frye was on a bus or train by then – a little splotch of blood would start to be visible on the target's clothing, most likely in the lower back under several layers of fabric. It could take a while for anyone to spot the stain. Most would think it a wine- or coffee spill. Some who examined the skin might think it was the case of a picked scab or a bug bite. They might suggest a test for Lyme disease.

The real bleeding would be internal. In an hour, the target might feel sleepy or nauseous. He or she might collapse and die before getting to the ER. Frye by then would be in the airport bar, possibly where he touched down. I thought of all this as I looked at him.

I wanted to kill him, too. I was sure I could take him right out. He was an assassin, not a warrior. I would have to watch my back constantly – I'd never get a second's peace – if he was ever after me. And the odds were good that someday he would be, at least if he was sitting here across from Jaap.

Surely he felt me evaluating my choices. And he looked back at me without a trace of fear. I can't tell you whether that was because he knew I wouldn't try anything or that he had a separate plan of his own – or that he had "danced with Death" so many times that it was habitual. I can tell you that most people show more than that when I look at them like I looked at him.

I met Albert's eyes under that broad, pale forehead and backswept dark hair. Nothing at all serious had ever come between us, and I'd say that maybe I spotted just a touch of regret that I and his for-the-moment colleague had come to potentially mortal blows in a Saratoga Springs parking lot. Either that, or he missed holding court at his trackside champagne brunch on opening weekend at Saratoga Race Course.

Jaap Simon cleared his throat. "We've had some difficulties."

At that, the Doughboy and I met eyes across the table. He gave me that simpering glare. I was tempted to ask him about his 'girlfriend.' That little blonde was the wild card. She had saved his ample bacon.

"There's no reason for difficulties," said Albert Frontiere. "We just have to communicate."

Everybody drew a couple breaths. I was shocked to think that Albert and Jaap Simon might be on different sides of an issue. I didn't even know Albert did business in the U.S.

"Eric… Danny," said Jaap, turning to us. "You have to call me if you're thinking about doing something radical. We could have avoided most of this."

"The Elders gave us clearance," said Danny.

"The Elders have their own agenda," said Jaap. "And this situation has problems it didn't need to have."

I have known Jaap long enough to recognize his stage-voice. Danny, though… He looked at Jaap like he was really wondering about him. "You can't let somebody kill a couple of kids," he said.

"You have no idea of the way that scenario was constructed," said

Albert.

Danny gave me that look again: *Give me a break.*

"This was one part of an operation," said Jaap to the table. "There's been a high-level arrangement. Albert and I have communicated on this. Until now it had nothing to do with any of you. We have to cool this one off and keep it that way."

He looked around and met everyone's eyes. "Does anybody want to say anything?"

"Where's your little bodyguard?" I said to the Doughboy. I still had a headache from his blows.

"Eric, please," said Albert. "We have work to do."

"What kind of work takes that kind of medicine?" said Danny.

I couldn't read Sia Lund – who on earth could? – but the women to Jaap's left were still. I knew they were disgusted. This may have been their first exposure to the little ring Danny and I broke up. I think they were worrying about Jaap for the first time. They would bolt on him or anyone in a heartbeat who allowed a ceremony that looked like the one Danny and I had foiled. "Looked like," was the key variable here, though. I think we all got that. We live in a world of deception.

I felt a bit of motion to my right, and Danny stood, his chair making a loud squeak. "I hope you work it out," he said, and left the room. I know it was no act. He was in his Townie life, his first one, and he didn't know any better. It was perfect, at least if we were trying to sell something to whoever Albert was representing.

"Since before most of the people in this room were born, there has been a standoff," said Jaap Simon. "Some very important parties have been holding onto items that other important parties want. Recently, there has been a negotiation, a way to keep people moderately happy and break the ice. It was one of those very rare cases where there was an outright trade of items."

255

"This exchange was being mediated between parties who have been traditionally uneasy about working with each other," said Albert. "One of the parties was hoping to get some information about one of the items just before making the trade."

I got it instantly. *The ceremony.* The thing Danny and I had broken up. Because we were recognized to be Jaap's agents, that made it look like he'd ordered it. Since Jaap was at least assisting with one of the trade-items, it looked to anyone else involved like he was pulling an end run of the sort I always had to look out for. Now he had to show – loudly – that he wasn't.

In the meantime, someone freaked and sent the Goon-and-Girlie squad after me. If I hadn't stopped the pair, who knows how far they might have gone? After Danny for sure, then maybe Jaap, Dana, Nadia... Then The Ghost and some of the other Linebackers who work for Jaap would have retired, gone on a revenge mission, or made a truce and found new employers. It could have rocked the College. A lot of the traditional trade networks could have been over. Everybody might have been looking for new arrangements.

"There is – or was – a group of individuals in the Upper Hudson Valley who were very good at gathering accurate information about delicate subjects," said Albert. "They have been in business for at least two centuries. They've been very useful when the traditional arrangements are not being made under conditions of trust."

I'd never heard Albert speak so formally. He's usually pretty irreverent. I got his code language instantly, too: when someone has to buy an item without seeing it. Take it or leave it. Untraditional circumstances.

"I thought you were a European suit," said Nadia across the table to Albert. "What's your connection with this outfit?"

"One of the items is of European origin," said Albert. "Its transport and verification was my arrangement."

"So you put those people up to that...?" said Nadia.

"My employer in this arrangement is one of the acquirers," said Albert. "This party has never asked anyone how they obtained information. For the record, this was who made the arrangement with that group. It was also this party hoping to trade for the European artifact. It was they who enlisted the aid of Mr. *Gollum* and his associate."

The Doughboy and I regarded each other. I could hear him snigger behind those low-lidded, dead-fish eyes. Had Albert really called him by the name of the Tolkien character? Was it *Column? Collum?* Until I see it spelled I won't know which. I still hated him.

"I'm glad no one was hurt," said Jaap. "But we have to put this behind us."

He turned to me, clearly addressing the full table. "Eric... Danny... I've told people that we've never had any trouble with either of you before. All the parties are satisfied that this issue was based on a lack of communication. What we have to do is to move forward."

He met everyone's eyes. "We have to take over the movement of these two items. Eric, you and Danny have to be involved with this."

I thought rapidly. So would I be working with these people? With Gollum? With Frye? I have enough wisdom by now to know that people you like at first can turn into bitter enemies, and people you don't like right away can become wonderful friends. Was I going to like Frye one of these days? I didn't see it coming at all with Hulk. I hated him. But I got the picture. "What to where?" I said with resignation.

"First, this has to be acceptable to everybody here," said Jaap.

Frye across from me was impermeable. My respect for him was going up. The Doughboy looked like the cat that ate the canary. My hatred for him was holding steady.

Whatever Albert was thinking, he covered it up pretty well. But he nodded to Jaap and made an expansive gesture that again convinced me that he had been born into some Romance-language society. "How could anyone do more?" he said.

Albert and his pair had filed out. "Can we get Danny back in here?" said Jaap.

"He's probably stomping around outside," I said, reaching for my phone. "He can't get too far. He rode in with me."

Danny didn't answer my call, and the two women got up and went out to look for him. I was about to get up, too, but I could see that Jaap wanted to have a word. I stayed where I was.

For the first time I noticed that he wasn't in his work outfit, typically a collared shirt, tie, and vest, jacket, or sweater. He was in a polo shirt. It was like he'd come in off the golf course – or on very short notice.

"Eric, I know you and Danny thought you were doing the right thing," he started out. "But you have to think about your actions. You have to communicate with me before you do things that could step on people's toes."

The two women came in with Danny on the echoes of Jaap's sentence.

"What sort of world are we in when we let people kill children?" said Danny as he took Albert Frontiere's former seat.

"It's not what you two did," he said. "It's that Eric didn't communicate."

"What were we supposed to do with bastards like that?" Danny almost shouted. "Take them out for ice cream? Love them down?"

"You had hours," he said. "Call the authorities. Secure the children. Go through channels. Anybody would have understood that.”

"We couldn't call the authorities," said Danny. "The Elders didn't know where they were within twenty miles till the ceremony started."

"It would have been over by the time the troopers got there," I said.

"How could we explain how we knew where they were?" said Danny. "They'd think we were in on it."

"People are going to read into the things you do," said Jaap. "You have to call me."

"I work for you sometimes," said Danny. "I walk the Medicine Path always."

"I understand all that, Danny," said Jaap. "You can decline anything I ask you. Both of you can. But neither of you is employed to be a policeman. You've upset a balance. I can't tell you everything about this because we don't have all day. And it's sensitive."

Danny just glared at Jaap. I looked around uncomfortably too, and I met Dana's eyes sharing the same mood. This really was our first "trip to the woodshed" with Jaap Simon. We all liked him so much that it was actually worse. He could see that we weren't handling it well.

"OK," he commenced, looking like he didn't want to go further. "There are people you don't even know about that I have to work with. Some of them aren't very used to working with each other. You two busted up something at the fringes of a transaction that's been a very long time in the making. It's fortunate that people tend to believe me when I say things or this could have really blown up. But now we have to make a little show of setting things right. It's gotten personal. *You* have to make a little show out of it." He looked at me. His glance included Danny.

"What are the items?" I said.

"One of them is a very old, very powerful Native American arti-fact," he said. "It's been with an old Collegian in the Mohawk River Valley for quite a few years."

"Don't tell me this is a Mask," said Danny. He looked like he was going to walk out again.

"It may well be something like that," said Jaap. "But whatever it is is going to be delivered back to the Onondaga Nation. I would think that would be acceptable to you."

Danny sat with his arms folded. He was all right with that, I knew, if he believed what he was hearing. The Onondaga near Syracuse are more or less the culture keepers of the League of Six Nations. They hold many of the most sacred items of the Longhouse in trust, includ-ing a collection of what whites often call, "False Faces." That's what they would look like, but the term doesn't suggest their purpose like what the Longhouse people call them: *Medicine Masks.* They are very sacred to the Longhouse Nations of the Confederacy to which Danny's Mohawk belong. As a category, they are also some of the most dan-gerous items in the magical toolbox.

"You have to meet this item, and tonight," said Jaap Simon. "At a local site. Take it to the representatives of the Onondaga. I think you should all be in on it. It has the chance of being a high-pressure trans-action. There's no way to sugarcoat this."

"What about the other item?" I said. "The swap."

"That's step two," said Jaap, looking right at me. "To be an-nounced." We had a few seconds of uncomfortable silence.

He resumed, addressing the whole table. "This meeting was sup-posed to look penitential," said Jaap. "A peace treaty. There were some people who had to see it, or at least report to others about seeing it. Your participation in it to the end seems like an acceptance of all aspects of the arrangement. It would help sometimes if you would follow my lead, Danny."

"Whose oatmeal did we piss in?" I said.

"A Trustee had interests in the negotiation you interrupted," said Jaap.

*Oh, no,* I said to myself: Him. *Puff.*

# Chapter 13

# The Magic Dragon

1

So. The Big Guy was making a deal. He wanted something transported. He wanted me to see to the delivery. It felt momentous. It was
also scary, for a number of reasons. I guess I better tell you something
about him, at least insofar as I know it. I knew we'd get to this point
sooner or later. With Puff.

That's my whimsical nickname for him, anyway, right out of the
Peter, Paul and Mary song. I call him that for a couple reasons. One is
because Puff likes to let on that he may very well be sinister, ancient, and
seriously powerful, and "the Great Dragon" is one of the nicknames of
the Devil in Europe. If people want to think that means he could be the
real Devil or whatever was behind him… Well, he's happy with that. He
loves it, actually. It keeps everybody scared of him. And I've sensed something huffy and inflated about him from the beginning, including his con-
ception of himself, whatever I can read of it. So for me, he's *Puff*.

Nobody knows what he calls himself. They call him a lot of things:
The Big Guy, His Lordship, Himself, the Commissioner (or *Commish*), the
Chancellor (or *Chance*)… With Puff it's so often just, *Him*, that or another
Irish reference to a boss or head-of-household, *Himself*, often accompanied by a nod or a chuck of the thumb over the shoulder like someone
tossing a pinch of salt. Sometimes the thumb goes even slantwise toward
the ground. When they say it like that – with the gesture – everybody
knows who you are talking about. Nobody but me calls him *Puff*.

The guy they sometimes call *Old Scratch* tends to pick up nicknames,
too. Puff may not be the Devil, but people in the College regard him
with a similar dread. They think he's plenty enough to fix your wagon
for you. I'm not sure they all believe in God, but they may believe Puff

is the character behind all the legends about the Devil, here since people started telling stories. That's part of his clout. People think of him as... More than any of us. *Beyond*. Maybe he is and maybe he isn't. He's sure got the whole College buffaloed.

Nicknames are by their nature irreverent – dropping all sense of title or formality. This one I use, I hear, has attracted some notice. Some people, when I use the term, pretend not to know who I mean and ask for clarification. When I give it to them, they always nod and go, "Oh, you mean..." and then use their own favored nickname which they sense is more respectful in case someone who might report back to the subject could be listening. Nobody runs the risk of pissing him off. Somebody might tell him if you said the wrong thing.

That reminds me so much of the way the old Irish used to talk about the Little People. They'd call them something flattering like, "The Fair Folk," "The Good People," "The People of Peace," or just, "Them." Makes sense. They're powerful shapeshifters. One of them might be in the same room with you listening and pop you out of nowhere.

I detected something a little off about Puff from the beginning of my work with the College, as soon as people started to feel free to talk around me. When I asked about this *Big Guy*, *BG*, *Beej*, or *Him* they were referring to (with the gesture), that's when some of it spilled out. A lot more has come out over the years. It's not the first thing people tell you about.

Even Jaap Simon won't talk about Puff. With Jaap, you get the sense he knows everything, but he has this marvelously discreet way of slipping out of conversations that don't seem designed to do any good for business. As for some of my other confidants... Dana, Nadia... They don't know any more than I do. Bella might, but she doesn't say much. They all say just to enjoy my life, do my work, and stay out of Puff's way.

So, perhaps hoping to draw Puff out, I started trying to get in his way. Through the nickname and a bit of irreverent speech, I tested him at a distance, and I didn't hear a peep out of him. It had to stand out. Surely somebody told him there was this macho jackass Freshman Arts Major who thought he could whip the world and was failing to pay him instant homage. People who seemed to know him have let on that I better watch what I'm saying, and that – when I really say the wrong thing and live without being struck dead by a bolt of lightning or made into an example some other way – it's because I must be too small a fry for him to be worried about. Or else it's *really* coming. So far there hasn't been any perceptible fallout – unless some of the scrapes I've managed to survive have been messages, if not ever-escalating tests.

If looking for trouble like that sounds offensive and stupid to you, well, it does to me, too – now. Don't forget that when I started out in this business I was a lot younger than most people who end up in the College. As a young collegian, a Freshman, I was testing the limits of everything. I was a little full of myself when I discovered the Gleam and the Beam. I thought I could take on a T-Rex when I discovered the Glow and the Glide. That had to be what started those feelings of invincibility, the Glide. It was really heady. You should have seen me when I got hammered. Why not get on top of a mountain and sing it to the world?

Plus the attitude I read out of Puff through his snotty, smarmy representatives gave me the sense of something exaggerated about him almost immediately. I could see quickly that some of them got a sense of self-importance from speaking for *Him*. I didn't believe that anybody who hid behind all the posing and did everything through surrogates could really be so tough. I thought there had to be something Puff or his agents didn't want people to see. I wasn't convinced that Puff even existed. I thought it was possible that he was a construct of people who claimed to work for him to get everybody else kowtowing. Maybe that explains my attitude: just wanting him to show himself. Like the British poet Shelley, I "call'd on poisonous names with which our youth is fed." Like him, I'm waiting.

Of course, I've mellowed a lot in all respects in the last five decades of my life. Thank God on a number of fronts. I haven't been out to get Puff's attention in any way. I'm a lot savvier and even somewhat stronger now, and I know enough to know that you don't go asking for trouble. Anywhere, any time, especially with power-people. And he's surely one of those, if not way more. If there is a Puff.

But in our College, there are long memories. Somebody who may have have lived more centuries than some readers have years could wait a long time to pop the wise-guy.

Puff may also be precisely who or what he lets everybody suspect he might be, another character who picks up a lot of nicknames: Splitfoot, Old Nick, Bogey, El Diablo, The Great Deceiver, Auld Scratch, Hoofie… Dat Ole Debbil… Lucifer, Beelzebub, "The Lord of the Flies," Clootie… You got it. If that isn't clear to you who we mean, remember SNL's Church Lady saying… *Satan.*

That's why he scares everybody, you know: They think he might be next level. Unbeatable. Immortal. Beyond us all. Untouchable.

Nobody knows. We Collegians may have "magic" and do some amazing things, but we're not that much different than you, Reader. We're people. We know what we've lived through, and there are some long lives in our College. But we can't look into the other realms and understand the Universe. At least I can't.

But in the traditions based around the Bible, it says that the Devil – Satan, "the Opponent" – was given power on earth. If there is a Devil, he could probably kill us all effortlessly, but that's not a bit of his goal. We'd all go to Heaven if he did that. That would be a total loss, at least for him. His goal is winning converts – souls – away from God, because

God loves all of His creations and this is a prime way to offend God, to keep fighting Him. Satan was granted his fallen-angel power on earth because people were given free will, and their reward for living good lives was to come. If Satan could pull the wool over them, they were all, regretfully, his.

It wasn't going to go well for the Devil after that, of course. On the Judgement Day, "the Last Trumpet," at whatever point that comes, it's all up. Gabriel's horn blows, Michael comes down with the flaming sword and takes the Devil out, and all the bad-betters out there head to eternal disappointment, if not damnation... The game, in short, is fated, which is why I never found the Bible compelling as either adventure literature or drama, no matter how much power I acknowledge it holds as a text. Till then, though, the game is his, at least on earth. And that's why everybody is so scared of Puff. I could see a way that he really is what he lets on.

Something started every story you will ever hear. In my own quest to make sense out of the senior members – the Administration – of our College and every other thing about it, I'm always looking at tradition, be it history, folklore, legend, literature, or any other possible line of insight.

Stories build like crazy off of earlier stories. By now we have layers of theme and subject upon which stories can build. The full architecture of legend and belief can be based like a pearl around a single grain of sand. But that original nugget, the real person or incident that started the whole thing off... That's what I am always trying to figure out.

Whenever I meet a vastly old Collegian, I wonder: Is there anyone famous in history or legend that he or she could once have been? Collegians pose all the time as famous people, and yet others... Probably did once bear famous names in art, literature, philosophy, or occultism, and they chose to live life out of the limelight for as long after as they could.

What are the parallels for Puff? I have a few thoughts.

Gnosticism is a freelance collection of religious/spiritual ideas among early Christian and Jewish groups of the first century AD. It seems to have been a network of sympathetic cults rather than a standardized religion, and there's a bit of variance among the Gnostic groups in their enclaves throughout the Roman Empire.

Gnosticism was OK with a number of early Christian presumptions, including the idea of Jesus as the soul of an enlightened being, basically an avatar, who came to the earth and was incarnated to take on humanity's sins and, by His sacrifice, give humanity at least a temporary "get out of jail" card. Other attitudes that Gnosticism seems to have shared with Christianity include a sense that the spirit was good and the body was iffy, and that the universe was a battle between good/light forces and bad/dark ones. It was day versus night, and both Christians and Gnostics were pulling for day.

Gnosticism had a few other tenets that weren't so appealing to the take-no-prisoners attitude of early Christianity. Christianity likes its absolutely good Good Guy and its so-bad-he's-revolting Bad Guy. Gnosticism held premises from Greek cults – the Eastern Mediterranean was a hotbed of ideas – that look to me to be NeoPlatonic, which are a lot less value-driven than Christianity. For the Gnostics, the Bad Guy isn't all that bad. Gnosticism also seems to have lacked the precise type of Dualism that's so vital to Christianity. For Christians, there's really only one God, and he's dramatically more powerful than His opponent. The first big battle is already over, and the Good Guy is fated to win the last. For most Gnostics, the two gods aren't so far apart; the Universe is a shifting power-struggle.

Gnosticism had a little trouble swallowing some of the other philosophies of the Christian orthodoxy, including the Virgin Birth and the

Resurrection. As for Jesus… Well, He was a real special guy for sure, but the Gnostics weren't all the way sold that He was *exactly* the Son of the Maker of the Universe or His personification in a human form. If you know much about the early Church, this became a very critical point. Still, Gnosticism thought of itself as in sympathy with the budding Christian faith. Christianity had its own ideas about that.

The first century AD was a precious time for the young monotheistic (one god) religion, Christianity, sorting out what it was and wasn't in the face of countless pressures. Its cousins could have seemed more of a danger to it than strangers. I get that, in a way.

The pagan faiths were bluntly pantheist (many gods/goddesses). Gnosticism was just enough like Christianity to steal its thunder. In fact, the early Christian church seems to have seen Gnosticism as an even more jealous rival to it than the pagan faiths. Somebody who didn't agree with them about Jesus and Satan was more of an irritation than somebody who had never heard of either one. Or is that, "One"?

The early Church did all it could to exterminate Gnosticism's documents and philosophy, if not, eventually, its most resolute disciples. (Never forget that Europe's last holy war, the Albigensian Crusade, was waged against itself, stomping out the Gnostic-derived Cathar Heresy in the Languedoc region of southern France.) It did a pretty good job. Most of what we know of Gnosticism comes from its root sources or its spin-offs. Then came the Nag Hammadi documents, the Gnostic Gospels, discovered in 1946 in an Egyptian town along the Nile. These were probably shocking to the average person who heard about them because they threw into relief the fact that an alternate form of Christianity had existed and been suppressed. It made the Bible look like not the only Word of God but the simple winner of a preindustrial turf war, as well as a post-New Testament PR campaign. Ah, laws, like sausages, they say, are better not to see being made. Maybe religions are like that, too.

When applied to religions, Dualism, to simplify things radically, is a term that means that the world if not the Universe is seen to be a battleground of opposing forces. The struggle is usually seen as a tossup, just like Spring versus Fall. They both get their turn on top.

Europe's indigenous pagan religions – the Greeks, the Romans, the Celts, the Germans – weren't Dualist. They had their dark gods, of course, and they could be forbidding; but they weren't seen as truly evil. People had to look out for them on the wrong day. Sometimes the scariest ones – like the Greek Hecate and the three-personed Morrigan and the Indian Kali – were just aspects/emanations/personae of benign and mainstream figures like Demeter and the triune Celtic earth-goddess and Shakti. Most of the world's religions I've looked at have been like that.

It's remarkable how Dualist the Abrahamic faiths – Judaism, Islam, and today's Christianity – really are. They are some of the most Dualist religions in the world. Those of us who grow up in cultures steeped in Judaeo-Christian concepts never realize how unusual that Dualism really is in the big picture. But it's our only picture, and it marks our thinking, even if we aren't religious. That's the way the world looks to us because of our societal upbringing. How else would it be?

The Abrahamic faiths have their bad guy – Iblis, Satan – who is really bad; and they have their good God, Who is really good. There's such a distaste with the Devil in Western concept that he even smells bad whenever he manifests. (Miracles of the good God, incidentally, smell like roses.) The Devil is a semi-animal morph, too, with sexual features and predilections that shocked and outraged some of the old-timers, at least publicly, with their fixations upon hetero sex and maintaining the nuclear-family.

One of the pre-Christian religious systems kicking around the Middle

270

East was Zoroastrianism. As far as I know, the Zoroastrians were the Western ancestors of all Dualism – the originators of this Dualist attitude to religion, meaning that life is an eternal struggle of good/light forces with bad/dark ones. Zoroastrianism predated Christianity by two thousand years. It is probably what influenced early Christianity and indeed all the Abrahamic faiths to be as radically Dualist as they were. It went into their roots and became incorporated into the tree and all its branches.

Dualism isn't the only aspect of Christianity or Judaism or Islam. They are all profound, developed faiths whose bases are in philosophy. They have a lot of messages. With any one of them there is a truly impressive architecture of thought, not to mention a powerful tradition of mysticism. But with Zoroastrianism, Dualism was its point. The world, even the Universe, is perceived to be an even struggle. All the philosophies spin off from that.

It looks to me like that takes Puff, if there is one, at least back to the Zoroastrians, meaning four thousand years. Unless that's just when they spotted him.

One of the most shocking Gnostic tenets, at least for the early Christians, was the idea that the Guy who made the universe might not have been the One who made the earth. Yes. I know there's a little debate about the degree to which all Gnostic cults and groups held to any of Gnosticism's major ideas; but in general, Gnosticism took the earth to be run by a different party than the maker of the Universe. They called Him/Her "the Demiurge," more or less, "Producer," "Creator." So in essence, the guy who rules the earth and who made the earth ISN'T God.

The first time I came across a paragraph holding that idea I had to read it a bunch of times before I was sure people were serious. So one guy made the Universe and another did the world? What kind of a wacky religious idea is that?

The Gnostics aren't even sure the Demiurge is all that good all the time. He might be neutral toward humanity if not outright surly. I can see their thinking. Surely you notice that life on earth isn't always a bed of roses. In fact, life can be so tough that it makes people even in my day believe that that there might not be a God at all, at least not a good one. Those people realize – because they're alive and they can think – that something made everything. To them the Universe must have had a material cause like whatever made every rock on the planet, and it's not any more loving or sentimental.

But you see where my thinking on Puff comes in here. If the Gnostic ideas should happen to have been correct – that there is a massive power on earth that isn't God and might not be very nice – maybe Puff is the one they mean. Maybe Puff was who the Gnostics sensed or even encountered. That's a reason to be scared of him.

I'm not sure Puff is the bad guy, but he's certainly not all good. You can tell that from the things he does in the world. He's after possession and power just like everyone. He pulls a lot of strings, and his specialty is getting people working for him without anybody being able to see where the strings lead. You can see that from the little ceremony Danny Montour and I broke up. Those people had done some horrible things and they were getting ready to do some more, I surely believe, and from the apparent fact of Puff's interest in the matter – I infer this confidently – he had a hand in it. Had Danny and I not blundered in, nobody would have known about it.

Puff has some long range plan in mind, and nobody knows what it is. Every once in a while he – or entities pretending to speak for him – deputizes somebody to do a little job for him: find this, fetch that, report on them, or explore there, usually someplace forbidding and dire.

When I started my work in the College I had that initial dread of him, too, though I never thought he might be a god. Then, as you know, he failed to show himself and I started tweaking him in my own punk way, half just to see if he was there. But as time has gone on and I've come into my growth, I don't think he's anything at all beyond the best of us in the College. I agree that he could be thousands of years old. I think he could be as old as the oldest record of some kind of negative god, some power eternally opposed to the good force of the universe. I don't think – whoever he is – he's the real Devil, because he would be utterly unmatched on the planet. There'd be no need for all the blinds, the surrogates. I do think that Puff – whoever he is – could be the source of all the world-legends about the Devil, Satan, the *Accuser*, the *Opposer*. His point is to be contrary.

He could go back to the earliest days of humanity's attempts to reach the other side. He could be the ur-Shaman. He could also be what he poses to be: the Father of Artifice. The Evil One. The Prince of the Air.

All I know is that the guy I call *Puff* rules the roost in the College. People either do what he wants, or else they go about their business in life and studiously avoid doing things he doesn't want.

He may be the Arch-Deceiver known in so many lands, the eternal opponent of the Creator and His noble representative on earth. He might be one of the henchmen, what, as Milton sonorously calls:

> *One next himself in power, and next in crime,*
> *Long after known in Palestine, and named*
> *Beelzebub.*

He could also be the Trickster-god, the Loki of the Scandinavians and sort of a Bacchus/Dionysus for the Greco-Roman world. He may not even be fixedly evil, as far as I can tell. He may just be selfish. He's in it for him and only him. I think that's for sure.

You want my take? I think he's the Arch-sorcerer. I think he's the oldest wizard in the world, at least the oldest one anybody knows about. That's where he gets all his mojo. The first.

Where Puff lives, if he lives anywhere, nobody's sure. He seems to have a number of strongholds around the world, or so we hear from people who report to him. All of the ones I've heard of are disarmingly simple above ground and alarmingly complex below it. Maybe a division of the U.S. Army plus a SEAL team could break into one of these and explore it, but I think nothing short of that could manage it. The College community would be afraid to go for it, at least without an invitation.

I don't know anyone I really believe has met Puff. I say this because when I ask people who claim to be in his camp what to expect if I ever meet him, I get such varied and yet uncertain responses. It's like people I knew in college getting so high they couldn't remember a thing about the concert they went to the night before except that it was "so awesome." Maybe there's a power of illusion, of deception, about Puff. Maybe he's a shapeshifter, a Protean figure who has no single form. Maybe he's even forgotten what it ever was. Maybe he can't get back to it.

But that's all people remember about Puff. And the way they let on around other people who say they've seen him makes me think none of them really have. People meet his representatives and they may even answer one of his summons to the place he's supposed to be, one of his classic retreats around the world, but I think they're just letting on. They know nobody else has ever met him either. They know at least that there's no consistent picture of him or what it's supposed to be like around him, except, maybe, for the "awesome" part.

I'm not scared of him. I'm wary, you'd best believe, but you have to be a bit fatalistic about some of these things. Besides, there's all the deception to be dealt with. I'd be ready to believe he's like the Wizard of Oz, a shrimp behind all the displays, but everybody's so scared of him that it's catching. It's like that bully you never wanted to mess with in junior high school. He didn't look that tough, but everybody said he was, and it got into your head.

But that's the trick with Puff, isn't it? You don't know how tough he is. You don't know if he can be beaten. But I've got a sense of comfort with the whole thing, even if I have done some things to piss him off.

If Puff had all that much power and wanted me dead, it would have happened a long time ago, and I'd never have seen it coming. I think I can sting him, and he's wary of me because he knows it. Then again, you also wonder if the whole plan might just be something he's cooked up, and he's only waiting to crack the whip.

276

# Chapter 14
# Snake Hill

1

East and south of the village is Saratoga Lake, just one of the things that makes the living around here so rich. Five miles long and up to one and half wide, Saratoga Lake is a scene of boating, sailing, swimming, fishing, skating, and a lot else. People live around it and party on it. I've sailed it, swam it, skied it, skated it… It's a four-season resource.

Most parts of the Lake are no more than a dozen feet deep. On bright and still days you can see the bottom almost everywhere, except for one conspicuously deep place where the bass breed and grow. Something dropped or weighted into that abyss would be there a long time. One of my fisherman friends tells me they've never really determined the depth of it. It's easy to find, my friend said. It's just offshore from Snake Hill.

Snake Hill and the underwater ditch at its foot make for a remarkable geological formation on an otherwise tender lake. Other than the unusual action of a glacier, I can't imagine how it was formed. The 200-foot-high hill itself is a monument on the eastern shore. It's so precise and abrupt that you'd suspect it to be man-made, which seems impossible due to the size. Not a single boater on Saratoga Lake is ever out of sight of it.

You can be sure that there are at least a few grim legends about any natural feature in the Northeast with the words *spook, snake, witch,* or *devil* in the name, and a good bit of folklore has gravitated to Snake Hill. Many say the 19th century story about it being a nesting ground for the Northeastern rattlers was fabricated just to keep people off it. The Mohawk and Algonquin both had legends about Snake Hill, typically related to clashes between their cultures. Lake residents today remark on mysterious lights seen occasionally on and above the hill. Lights and legends everywhere else are associated with the sites of ancient earth-and-stone constructions, and they say there is one at the top of Snake Hill. Monuments like those of the Hopewell and Adena are pretty rare in this part of the Northeast, adding a bit of mystery. Who put it there?

When you get close to Snake Hill, its lack of human occupancy is the first thing that stuns you. Lakefront property is precious around here. Anyone interested in clearing half the trees, running a few roads through it, and putting up houses or condos – with lake access and magnificent views – would clean up. The realtors would be salivating. But today Snake Hill is shut off like Chernobyl. There aren't any roads heading onto it, and its trees appear to be old-growth. There's not even a good track leading to the summit.

A few people live across the 9P from the landward foot of Snake Hill. They say the State Troopers arrest trespassers. Otherwise, they dislike talking about it. Word in town is that the Hill might be owned by the family that founded an empire of gas-and-ice cream shops about the Northeast. It certainly figures that they would have the resources, but why Snake Hill should be important to them to hold but never use is a mystery. It's almost like there's something on it that they want to stay hidden. Could they have made a secret treaty with a Native American group? Could the family be a little more mystically-inclined than we stereotype of capitalists? One thing is for sure: Nobody wants you on Snake Hill. As I climbed to the summit beside Dana Lambert, it seemed a good reason for it to be chosen as a meeting site for the first stage of our peace-making mission.

Whenever you have anything to do with Puff, you start thinking about the Devil. I know that's making him happy because it adds to his mystique, but I couldn't help reflecting on it as we picked our way through the pines and maples. There's a good bit of Devil-lore in the Saratoga region, even in the little corner of it we trod.

Stories of magic and enchantment of many types came from Bear Swamp a few miles north of us. We'd passed through it in our rented SUV to get to Snake Hill. Bear Swamp was a lot more formidable in the old days, and the Native Americans of the region were never fond of it. It was said into the 1800s that if their quarry fled into the swamp, the Native hunters let it go.

A Bear Swamp resident, Nelly Jones, figured in one of the most famous Devil-tales of the settler-era. She was said to have been a scold, and her husband was so eager to be rid of her that he made a deal with Old Scratch to take her. Now, female scolds are usually figured to be a match for the Devil, at least in folk literature, and when he showed up at the house Nelly Jones did a number on him with the fireplace-tongs. Still, Scratch managed to get the best of this one, swishing Nelly Jones up into the magically magnetic saddle that was curtains for many a sinner before. Stuck riding behind him on his fearful mount, Nelly Jones set to twisting the Devil's pig-like tail and so tormented him that he had to pitch her out. She looked up from her tumble just in time to see the diabolical horse and rider dive into the earth at White Sulphur Spring, later to become the focus of a Victorian-era hotel and spa. The boarded-up remnants of the lakeside spring house were such an easy walk to our south that we'd parked our SUV by it. Ah, the native Saratogians tended to hand it to the Devil! No doubt he made up for it with tourists at the casinos and the track.

The early evening was bright off the Hill, but the trees were thick on it, and Dana Lambert and I climbed through a disconcerting gloom. We went carefully, too. Long experience has shown me that when you descend from a hill you could come down a long way from where you meant to. I wished we'd had Danny Montour with us, but we were limited to two at the handoff, a stipulation that baffled me. This wasn't supposed to be a tense one. This was supposed to be a peace offering, a simple pickup, all arranged, with only the most cursory validation called for. We still had to "check the transcripts," which was why it had to be Dana with me. If you ever once suspend the validation for anybody, you enrage everybody else down the road.

Dana and I are both hikers. We had our off-road trainers and outdoor clothing, most of mine out of the EMS at the Wilton Mall or High Peaks up in Placid. The idea that we might have more worries than a split seam or a turned ankle was coming to me.

Shadowy forms moved in the half-light around us. They were fast for their size. They had to be Trolls: supernatural protection agents like others you've heard me describe in these pages. I couldn't tell if it was a crew of them or just two or three fast ones.

As we neared the top the light was a little better, and I got a look at one darting between some trees. I didn't know what to think. It was out of bounds, at least with the people we had made our deal with. There was no need for security besides us. It almost looked like we had a third player – or that this was a setup. I stayed close to Dana.

I wanted to throw on the Glow in case I got jumped from behind, but I dared not. If I'd brushed Dana as we walked, it would have been agonizing. I could have thrown an arm around her and pulled her inside, but that would have made it almost impossible to walk up this wooded hill. Plus, any Collegian within fifty feet would know that I was on edge, and I wanted everybody thinking things were still peaceable.

A few yards from the top I could see someone above us, a middle-sized man standing by an abrupt rise in the natural earth. It was clear that the rumored earthwork was here on Snake Hill, and most likely in the position of the bump in the treeline suggested by the profile of the hill. It reminded me of the tumor-like formation atop Maeve's Mountain, Knocknarea, against the horizon, way back in Sligo County on a day that seemed like lifetimes ago. Who knew what legends and traditions the ancient people had linked to this one above me? It had slumped a bit, I presumed, since the last time anyone had tended to it, and it sprouted trees that looked to me to be centuries years old.

I was surprised to find that the man was "Hawkeye" (sometimes, "Hawkie") Jacobs, the ominous-looking Onondaga with the dense, blue-black tattoo of a bird with spread wings across his countenance, completely covering the left eye, half the right forehead, and most of the left cheek. Inked down to his eyelids, he always tried to tell people it was a heron in honor of his clan, but it looked to everyone a lot more like a raptor, and it accounted for his nickname. I'd seen him six hours and a day before at the Elders conference in Vermont. That, too, felt like a whirlwind in the past.

"Ho, ho, ho!" called out Jacobs. "We gonna make this roundup?"

"That you, Hawkie?" I called out merrily. "Let's check this diploma and be out of here." I felt hollow when I said that, though, like I could have given something away. Using the slang of the College was a pretty good sign that I was in it. Besides, whatever mirth I had was dampened when I spotted a couple shovels and the signs of an opened space in the tumulus. Someone had been excavating here, within hours. It was as if they had used this ancient sacred space to store whatever we were here to pick up. I had the impression that whatever had been buried here had been periodically taken out and returned. I could feel Dana tense up. Any monkeying with an ancient monument is pretty taboo, at least for people in the know.

"Why the Trolls?" I said as we drew up to the man.

"Just keeping an eye out," he said. By his right knee was an open trunk that looked really old. Inside it was a leather satchel that had been waxed to protect it from the wet. In it was a wooden box that could have held a very big book. I hadn't been told much about the item we were transporting other than that it held high metaphysical gravity – a lot of

*Source* – and that it was to be entrusted to the Onondaga, the treasure-keepers of the Confederacy. I presumed it was a Medicine Mask if it was an Iroquoian artifact. The Iroquoians seldom embodied their spirituality in objects, and the most prominent items in their society that suited all these parameters were Medicine Masks. There were many grades of them. This one, if such it was, had to be important.

The grey-haired man picked up the valise, held it by the sides like a painting, and pressed it outward. Dana stepped in, held her left hand across it as if feeling for heat, and then moved it like someone clearing steam from a mirror. "It's there," she said.

"Where we going?" I said.

"Just get yourself to the 90 East. You'll get a call on the way."

That surprised me. Onondaga Country was just about straight west. I didn't blink. I reached for the old box. He handed it to me like a pizza, on its back.

I looked at "Hawkie" with astonishment. He just smiled. No Medicine Mask is ever rested face up, the traditional position in which the dead are laid out. It might "get ideas," as it were – and start using its power to assist living people and animals in its sphere to assume its pose. Everyone in the know about Native spirituality in the Northeast knows that. He was either testing me, or... I noticed his tattoo fading. *What?*

"Eric! Dana! We gotta get out of here!" called Danny Montour from fifty feet below us. So he had followed us.

I heard a crash in the trees about forty feet behind me. Dana and I looked quickly. It sounded like a deer, but in the aftermath of a couple of bushes waving, I had the impression of a manlike being rushing toward something behind a tree. Then something blurringly fast like one of Sia Lund's chest-press-punches shot out horizontally to meet it. I could be sure of nothing, but I had the idea that The Ghost – yes, he was here with us, one of our own little surprises – had taken out one of Hawkie's critters, or else the reverse, in which case we were all toast. My money was on Mr. Bronze Hands. But the gloves were off.

The ever-so-slowly altering Hawkie Jacobs just stood looking at us. I thought about giving him a shot of the Beam, but he made no move to attack me. I was so uncertain about everything that I decided to just make tracks. I restored the parcel, really an old-fashioned briefcase, to its up-right position and tucked it under my left arm as we retreated down the trail. It suited the weight I would expect of the typical False Face, none of which I had ever handled.

Danny forged in front of us as we moved down the hill. I knew The Ghost was looking out for us from the rear. I thought about throwing on the Gleam but I had no idea what sort of effect that might have on the already powerful item I held.

At about the midpoint of the glum descent, Danny made a quick cross-move and dropped something flashing toward him from his left, a dark humanlike form that had an animal head. He'd moved in an eye-blink, and only after the stroke did I see that he been carrying his little Mohawk "turnip" war club, doubtless the one he'd had on him the day before during the adventure that had kicked all of this off. I took a quick look at whatever he hit as we passed it. It looked like a six-foot roadkill, with panther-ears and -teeth and a caved-in skull. I'd never seen a Troll like it.

A few seconds later I heard another clash-crack-and-thump uphill behind us and figured that The Ghost had struck again. He was some-thing. He was at the very least one of the greatest martial artists in the world.

2

As we neared the foot of the hill we were surprised to see how much daylight was left. We had all made it through with no injuries but a scrape or two from branches, which seemed really remarkable.

As we set foot on the 9P that rings the east side of the lake, someone thought of calling Nadia and having her drive to meet us. We had left her by the White Sulphur Spring behind the wheel of the big SUV Jaap Simon had arranged for us. Nothing but first-class for that lad, plus deniability. Nadia met us, and we all piled in, heading back the way we'd come. Dana Lambert took charge of the package, resting it beside her and even belting it in so it never lost its upright position. I was shocked to notice that she was still shivering. I bet that was the first *hazing* she'd ever been part of, which is what we drily call a bushwhack, or any College-style clash involving Linebackers. Don't forget, she's not the muscle-end of the College. But I think we were all jittered, except for The Ghost of course, whom you could never read.

As the crow would fly, the Northway is really close to Snake Hill. You have the water between you and it, of course, and the entrance ramps have to be considered. If we'd had our wits about us and were determined to head in the direction we'd been advised, the quickest way to the eastbound 90 was to continue south along the east side of the lake. No one thought of that. Some wizards, right? I guess a fight in the woods with werewolves or the suitable like thereof will do that to anybody. We headed north, back toward the ramp we had passed getting to Snake Hill.

We talked as we drove, with not much consensus. Whoever was out to disrupt our transaction had really underestimated us, but it could have gone far otherwise. If we had kept to the letter of the arrangement – sending only me and Dana to the top of the hill – the package could have been nipped and at least the two of us killed. It looked like that was somebody's plan. "What just happened?" said Dana Lambert.

"I'm having trouble with that myself," I said. "This was supposed to be a handoff. Who sent the Trolls?"

"Not sure that's what they were," said Danny. He hasn't been around all that long, meaning, "in the College," but he knows Native stuff.

I agreed with him. "The Trolls I've seen or heard of come in a couple patterns. These fly. These climb. These are like Bigfoot. Sorta. None of them were like the beastie I stepped over."

"I coulda swore I dropped a Shapeshifter," said Danny. "Never seen one up close, but that's what everybody says they look like."

The Ghost conceded with a nod that he had fought something like it. "That or a Skinwalker," he added. He's been all over.

"Not sure there's that much difference between them," said Danny.

"These guys backed off when they saw what kind of heat we had," I said. "The Trolls don't back off just because you drop a couple. They do like they're programmed."

"Somebody coulda recruited some specialists from out West cause they couldn't get anybody local for the job," said Danny.

"Or didn't want anybody local to know," said Nadia.

This had surely been an attack from Native American factions. This put a whole new light on things. Had we been conscripted into doing something that went against the Elders? And this was no long-range dispatching of bio-lab beasties. There would be a human being under the transformation, which was running a risk for him or her. If one of them took a wound while in-form, it took when they shifted back. He or she could be killed.

The great shamans could all make the change. So could the great Medicine People. If we had put ourselves into some act that ran against the interests of the Six Nations, we had been misled. But great witches can do the same thing, too, and in fact they are said to be much more likely to do so, at least when they're on the no-good. One thing was clear: Something had gone wrong up on Snake Hill, and everything connected to it felt fishy. I was starting to worry about the information we'd been given by Jaap Simon.

The sky was sublime and captivating, alternately blue, grey, white, and gleaming orange, with all tones in between. It was one of those Asgardian sunsets that gets me thinking of the astral kingdom of beams and rainbows. On a less stressful night I bet we'd have found a high point for skywatching. When we reached the overpass by the ramps onto the Northway, Nadia pulled us over. "I'm just going to sit us all here until we agree on our next move," she said.

"I got one," said Danny. "No more deals with Hawkie." The Ghost and I chuckled.

"I never met the man," said Dana, "but that didn't feel like who it was supposed to be. There was something really off about that whole interchange."

"Besides the boogaloo with them Loup Garou?" said Nadia.

The crossfire conversations going on ahead of me made me feel a little alone in the back row. The only thing that seemed certain was that the item with us was the real deal. The big picture of the arrangement was still in force. As for its new rightful owners, the Onondaga... The hit-try, the hazing, wasn't their problem. That was what we were there to prevent.

As I tried to listen to something Nadia was saying – she was the only one of us who hadn't seen anything on Snake Hill – I looked around, even dropping my gaze into the driver's mirror at the top of the windshield as if it was a tiny TV. It was a likely place for me to rest my eyes while looking forward. I mentioned to you earlier my bemusement with skyscapes. Something strange was going on in the east, behind us.

I turned almost instantly to look at it through the hatchback window, which should have been a much better view. I saw nothing strange. I looked back to the mirror. The formation was unmistakeable. It was a peculiar, symmetrical cloud bank that resembled a ponderous winged creature hugging the horizon.

I got the absurd image of a marshmallow Mothra, resting its wings on the peaks and peering over for its next target. I never settled on my own impression of the thing, whether it appeared to be crouching over the Adirondack horizon and readying to launch itself at us or swooping over the curvature of the earth from far beyond them and glacially closing in.

I nudged Danny in the middle seat to my left and pointed behind us. He took a good scan of the sky. Then I directed him to look into the mirror. He did, then looked back again a couple times and did a double-take. "Oh, man, this is not good!" he said. "I've never seen Medicine like that."

I called everyone to look behind us, to the east. They saw nothing. "Nice sky," said Nadia.

"Now look in the mirrors," I said. It took a bit of craning out of everyone, particularly The Ghost in the passenger seat. We had to move carefully to keep from blocking each other's view, but one by one they were all astonished to see what I did looming on the eastern horizon. Someone thought of checking the side-mirrors, and we could all study it at the same time.

To me it looked like nothing other than a vapory, bug-like Rodan, another Toho film monster. Its grey-shaded outlines suggested a pair of broad, suspiciously smooth (for clouds) wings, mostly concealed behind the mountains. Perfectly positioned between them was a globular head, with two almost identical grey puffs in the precise position of compound eyes, giving it a menacing expression. I could even believe I saw something of the same tone suggesting a smudgy, snub-nosed little beak.

I had a laugh, thinking of the Pilsbury Doughboy of the *Ghostbusters* film, but this was real, and a lot more sinister, belly-scraping the green foothills of the 'Dacks and heading right toward us. I could see the ballooning head above the green ranges and got the sense of a dirigible-

THE PRINCE OF THE AIR

like body behind it and mighty, gliding wings mostly hidden by the peaks. It was the most remarkable simulacra I had ever seen. Or was that all it was? It loomed ominously, still a long way off, but… It appeared to be heading right toward us, and with its own momentum, faster than the rest of the banks in the sky. If we stayed put, it seemed like it could be on us in minutes.

"Anybody besides me think that's a little wacky?" I said.

"The guy on the hill told us to go east and wait for a call," said Dana.

"Yeah, and if we did, we'd head right into it and never see it," said Nadia.

"To me, that says, 'Head west,'" said Danny. "I think we're crazy to go any direction but away from that thing. Onondaga turf is west of here, anyway."

"Call your dad," I said to Danny. I saw Dana start dialing, and I knew she was calling Jaap Simon.

I couldn't track either conversation, though once Danny shouted, "Yes, only in the mirrors…!" Both wrapped up fifteen seconds apart.

"My dad's calling a council," said Danny. "It's going to take time to get anywhere, even if they all do it on speaker-phone. Something has really blown up, that's all he told me. He did say he has a friend at Onondaga who's waiting for the delivery. It's Hawkie Jacobs."

Dana and I looked at him like he was crazy. "Didn't you know that's who we met on top of that hill?" she said.

"I saw you with *somebody*," said Danny. "Things were just a little crazy up there."

"Hasn't been all that normal since," said Nadia. "We figured out what we're doing?"

"Jaap doesn't know what's going on, but he told us to duck the trouble," said Dana. "Drive west. All night if we have to."

"This thing has to get to the Onondaga," said Danny.

"We won't find as many obstacles if we at least try," said Lund.

"I think they're on it," said Danny. "They've been waiting centuries for this one. That my dad did tell me. We just need to get there."

"That juju-storm's not getting any farther away," said Nadia. "We gonna sit here in the cross-hairs?"

She was right, or at least it looked that way. In just the five minutes that we had sat where we were, the formation seemed closer and more forbidding, even in the small screens of the mirrors.

"Straight ahead," I said. "We're going through the village to Ballston Spa and picking up the 90 West at Amsterdam. Then we're heading out at highway speed."

"I don't know who we were talking to on that hill," said Dana to me as we pulled out. "Did you see him touch anything? Pick up anything?" I saw right where she was going. Some of the people in our world are quite good at projecting apparitions.

"He handed me the box," I said. "He was material." I was grateful again that I hadn't done something impulsive like lancing the figure I spoke to once the scene went south. It might have been the wrong move, and it would have made a statement I had no interest in making.

The delays we encountered on our route through the village of Saratoga Springs were agonizing. Even at nine on a Sunday, in race season, they're busy. I don't think we thought any piece of meteorology was going to hit us at a stop light in a village of 28,000. I think we thought we could outrun it once we hit the Interstate. Even a supernatural cloud-form doesn't go 70, particularly against the natural direction. The weather around here almost always comes at us from the west and south.

"So what can your dad tell us about this Hawkie Jacobs?" called Nadia back to Danny Montour.

"The real one," said Dana.

"I can tell you about him," said Danny. "Good looking guy when he was young. Good singer, good dancer. The women like him, least they used to. Always had a good-looking one with him. Got with the arts, did some teaching and acting. Hasn't been able to keep himself outta trouble. Real impulsive. Least he always was. He's been in prison."

"Prison?" said both women at once.

"Yeah, at least once," said Danny. "I think that's when he got that tat. Started taking up with the Indian prisoners. Finding his clan heritage. Started thinking he was Heron Clan, and nobody knows anything about that. I'd always thought he was Wolf or something. I wasn't even sure he was Longhouse. I thought he might be Algonquin."

"How did he get in prison?" said Nadia.

"Not all that sure about it," said Danny. "Could have been a lot of things. Just couldn't take his warnings."

"Warnings?" said Dana.

"Life gives you warnings that start out little and then pretty soon they turn into big ones if you don't listen. My dad used to like him. Everybody liked him. My dad used to look out for him. Tried to help keep him on the straight and narrow. But he was always looking for shortcuts. Never liked it when somebody told him no. Right now he's got kids with three or four different women, and he never sees them, which isn't really walking the Medicine way. But we thought he was straightening out. Finding his heritage. Walking with the Medicine."

It was be a smooth shot west-southwest till we hit Amsterdam and picked up the Interstate. Somewhere past Ballston Spa, Danny's phone rang.

"My dad's got some people from Onondaga to take over the item," he said after a quick conversation. "We're meeting them right off the highway in Onondaga Lake Park."

"I think we need a committee waiting for this one," said Nadia.

"My dad'll have the whole Medicine Society out there," said Danny.

I knew the area well. "There's a rec path on Onondaga Lake," I said. "It goes under the 90 right at Maple Bay. It'll be dark when we get there. It would be the perfect place for a handoff. We could pull over right on the shoulder of the westbound and run the item under the highway on foot if we have to. If there's another jump scene, we can just pull out and scoot. Can we set it up there?" Danny reached for his phone.

If there was this much tension over its handoff, I was sure that whatever was in our case was one of the most important of the old False Faces still in existence. I presumed that whoever had been holding it was allied to Puff, but why the Onondaga would have waited so long to make a deal, all that was a mystery to me. But I know the Elders are patient, so patient that the Euro/Western mind, even that of Collegians, sometimes has trouble grasping it.

3

All through our 40-minute journey to Amsterdam, Danny and I checked on the sky behind us in the mirrors of the SUV. We hit a high point in Malta and the ominous cloud bank was still low on the horizon, even clearer in the light grey of the twilight. Its shape hadn't changed like you'd expect in thirty minutes, and it looked if anything closer, which ought to have been truly impossible. None of us had ever heard of a weather effect that could make time on a car, at least one running counter to the natural flow as if it had its own motor. I wondered if anyone besides us could see it, even in the mirrors.

We all thought, of course, that it was the sign of something very powerful stalking us. It was a titanic application of *Source* if nothing else. Whoever could do a thing like it had to have scary clout. We were sure it was the tool of someone wanting to prevent the delivery of the item we had. We weren't sure it was the same party that had set its agents after us on Snake Hill, but it was likely.

All the while we kept conversations going with anyone who might help us. Danny had updated his dad several times and described the strange cloud that haunted us like a shadow and was visible only in reflection. Ed Montour had arranged for the handoff where we'd asked for it and advised us not to pull anything fancy on the Interstate. He told us to take the exit any other driver would, pay our tolls, and make our way to the lot at Long Branch Park, a hundred feet northwest of the head of the Onondagas' sacred lake.

It was a tense drive. We presumed that aerial thing was going to pick its moment and then attack us somehow, possibly along one of the more rural stretches of the 90. If it drove us into woods or off a bridge into one of the rivers, it could be a good while before anyone found us. There have been many cases of cars lost beside the Interstate for long periods, even in the hospitable months. If that happened to us, someone could round up our package at their leisure. We thanked the gods that it was otherwise a peaceful night.

Twilights are late and long-lasting in August, and parts of the sky still had a gleam as we crossed the Mohawk River on the way to the ramp to the I-90. Danny and I had been keeping our eyes on the mirrors, getting different looks at the cloud-form kaiju as we turned briefly to the south. A light held us up for a minute just over the east bank of the river, and someone checked on the formation. It was gone. It had vanished like an effect of light and shadow that you had to be in exactly the right position to see.

"What the...?" called Danny, craning his head to get better looks in the driver's mirror.

Dana on the middle row looked into the dashboard mirror in time to agree with me that the sky in its former position was vacant. As our SUV made its entry onto the bridge over the river, everyone spotted our celestial pursuer again in the expected place, fading back in like an illusion.

I think I swore. "Was that all my imagination?"

"I don't think so," said Dana.

"What was that we crossed?" asked Sia Lund from beside the driver. He was not a native of the upstate.

"The Mohawk River," said Danny, as if thinking. "And Route 5."

We hit the Interstate about 9:30 and started to break speed records. "What are we going to do if we get pulled over?" yelled Danny. He was the only Muggle with us. At least I think he is.

"Got bigger worries," called Nadia, doing 85. "Let them catch me." Fortunately for us, no troopers answered her challenge. They are said to be making their quotas only late in the month.

A mile before the Canajoharie exit, the odd formation in the sky looked no farther behind us, which should have been impossible. We were forty-plus miles straight west of where we were when we first spotted it. Danny hauled up his phone again and got through to his dad. I was looking so hard into the mirrors that I didn't pay attention to anything they were saying, other than to hear him mentioning the river-crossing and Route 5.

# Chapter 15

# The Iron Trail

## 1

I stood on the paved recreation path under the eastbound overpass of the New York State Thruway. Cars and trucks howled right over me. My uneasy colleagues occupied the only vehicle behind me in the forty-car lot to the north of the westbound lane. It was the perfect meeting spot: somewhat secluded, but yet with surprisingly good light for ten o'clock.

I was expecting a peaceful pass-off to a handful of Elders grateful on behalf of the Longhouse Nations. There might be a small tobacco ceremony, puffs of smoke, and pinches of leaves tossed in the air... There might be prayers, chanting, even drumming, maybe a little fire...

I was surprised to find only a single emissary, a middle-sized, pony-tailed man, gazing away from me toward the city across the water. He was the same size as the Onondaga Elder Hawkie Jacobs, as well as the man I'd seen hours earlier on Snake Hill. I wished I had made better note of the clothes. The hat was the same, but no one impersonating Hawkie Jacobs would have left out the hat – or the tat, though I couldn't see his face.

"You beat us here," I said as a bit of a joke. "Didn't know you had a Vette."

The old lad chuckled, looking away fixedly, but there I thought he revealed something. The fake Hawkie Jacobs could possibly have beaten us here from Snake Hill, but the real one would not have known what I meant. I tapped the case I was so carefully holding.

"Let's have a look," the man said cheerfully, still facing away. He seemed to want me to bring the package around from his right side, and something felt off. A patch of bushes extended from the abutment of the overpass. If I turned to face him, my back was exposed to it. If I looked that direction, I couldn't watch him.

"I thought we had some Elders coming," I said. I stepped a bit closer, still to his right.

"Oh, they're here," said the figure with Jacobs' voice. "They're keeping an eye out."

I stayed where I was, a foot or two behind him. "This is something for the whole Nation," I said. "For the Longhouse."

The man I studied just looked ahead in the grey light. He peered over the lake outlet to our left like its airs and ripples played the pageant of his ancestors' visionary history. He watched the city skyline, just visible in a corona over the southern end of the fabled lake at the core of Confederacy turf. Whatever gleam came from it would have illumined his forehead and revealed his expression, could I have seen it. I took another step to try to catch his countenance.

I had been holding the package in my left. Something hurled itself onto me from the foliage to my right, its chest bashing my shoulder, attempting to slash and fang my throat. Poor decision. I lashed out with my right, the Axe-hand, into the torso of whatever it was. I heard a not-totally-animal-like squall, and the creature dropped to my feet. Only my last-instant application of the Glow kept me from being covered in a gush of blood and guts. I was fairly sure it had been a human being, just in an altered form.

I took a quick look back to the man I had come to meet. It was then that I spotted the legs of three people projecting from the bushes under the underpass. If those were the Elders who were supposed to take charge of our package, I was surprised that they had been such easy prey. The man in the hat made no move, but he did start that slow, low laugh. There was almost something canine in it.

"This was never about the Nation," I said, wondering what to do with him.

"Go easy on yourself," he said, as if speaking was hard. "Set it down. Walk away."

I could hear snarls, shrieks, and falling blows fifty feet behind me. I heard Danny Montour yell something. Then I heard a couple gunshots.

"I'll just hang onto this till we figure something out," I said grimly, trying to watch him and look all about at the same time. I hustled to the parking lot.

My number one weapon against just about anything is the left, the Beam. It keeps things a couple of feet off, at least if they don't have a ton of momentum. I was holding the package with that hand, and I didn't think to switch sides with it. That glowing right, the Axe-hand, was almost a beacon lighting my way back through the dim underpass.

I found Danny and his little trouble-club balanced expertly outside the open hatch of the SUV. The Ghost stood in front of the vehicle in his usual sideways battle-pose, back straight, palms chest-high, the right out, the left in close. It looked like he had confronted at least one attacker, possibly one trying to get around to where I expected Nadia to be sitting ready to roar out at any moment. A second one just outside her door seems to have gotten a different surprise. Nadia, I knew, was "packing," as they say. That explained the shots.

Dana was the true non-combatant among us, and I was thrilled to see the others so protective of her. I set the package beside her and clambered back to my station. As we pulled onto Long Branch Road and started moving west, I spotted the legs of one dropped attacker retreating like snakes into the undergrowth. Clearly something was hauling him or her off. *How many of those things are there?* I thought to myself.

"This was a sting," I said to the rest.

"*No*," said The Ghost. He can pick the most bizarre times to be a wit.

"There's nobody left from Onondaga to pick anything up," I said. "I think the Nation ought to know about this."

I could see both Danny and Dana on their phones. I was sure calls were in to Jaap Simon and Ed Montour, and that a network of calls and conferences would be going on behind the scenes after that. It gave me a window to think.

From the bodies I'd seen, I thought these were more shapeshifters, power-people who could alter their forms and be deputized to be super-human assassins with full deniability. They were witches. They also represented real human lives we had taken. People were going to be missing family members. This had been a big operation. It had taken a surprising degree of both secrecy and coordination.

I knew that the shapeshifter tradition was still extant among many First Nations societies, but I wouldn't have bet there was more than a handful of people left on the Onondaga turf who could still do it. This raised a bunch of uncomfortable possibilities in my mind. One of them was that we might not be doing the right thing with our package. Another was that the whole Native Northeast might be after us. Clearly, several factions had designs on the Mask.

Every time I looked to a mirror revealing the eastern sky I saw the ominous cloud-formation. It shouldn't have been visible at all in the night sky, but an unusual illumination made it stand out. I was reminded of a tent with a faint lantern glowing within it, where the skin is a fairly steady hue and the ribs and folds are dark. In this case, something filled the billows with a consistent tone and just a few joints – and that pert beak and those eyes! – were the color of the indigo night. It was truly remarkable. It was also scary. It seemed to have gained on us in our little stay in Onondaga.

We spotted a sign announcing the 690 and a return to the Interstate.

"If we had just left this package back there, would that thing still be after us?" I said.

Danny folded up his phone. "Get to Route 5," he said.

"They got a war party waiting for us?" I said.

"Off the highway?" said Dana, almost with a shriek.

"Yeah, I don't know about that one," said Nadia.

"We're going to hit cross-streets and stoplights and everything," said Dana, who is an upstate resident.

"My dad just said do it," said Danny. "Said he had some Medicine on it."

"He give us any directions?" Nadia just about shouted.

"Anything that heads south."

We were all acting panicky. None of us are Syracuse residents, and we didn't make the best driving choices. We compared notes as well as we could.

"Why didn't Jacobs try to clip the package?" said Dana.

"He did," I said. "Or someone did. One of his goons tried to hit me from the bushes. After that, I think he could see it wasn't going to work that way. I think he or whoever he works for has some plan past that. One that doesn't involve getting himself killed."

"What makes you sure he was even there?" said Danny beside me. I hadn't seen the second manifestation of Hawkie Jacobs do anything that would reveal that it wasn't an apparition, either, a virtual ghost. I wondered where in the Upstate the real Hawkie was.

We drove generally westward through a maze of sprawl – car dealerships, strip malls, fast food, and manufacturing companies – until we came to one broad intersection and a numbered route that seemed to promise a straight shot south. That we took for just a couple of miles until we came to Route 5, a virtual expressway at that point and for a number of miles in either direction.

Why we ought to prefer the slower, sometimes two-lane thoroughfare to the hurtling Interstate was lost on me. Then someone thought of checking on the sky behind us, to the east, and the two women gasped joyfully. We had shed our meteorological pursuer. It had followed us for 150 miles on all our other routes, and it was either gone or invisible once we were on the lane prescribed by Danny Montour's mystical father. What was up? A picture was forming.

Somewhere underneath most parts of today's New York Route 5 lies one of the most important ancient footpaths in the Northeast. The first Euros to see it described it as a dirt trail a foot or two wide, packed rock-hard. In the nearly impassable old-growth forests of the preindustrial Upstate, it was the major route of land travel along the underbelly of the Great Lakes and a natural east-west migration trail for anything on feet. The Jesuits called it "the Iron Trail" because of all the military hardware that clanked along it during the Colonial wars. So old that it may have dated from the era of the glaciers, this foot-track may have been made by the animals, even many extinct ones, megafauna like the mammoth and Great Elk and short-faced bear. Things felt a lot more peace-

able on it. Maybe this was some part of the plan.

Thirty miles west of Syracuse Routes 5 and 20 start overlapping, and they share a course for another seventy. The point in Auburn at which they meet can be confusing to stressed newcomers like our New Orleans-based driver. We followed the flow of the route but found ourselves un-expectedly on quiet residential streets, some of them one-way. Nadia made a couple turns trying to get back to our intended course and gave up, pulling us over at the foot of a big hill spiked with tombstones that gleamed under the near-full moon.

We stepped out, stretching our legs and hoping to catch our bearings.

I knew instantly where we'd landed: Fort Hill, a strange, powerful place. The layers to it are deep.

Years before I'd taken an interest in Auburn when I thought about writing up a tour there. I looked up and reflected on the mid-sized mountain the whites had usurped for their own cemetery hill.

At the ominous summit the Cayuga had maintained one of their own Northeastern-style fastnesses into the Contact period. The first Euros reported finding a several-square-acre fort with tree-trunk palisades and stone foundations. It might sound flimsy, but one of those – backed by the sturdy Iroquoian warriors inside it – could be remarkably resilient until the era of massed cannon fire made even Euro-style castles obsolete. That was just a piece of the mystery.

The Cayugas' name for the place at the outlet of Owasco Lake is unpronounceable for most Americans and unspellable in the English alphabet. It was said to mean, "The Place where Men Are Killed," and the early historians of Cayuga County speculated that it must have been a site-memory of at least one grim, grand event. Was Fort Hill one of the well-known torture-posts? Was it a pre-Columbian clash-site? Was it the spot of a massacre or even – rare to non-existent in Longhouse country – a sacrificial site? Was it something remembered from an earlier era? Was the name inspired by something the first Iroquoians found here?

Ringing the Iroquoian fortification had been a much more ancient and massive monument, an earth-and-stone formation the first Euros started calling "Fort Allegan." Its builders were an earlier society to the region, either the indistinct folk often called "the Mound Builders," probably the Adena, or an important local population influenced by the mound-building culture. The Adena are truly mysterious. They were Native Americans, of course, but no one knows where they went when they abandoned their communities or who their surviving descendants may be.

The purpose of the older ring may not have been military. It could quite well have been religious, which elevates Fort Allegan into the category of ritual landscape architecture. This mighty site could have been a spot of vision, ceremony, and procession. Sites like it all over the world are zones for what Paul Devereux calls "exceptional human experience," or EHE. When near or on these "places of ancient sanctity" (John Mitchell's term), human beings tend to think they experience things that are quite out of the ordinary, and bodies of legend and folklore pile up.

As my friends checked their maps in the opened door under the light of the SUV, I thought about listening for the Chimies just to see what they could tell me. In the stress and frenzy of the preceding three hours I had barely thought of them. I would have been in big trouble in my life if I hadn't figured out a way of virtually turning them off. They hadn't reminded me of their existence by bursting in, which didn't surprise me on the 90. Most parts of the Interstate are spiritually dead, at least in New York State, and not only because of the speed. The I-90 is a fairly artificial construction and seldom overlaps anything truly historic. The modern Route 5 sways a bit off the ancient track, but most parts of it are pretty active, and we were still near it.

Warming up to be able to listen for the Chimies is like trying to detach from a busy day during the relaxation before a yoga class. It takes some grounding. When I could calm myself enough to hear them, I found them apprehensive, even agitated. I was starting to be surprised that they hadn't come to me before. What could be so urgent?

I looked toward the top of the snaggle-toothed hill, envisioning "Logan's Monument" at the top, the native stone obelisk to the memory of the melancholy Cayuga with the Anglo name. I got a shock. The hideous cloud was back, even closer than before, looming over us from above, and I could see it directly. I stared at it for seconds before I could say anything.

I don't scare easily, but I could not imagine trying to protect myself and my friends from an apparent force of nature somehow conscripted to move against us. It emanated such a sense of malice and latent power.

My first impulse was to presume that the thing had never dissipated. It had been looking for us the whole time. It had simply been invisible to us, as we possibly were to it. We could see it – and it could detect us – because we had gotten off our prescribed course, the ancient Native track that must have had some kind of power to conceal us if not protect us. Or else we had blundered into its trap. It had not just overtaken us – it had found us, and we needed no mirrors to spot it.

The puffy form had an eerie tone, a staticky, illuminated grey. The virtual face was just a spherical bulge in between the by-then sloping winglike limbs, resting their tips as if on the earth a mile to each side of us. I could still see the faint hornlike appendages at the back of its would-be skull. I had no idea what direction I faced, but I presumed the thing still came on us from the east.

I stepped off the sidewalk, stood six feet from the spiky metal fence, pointed uphill and called to my colleagues. They registered the sight at their own speeds, alternately cursing and exclaiming.

Thirty seconds into their conversation, I felt a new bolt of fear. Something was changing in the remarkable cloud-formation, specifically at the irregular, rhomboidal eye-spots, which I had thought were smaller, denser clouds, coincidentally placed. They were starting to come apart. It couldn't be but... Yes! I was sure of it.

It was as if each of the apparent eye-simulacra had been a ball of smoky twine that was starting to unravel itself and descend toward us in two thin wires. Or... No, because of the particular nature of the apparition, it looked like two separate masses of pepper or even dark metal shavings being emptied in a spiraling umbilicus like water swirling down a drain. These two files of particles were converging toward us.

I can't judge how far away from us that formation was. But the longer I looked at the sloping sky-wires, I realized that each had a sense of internal motion. When I saw what appeared to be flapping wings on the closest, I realized what was up.

In a flash I processed the folklore and supernatural experience that could be connected to what I was seeing. I was astonished to remember one of the oddest of Auburn's traditions, and this is no legend: the coming of the crows. Twice a year, in late fall and early spring, up to 100,000 of them swarm Auburn and this cemetery as a stop in their migrations between the Maya territory of Mexico and somewhere in eastern Canada. It's an unwanted wonder, these hordes of scavenging bio-bombs that plague the city for two overnights a year. Why do they target it?

These battlefield-birds, crows and ravens, are everywhere associated with war and destiny. They know where death is soon to take place and where bodies are to be had. Was Fort Hill the site of a prehistoric battle, one so gigantic that even the crows, accustomed to their seasonal feasts, remember it in their imprinting?

I could tell that these weren't crows, at least not normal ones. The approaching file had to be some tool of whoever was working to disrupt our delivery. But why were they coming to us here? The answer could only be that we had run into their trap. We had entered a portal. Fort Hill qualified on every level. I remember vowing to myself, if I made it through the night, to try to understand what else about about Fort Hill – or in or on it – might account for its apparent power.

My colleagues were spellbound watching the transformation coming over the effigy in the sky, eerily self-contained. But when they saw some components of the thing starting to head toward us like a detachment of witches or the Wild Hunt itself, my colleagues exclaimed, probably cursing again.

Nadia must have already settled on the best way to get westbound on the 5 and 20, because we made it there in a single straight move through two slumbering blocks. We had swiveled my seat in the back of the SUV so I could police the rear window, and at one point I wondered if any citizens of Auburn might have been looking up and seeing the same thing we did. I doubt that one of them would have said more than, "What a weird cloud."

"Jaap doesn't know what's going on," said Dana before she'd even put down her phone. "He says to keep going west, into Seneca country. We'll have to hold up till daylight."

The 5 and 20 overlap goes from near-highway speed to 30 and back again several times. It's the main street of many a little upstate town, and it cuts long swaths through farm country. I didn't know how fast those critters could fly, much less what their master plan was. But the slanting column of them made headway on us whenever we coursed at village-speed. It was agonizing to see the twin flocks of air-beating creatures join into one pointing right at us. At least they weren't all going to hit us at the same time.

I caught a look at the strenuously-flapping advance guard. They were what we often call Bogies. A horde of them. I couldn't see any of the frontrunners well, but I could tell from their awkwardly nodding heads that they weren't birds, at least none of our era. I got the impression of aerial manta rays, beating and bobbing their way through the silvery air. This was very quickly looking like a desperate situation.

My seat in the back hatch was not just a good place to watch whatever was overtaking us. It was also the best place for me. I'm the only one who could do anything to drive the Bogies off without opening a window or getting outside. My Beam works perfectly through glass, passing through it as if it isn't there. I was ready when the first of the giant flock hit us. "Incoming," I said as sort of a joke.

The first handful of critters closed on the back window. I dropped a few with my Beam when they got within five feet of us. Four or five others tried to fly through the window at first as if they didn't understand what it was. Others thrashed around, trying to attack our big SUV like it was a living thing. They clutched for holds on windows, racks, and door handles with prehensile claws on their pterodactyl-wings and back legs. Their beaks and stingray-tails battered at the body. I lanced the ones I could reach off us, watching their wings peel back, their shark-pale bellies turn up, and their bodies slap on the pavement.

We were a mile or two outside a village and only going about 40 when more of the critters started closing in, all variations of the leathery-winged Bogie I'd seen a few times before. Each one was about the body-size of a house cat, but there the similarities ended. Each one had a knobbly beak almost like the water-breaking bow of a submarine that ranged out over the jaws and eyes like a nose that jutted out of the fore-head. They were shockingly clear in the brilliant moonlight, and I got good looks at a couple of the thrashing goblin shark-faces, peering in on us with their wild, side-mounted eyes.

One of the little devils latched onto the door handle of the middle seat on the passenger side, right in front of Dana holding our package safe in the center. She gasped, and the dark form took a peck at the glass right in front of her. It didn't crack, but I didn't want them figuring that trick out! I reached over her and gave it a taste of the Beam, glimpsing the raving eyes rolling backward in its ship-prow of a head. I watched it fall away and splat like a wet T-shirt on the highway.

Another right in front of me clutched the back wiper, stretching it out and spreading its wings as though it meant to brake us. The force of the air peeled it off us. It made a massive thunk on the hood of a white pickup that had been following us. The driver pulled over to try to figure out what he'd encountered, then ducked back in terror as the storm blew over him. Lucky for him they were after us.

By then the rest of the cyclone was catching up, a few at a time. Danny was dying to open the sunroof, wade up into the open space, and whack a few blasties out of the night air with the turnip-club he'd used twice that night to good effect, but we ruled against this.

I studied the forms that flapped alongside us. Though along the same general outline, they weren't cookie-cutter. I'd bet there was half a pound of weight difference between the big and the small, which is a lot for an aerial critter. The bellies were all pale, but the skin tone varied. So did the shape and size of the heads and beaks, though the beak, most likely a tusk or horn, was always above the jaws.

I honestly knew no Collegian who was ever acknowledged to have sent these fiendish creatures, Trolls or Bogies, like the ones clearly beleaguering us. It's not an operation of "legal" commerce. You make a deal or you don't, and you go from there. I wasn't even positive these things were truly manifestations of anything College. They may be used by people in the College, but I really did think again about the bio-lab that brews these things up out of DNA and beams them on missions at the behest of connected high-rollers.

Their employment here, though, was clearly a case of someone trying to "poach a recruit," as they say: an unknown party trying to nip a package mid-stream. One thing lost in the immediate shuffle is the fact that this pisses off parties at both ends since it's a double-theft. The risk had better be worth it for that marauder-in-the-middle, and he, she, or they better stay scarce.

Routes 5 and 20 had opened up and become a fairly fast two-lane road, with gas-and-convenient stations at some intersections, a few traffic control signals, and speedy dark stretches through agricultural country. A few of the critters were still with us, trying to peck at our vehicle like it was an animal they were hoping to deal the death of a thousand cuts. Thankfully, none of the idiot creatures got the idea of mobbing our windshield and blocking Nadia's vision. We were dead if we ran off the road.

The traffic around us was light. I didn't notice any vehicles behind us or oncoming menaced by the beasties, but the occasional drivers were surely getting freaked by our speed, and our weaving, to say nothing of the storm cloud of batlike attackers that chased us like a roused beehive. I do think at least some of the drivers could see them. Every now and then a car in our wake pulled over, some of the drivers remembering to use their flashers.

It would have been wiser of those drivers ahead of us to drop out. Nadia almost toppled us several times in her Devil-may-care passes. I was almost as afraid of her driving as I was of our general predicament. But she was good. She would have made a righteous getaway driver.

Whenever our route cleared we pulled ahead of the gnarlies. Fifty is really fast for a winged creature, and we were doing more than that when Nadia could open it up. They gained on us in the slow stretches and when we got caught at the occasional traffic signal. There are a few of those between Auburn and Seneca Falls.

One of the first critters to catch us after we made a break from a light managed to latch onto something, maybe the rack above us, and clamber over the front window, pecking downward at Nadia in the driver's seat, impeding her view. Out of reflex she hit the wipers, which made for a crazy scene. I leaned forward, reached over Dana and our package, and shot the Beam into the beastie's core, which dropped it to the wayside, but this was a desperate situation. Nadia had had to slow down a bit, and a few more of the critters mobbed the top of the vehicle. They seemed to be learning as if they shared a sort of collective awareness.

The Ghost is usually the rock in these situations, but there was nothing he could do without rolling down a window, which wouldn't have helped anything at all. "Eric, you have to do something!" called Dana. Someone had to get on the outside of the SUV and keep the critters from mobbing us.

I don't know if The Ghost would be hurt by a fall from a moving vehicle, but most of the time I wouldn't, not if I had the Glow on. Dana was right. I had less to lose than any of them.

"Pop the roof," I said.

The Ghost tried to help us open the sunroof, and inadvertently let down his window. One of the critters stuck its beak in and tried to jab him, and for once he looked almost abashed. He gave it one of those speed-of-thought lefty palm presses and it squawked and flopped back out. He fumbled for his own switch and shot the window back up, but Danny and I laughed, in spite of the situation. I don't think The Ghost has ever owned a car. His students drive him everywhere he goes, and auto mechanics wouldn't have been on the menu in that 17th century dojo in which everyone thinks he was trained.

In that SUV someone could straddle the middle seat under the sunroof, hold onto it with their knees, and stand up through it. Nadia took a hand off the wheel and got the roof partway open. "Keep that temple-thumper handy," I said to Danny as the glass receded.

I climbed over and stood into the gap, Beam brandished like a lightsaber, though one only I could see. I turned toward the front of the vehicle and lanced a few of the nasties off the hood and windshield, which was mission number one. A couple tried to spring at me, but between the Beam and the rush of the wind, they were clear of me pretty fast. I could see others getting the picture and starting to flock toward me.

Nadia had taken to making sudden lane changes to shake off critters, which was partly working, but having its own problems, including threatening to spill me out. My center of gravity was close to the lip of the open roof, and I was having trouble staying on mission.

"Nobody touch me," I said, ducking my head back down. "Nobody." Then I threw on the Glow. I didn't know what any of them knew about it, and I tried to focus on it forming exclusively on my upper quarters, but I had no idea if that part of the move was working. The peckers started bouncing off me, probably killing themselves in the process.

So far, so good, but there was no end in sight to this. I'd estimate that I'd thinned out a fifth of the horde. The rest of them were drawing towards us, a few at a time. At that rate, we had hours of torment ahead, with the near certainty that something was eventually going to get through. Sooner or later we'd stall out somewhere and the whole crew would descend on us.

Speeding in an SUV is reckless enough in daylight, much less at night with things trying to block your windshield. The tires, too, were vulnerable. If one of those critters ever figured that out or just got a reflexive shot on one with a beak, we were curtains. I didn't know what kind of intelligence they had, and I was betting it wasn't high. But I was growing even more certain that the live ones could learn from the mistakes of their late flockmates. The odds were not on our side.

Most of the wingy-thingies, the Bogies, I've seen have been of the venomous type. Send a dozen of those at almost any living critter and you usually get the job done. All it takes is one sting. They're marvelous site-protectors and assassins. They wouldn't be any good at tapping out windows on an SUV, though, and the nasties we were seeing had solid beaks. The goal was putting a halt to a fast-moving, earthbound vehicle. Someone had played this beautifully, I reflected. They'd tried the subterfuge and the stealth approach – those human-animal morph assassins – and kept the ace card in reserve. Now it was all in the open. The mob.

But a funny thing happened at about the time I had the above reflection: The horde of attackers had thinned, and I don't mean in number, but in appearance. They were faded like someone had applied a filter to their images on Photoshop. They couldn't spot us, either.

I can't tell you how quickly or at what point I noticed the transformation. It was before we came to Geneva. What I noticed was that the cloud of beaked tormentors seemed to be less focused on us us as though they couldn't see us. Once we hit a stoplight at Route 5, the night was still. It was as if our attackers had simply dematerialized, or else gone back into whatever realm they were sent from. I dipped back into the cabin.

Everyone but me looked around and cut loose with a laughing sigh. Danny grinned like the Cheshire Cat.

I stood back up, enjoying my roof-ride through the moonlit country. All was still, all but for the warm breeze coursing around me. I had a moment of reflection. It was as Danny's father had said: Get to Route 5. It had taken awhile, but it had worked. What could he have meant? Why was this the tactic? Then I got it in a flash. I know about the power of landscape. It's almost surely related to *Source*. I know the Native Elders of the Northeast can work with *Source*, probably as well as most people in the College. I was sure Danny's father had called such a conference into action.

The cloud-form that had been so disturbing to us had shadowed us, as if waiting its moment. It lost us when we were on the power-track. When we got off it, in Auburn, it could find us again. It or whatever force was sending it could also reach us with its creatures, at least once we stopped near the power-mountain that had some connection to winged beings in its legends. They beleaguered us afterward whenever we strayed from the route of the old trail.

Even if we stayed religiously to the signed and marked Route 5, we could stray without knowing it. The exact route of the old foot-path of "the Great Indian Trail" can't possibly be 100% under any contemporary roadway.

I chuckled to myself when I reflected that a guy wrote a book about the enchantment of the 90. The 90 runs largely along the old Erie Canal, a man-made route that just happens to exploit the course of handy waterways. It's Route 5 that has the mojo. The only reason the 90 seems to have the spookery it does is because it's so close to Route 5's aura.

A cynic would say the reason so many battles, sacred sites, major villages, and haunted sites chance to be on Route 5 is because it was such an important walkway. How else would you get around in the preindustrial Northeast? Upstate New York was fiendish for travel off the trail. The woods were said to be so thick that a squirrel could get from the Hudson Valley to Pennsylvania without touching the ground. There was no Erie Canal.

A cynic might also ask why something used so commonly for mundane purposes like trade, travel, and warpath could still be considered sacred. There I have the answer.

The Euro mind is nurtured, whether it knows it or not, on Judeo-Christian dualism and Greek logic. Things may share qualities, but they are this or they are, most often, that. The Native American mind had no such exclusionary quality. The Native American mind was quite comfortable with something being significantly one thing and also significantly others. Route 5 is a power-track, then and today. As long as we were really on it, we seemed to be protected.

One of the fundamental apprehensions about "magical" ceremonies is that their effect follows the earthly flow, either of natural avenues like rivers and valleys or man-made trails and roads, at least important ones. Ed Montour could have arranged supportive ceremonies to be held at various points all along the 5, possibly between us and our destination. There were Elders living by the sacred spring, the Kateri Shrine, in Fonda. They could have set something up in their back yard. For all we knew, Ed Montour was with them. If the Six Nations Elders had launched some sympathetic mojo, it would have been the equal of anything like it in the world, at least on their own turf.

For that matter, maybe even Jaap Simon was in on the act. I didn't know for sure that he was ever involved in anything more than the business, "the Registration," of the College, but I know he's always pulling for me and all his team, and Route 5 does turn into State Street in Schenectady. It runs right into the Old Dorp, and Jaap Simon's office is on it.

For most of the drive to Geneva we were untroubled by any assaults.

It truly did seem as if there was some spell that worked our way as long as we we cruised on top of the original trackway under the many-times graded and repaved surface that became today's Route 5. It was a lot more comfortable, too, despite the delays of stoplights and speed limits. We felt safe enough to stop at a 24-hour convenient and load up on gas, water, and the like. The clerk had just put on a fresh pot of coffee, too, which lifted everybody's spirits. Even The Ghost took a couple sips. He was rigidly and mockably off caffeine.

We switched our seating when we hit the road again. The Ghost moved to the middle seat beside Dana Lambert, keeping the package between them. I took his former spot beside Nadia where I could keep the windshield clear just in case we met with another Bogie-barrage. Danny replaced me in the reversed third seat. We hadn't thought of the re-arrangement before because everything had been coming at us so fast. Another aspect of the furious evening was that I was getting tired. I'd never needed to be so on with all my faculties for so long. Most of my fights are quick.

I was starting to share the impression with my fellows that very few of our human companions on these roads and streets had seen the critters we had seen. Even if some of them had, a hectoring pack of crows would seem remarkable but not paranormal enough to call in 911 or the National Guard. We felt like our tormentors weren't too far off, though. On a couple of occasions we thought we spotted semi-material shadow-forms buzzing us. I wondered if that might have been the sign that we had swayed from the track of the old footpath and whatever Native medicine channeled through it.

314

# Chapter 16

# Lady Justice

1

The east behind us seemed the direction of all our troubles. I had the feeling that something was trying to claw the item we had back to a source in that direction, too. What that meant, I had no idea. But something felt incomplete and misguided about our flight. I wasn't the only one.

"What kind of plan is it to just keep going west?" said Nadia as we were leaving the Geneva city limits.

"We'll be in Buffalo before daybreak," said Dana.

"Then what?" I said. "Just keep going?"

"Something's got to happen before that," said Nadia. "This isn't any good at all."

"New York Route 5 turns into Pennsylvania Route 5," I said, looking at Danny. "Does the mojo cross state lines?"

He was about to say something when his phone rang. It had to be his dad. "Canandaigua," he said, hanging up. "The 5 goes right through it. Some Seneca meeting us there. Medicine cooking."

"Big village," I said. "Where in Canandaigua?"

"I'm told we can't miss it," said Danny.

Somewhere after we left Geneva I saw a sign for a place called "Seneca Castle." Soon after that I saw another for a town evidently called "Hopewell." My antennae went up.

Place-names can be quite suggestive in the Northeast. The region we were touring had been strewn with ancient earth-and-stone constructions, and both those names were suggestive of them. I tried to remember if I had spotted others like them.

Some of these structures were post-medieval and truly built as forts. Others, usually the older ones, were often mistaken for forts, but they were ritual earthworks designed as religious monuments. The Empire State's done a poor job of preserving them, but their sites, whenever they can be found, are still places of power. While I think whatever force they have generally favors the causes of balance and compassion in the world, their energy can be conscripted to almost anything. People in the know can hitch onto them. They'd be like a combination of magnets and generators for the right Collegians. Someone with an exposure to indigenous mojo, particularly of this continent, could set up a Hell of an ambush at one of them.

Right about the time I was reflecting that, we got a nasty surprise of the material variety. We were just a few miles east of the village of Canandaigua.

You've heard of those slasher-films, *Maniac Cop* and *Psycho Cop*? Well, this looked like Wacko Trucker had had an episode. A huge trailer was jackknifed and waiting for us just before the intersection of 5 & 20 and some substantial-looking north-south route. The road was completely blocked. I wondered what the driver had seen to cause such a frenzied turn. Everybody braced for an assault from shadowy forms as soon as we came to a stop. The fact that the pounce was not instant comforted no one. They were just as likely to be picking their spots, even herding us.

Nadia just swore something, switched the SUV into truck-mode, pulled off the 5 & 20 behind the stop sign, and motored us unevenly back and up to the paved surface heading north. They call them SUVs for a reason.

We knew there were several well-traveled routes converging from the east into Canandaigua. If we went north we were bound to hit one. But we worried that the harrowing could begin again off the protective bubble of the 5.

In a quarter mile we saw the first of the Bogies. This one seemed to recognize the driver's side as a control center. It gripped the hood at the base of the windshield in front of Nadia and gave the glass a few testy pecks. That beak sounded dense enough to break through. Then it tried to peer into the cabin at us and we got a good look at its ghoulish pterosaur face. I lanced it through the head and it peeled off of us. It was another sign of progressing strategy out of them. The rest had been attacking our vehicle like it was a burly animal they were trying to bleed out.

The flock was thin, though. With my Beam I was able to keep the viewing field clear in the front of the vehicle. The real danger was that the occasional beastie would cause us a collision or, worse, get in and get at Nadia. We veered crazily at least once.

In a minutes of leaving the 5 & 20 we came to a high point on a ridge and took our left turn to begin the eastward approach into the core of the village. A beacon stood out for us like a gigantic melon, an amber gem on the horizon visible across the landscape for miles from the right vantages. In spite of our turmoil, harassed by otherworldly beings, I was inspired by the sight of it, every time we spotted it again after a dip in a valley. It could only be the illuminated dome of the monumental Ontario County Courthouse, one of the most significant buildings atop one of the most marvelous sites in this part of the state. It's also outrageously haunted.

That glorious jack-o-lantern in the distance fascinated me. I barely noticed that we were no longer being pestered by the winged creatures. I suppose we all thought we were outrunning them, or else that we had drifted onto another protected trackway. When we entered the city limits and parked at the foot of the expansive grounds, I understood. They were waiting for us, as if they had known our destination. I stepped out.

A vast flock of the grim creatures languished. Their ominous latency reminded me of the scene at the end of Hitchcock's *The Birds*. Their numbers were awe-inspiring. They perched in every tree, rested on every bit of open roof, and littered the lawns like autumn leaves. I even saw a handful propping themselves on the sacred boulder, the signing-point of the "Calico Compact," the 1794 Pickering Treaty.

I wasn't shocked that no crowd was here studying them. I wasn't sure everyone could see them. This part of the village is pretty quiet at midnight on a Sunday, anyway.

From the mass and volume of the psycho-physical critters around us, I knew there was enough protoplasm – or ectoplasm – to just about lift our SUV and tote it back to Neverland, at least if these things could find enough to grab onto. Flying off with the package we held would have been effortless.

Danny's phone chirped. He spoke a few seconds in the angle of the open door, then held the device out to me. The voice on speaker mode was that of Ed Montour. "The Elders have this one figured out," he said. "We have to get the item to the top of the dome."

I was the only one he could have meant to do it. I was not looking forward to it. I may look like Superman to those of you with Muggle abilities, but some of the stuff I have to do with mine is pretty scary. "Then what?" I said.

"Then, I'd say…" said Ed Montour, "it will 'open its eyes' if it's where it belongs." Then he was off. I had been comforted by talking to him, even briefly.

I stood and gaped again at the domed, illuminated, Greek Revival Courthouse before and above me. It's always awe-inspiring at night, and its space has its own energy. I remembered what I knew of it and its site. Besides the signing ceremonies of the Pickering Pact, it hosted a number of pivotal trials. A gigantic, pre-Contact fort had once occupied the vantage overlooking Canandaigua Lake, the Senecas' creation-site, with its mighty serpent. It was as if some magnetism about the spot drew all these historic and prehistoric events to it. The town's main street on which we parked had been another old Native footpath. Once called the Rochester Road, it joined the Seneca town on the lake with the villages to the north along the Genesee.

*It will 'open its eyes'?* I sorted that. Despite the fact that all the sites and personalities and circumstances we'd dealt with that night were native to the American landmass, this scenario felt like an occult clash that also had European elements. It felt like a clash of continents, in a way, at least of the energy behind it. I thought this because I sensed that Puff was in some way involved, and that no matter where he dwelt, he was Old World. Really old.

We were in one of the northeastern hearts of Native power. It felt like there was so much of it here that no supplanting force could menace us if we were doing the Nation's work. But were we? I questioned that. Almost as quickly, I came back to myself. I had to follow the leads of the people I believed in, including Jaap Simon, the Native Elders who spoke through Ed Montour, and whatever felt like justice to me on the planet. This wasn't the Longhouse that had massed its forces against us.

"Let's get a look at our package," said The Ghost.

Dana Lambert started unfolding the wrappings. The layers looked like they were recently applied, but I knew this made sense, no matter the age of the artifact. This one had been handled, recently and frequently. Medicine Masks cannot be stored like furniture. They are re-garded as powerful, even sentient beings who must be routinely and reg-ularly honored with the proper ceremonies, lest they get agitated and cause disruptions in the environment around them. These disruptions would be dramatic with a Mask that was the focus of a centuries' long standoff between the Elders of the Six Iroquoian Nations and Puff, as I call him, "the Archimage."

The two women held the Mask properly and carefully. There was plenty of ambient light coming in by which to see it, including one beam from a streetlamp that fell right on it through the sunroof of our vehicle. Danny saw it just before I did and said something, surely, in Mohawk. I gasped when the wrappings fell away. It was the most unusual Mask I'd ever seen.

The Iroquoian Masks are thematic takes on animal heads or one of a handful of mythological characters. No two are identical, but they are in categories, and each has a message. Though fashioned almost surely out of the traditional material, basswood, this Mask appeared to be, like some of the iconic Moche pots, a very lifelike portrait of someone who had once lived – a white-toothed, aquiline-nosed man, stern, content, and arrogantly handsome. This man had been a chief. Most of these masks are fitted with fright-wigs, too, manes generally of corn silk or, since the coming of the Europeans, horse-hair. This one honestly seemed to be the long, heavy locks of a human, possibly even those of the man after which the Mask was modeled.

It was not only the most unusual Mask I'd ever seen, it was also the most *alive*. It took on its own virtual glow. I had heard about an incident in which a famous Tuscarora medicine man recognized a Tibetan mystic at a crowded conference by some metaphysical light-forms that looked to him like green dragons, framing the man's throat-chakra like a horse-collar, like a Celtic torc. I've never been able to see effects like that, but I could fancy that I saw this Mask acting up. I got the sense of motion about the locks framing the triumphant face, like luminous, coiling serpents within the mane. I recalled the old tale about the snake-haired Onondaga wizard-king, the Tadodaho, the Longhouse Medusa, whom the Peacemaker had to bring into the fold before the great League could ever have existed. I wondered if I could be looking into his face.

It was above Canandaigua Lake that the future leaders of the Longhouse League had gathered to plan to approach the witch-chief and bring him into the alliance, bringing healing to the Longhouse Nations and making brothers and sisters out of cousins. Were we on the very

spot? Had we walked into a mythic re-enactment? Were we being deputized to take over a new message of healing? Was the Mask in some sense
coming home?

"Time for duty," said The Ghost, standing guard.

Danny said what seemed like a little prayer in Mohawk and lifted the
item like a heavy, fragile vase, by its middle – in this case the cheeks –
with no more than the weight of the thing holding it in place. He didn't
grip it at all with his fingers. He presented it to me facing his own body-
core.

"How do you hold one of these?" I said, shivering like my 12-year-
old self being handed the first infant he'd ever held.

"Don't look it in the eyes," he said, transferring it to me. "Hold it outward."

"I'm paranoid," I said, holding the item on my chest and starting to
step toward the spectacular Greek revival structure. A thousand beaks
snapped toward me soundlessly, and I braced for an assault. Nothing
came of it. The birdlike beings held to their positions. I would say their
poses implied that this move we were making was acceptable to them, as
though they "thought" – like they think – I was presenting the item as a
gift.

"What if I do something wrong?" I said after a pair of steps.

"This one will understand," said Danny.

I looked back at them all as if to say, *Why me?*

They looked back as if to say, *Well, you are the only one of us who can fly.
Sorta.*

"You want me to take this up to that dome?" I called back.

"Unless you can get in the place and walk it to dead center that way,"
said Danny. "That's what the Elders told my dad. It has to get there.
Right on top of that exact spot."

"Nice of those white guys to put a building over it," said Nadia.

"Try to stand right by that statue," Danny said, meaning the Lady of Justice with her scales.

"At least they gave you something to hang on to," said The Ghost. *Funny.*

"Be peaceful with us, Old Brother," said Danny after me. "Help us get you home."

I took my first few steps outside the SUV and considered my options. I could easily break into the Courthouse. I could take any door lock out in seconds with my Gleam-hand. I would probably have to axe my way through several interior doors after that to reach the special spot. There would be alarms, even video. How long would I have to stand in the pose? What then? There would be armed troopers and police within minutes. How could I avoid injuring any of them? And what was keeping the bird-things out after that? The breaking-and-entering scenario seemed worse than a levitation.

I took a few more steps, wondering what we had arrayed against ourselves. I stood before the glorious structure like it was an altar. I could see hundreds of beak-horns pivot toward me like the barrels of snipers stationed in all directions. I'm sure all the ones I couldn't see did likewise. I expected to be mobbed. None moved. If I had to describe their attitude with a human mood, I would say that they were gloating. This was what the shadowy wingers wanted: me stepping toward them, Mask in hand.

I'd never felt so opposed by psychic/supernatural forces. The moment, and the site itself, was all over me. The night air seemed to bare teeth. *Power is simply power,* I told myself again. The building may have been young in European terms, but the Native influence of the site is not, and I felt the force of it all starting to surge through me. It still felt like things were in the balance. Did whoever controlled those things think I was giving up? Getting ready to hand the Mask over? In spite of my desperation, I chuckled. *Yeah, right. Come get it, fuckers.* I threw on the Glow.

I gave a little hop and a big wish and started to rise. It was awkward, keeping my elbows in to hold the mask so carefully. Usually I spread out like a swimmer.

Of course the Bogies detected me with the package they had been programmed to crave, and they rushed me in handfuls. I don't have a lot of weight when I levitate, and they kept me from catching my bearings. They knocked me off my drifting, that's for sure, pinballing against me in the night sky. Some of the horny beaks came startlingly close to reaching me through the Glow. The critters all bounced off, though and splatted. The lawn to the street-side of the courthouse was starting to be littered with them. By the time they wised up enough to know they were only hurting themselves by bashing into me, I lifted above what seemed to be their comfort-zone and drew myself to the second level of the building. Maybe the dome had its own force.

I can't lift a lot when I go into the Glide. You might be asking yourself why the critters or whoever managed them would let me get off the ground with that package without a mob attack. I ask it of myself. My only answer is that whoever pulled the strings didn't know what I could do – another reason to keep my abilities as secret as I can.

I skimmed the sides of the grand courthouse, imagining its transitions under the handiwork of the Genesee Valley's prime father-and-son teams of sacred architects, first the graceful Searles, then the monumental Warners. As simple as the virtual temple looked, I knew there were mathematical subtleties within it that might never be explicated and that could certainly enhance its geomantic power.

I rose to the level of the glowing dome and drifted close to the statue, Lady Justice, *Justicia*. Her scales were said to have clattered down the sides of the building and clanged on the earth when the verdict of the 1873 trial in this courthouse was read, finding Susan B. Anthony guilty both of being a woman and voting. I was surprised at how big she was. I could stand precariously on the octagonal cupola beside her. The views of both village and valley were so stunning that I would have loved to have spent a bit of time in my reflections. But the moment was upon me.

No matter how many times I pull this move, the Glide, I never lose my fear of heights. I was tempted to reach a hand over and steady myself on the statue. I didn't dare. If that Mask fell, everything was lost.

I studied *Justicia* idly. She was at least ten feet tall. Up close, a position almost no one ever reaches, she was looking worse for the wear, even in the glistening moonlight. I knew the Finger Lakes winters would give her a beating, but she looked a little hangdog even for my expectations. There wasn't much room beside her, and I had to stand straight up. I wouldn't have been able to stay there long at my natural weight without hanging onto something. I'm light when I go into the Glide, and you'd think it would help me stabilize on top of a narrow perch, but it was worse under the circumstances. The item I held, the one I'd been led to believe was so delicate, was throwing off my balance. Its weight was tugging me forward into a fall or another Glide like the one I'd done upward to get to where I was. And I had to hold it with two hands.

*So what now?* I asked myself. I had one of the most powerful and valuable occult totems in the Native world in my grasp, perched what felt like seventy feet over the ground, waiting either to tire or be swarmed by a flock of supernatural attackers that, if it rushed at once, might knock me over or separate me and my burden. I was tired. The power I have that's most impacted by mood and energy is this one, the Glide. I might even drop like a Muggle. This was a losing game. But the driver of the Bogies had never impressed me as a patient force, and I sensed that another play was coming. With those thoughts I noticed things starting to change.

At first I thought I might be getting dizzy from the height, plus standing with my elbows in, holding up that precious and fragile Mask. I leaned back into the statue, nearly getting stuck in the leg by Justicia's sword. Against myself, I looked down, which was dumb. When I looked back out before me to try to orient myself, I noticed something odd.

All the birdlike beings who could still get airborne had risen into the sky around me and arrayed themselves against the indigo sky like wallpaper designs, perching in their niches like dark stars in an almost perfectly symmetrical heaven. Everywhere I looked it was the same. It was as if I was the focus of a three-dimensional mobile moving with my vision whose invisible supports held its elements in a perfect equipoise. They were interesting, even fascinating. Then they started to bulge, recede, and spin. They were hypnagogic. It was hard taking my eyes off them.

All of you have seen countless special effects in the visual media. What was psychedelic when I was a kid is mainstream animation now. Try looking at effects like that in the natural world around you, especially when you are free-climbing a Greek Revival monument that towers over Canandaigua Lake and trying to hold onto one of the most important totems on the continent.

The world spun. I tried closing my eyes, but that made standing in position even worse. If I dove out and tried to Glide to a safe spot on the ground below, I was breaking the advice I was given – and the torment could begin again. If I slipped, I really might fall.

These Masks are major storers and channelers of *Source*. Sometimes some of them even work like weapons. They all have to be handled precisely. I had been told never to hold one face upward, but something out of nowhere told me to do so with this one. I held the Mask over my head and held it open toward the night sky and the direction I associated with all the torment. I didn't dare look in its direction,. but I could sense things starting to change.

I could hear the women calling to me from the street below. Danny was yelling something in full throat. Then I couldn't hear anything but a massive whorling. I could hardly even think. All I remember is feeling some invigorating force radiate upward and outward through me like it came from the ground and channeled through my upraised arms into and then out through the Mask. I had never felt such a channeling of *Source*, which I envisioned turning into a 180° emanator of radiance that scoured the heavens above it of all hostile intentions. When all was still,

I opened my eyes. I saw only the sky I would have expected above me and the city below. I checked my perceptions, sensing a trick. The night was clear.

You might think the scariest thing about the Glide would be soaring to a height from which a fall would kill you. You might think it would be leaving the ground in the first place. You would be wrong. The scariest thing about the Glide is stepping off of a height into bare air, not really knowing if it's going to work. Nineteen out of twenty, no problem. That one time it piffles out makes all the rest of them scare you.

That time it worked. I drifted out and touched down a few feet from my friends. I had a little more momentum than I'd hoped when I came in and could have blown the whole deal if I had dropped the Mask. Fortunately, The Ghost caught me under the shoulders from behind with those rock-hard palms and held me up like someone swinging a toddler. He is quite strong, and the fading Glow didn't seem to bother him.

I passed over the Mask and fell into the arms of my comrades like a place kicker who had just won the Super Bowl. They told me that when I had raised the Mask over my head and laid it on its back, the position of death, it had radiated a faint, gorgeous, lime-green force in a perfect hemisphere above it, lasting just a handful of seconds and then lapsing. Our airborne tormentors faded and disappeared. None were left on the ground around us.

The two women started to repackage the Mask, which, after that display, felt like an old friend. At that point the shadowy forms of several men came up to us from around the south side of the building. The Ghost and I braced wearily for more action, but Danny gave me a little tap on the right shoulder, and we both stood down. When they came into the light I saw that the newcomers were all casually-dressed Native American men who looked about middle-age. All were solidly built, though only one was tall. It was quickly clear that these were friends of Danny's and that this meeting was by arrangement. I gathered either that they had just arrived or that they had had to stay clear until the combatics were decided. No one could be blamed for wanting to duck those horrible creatures. I knew exactly what would become of all the corpses; they would dematerialize and fade back into the realms that had sent them, leaving no trace of themselves except whatever damage they had done.

The foremost of the newcomers and The Ghost nodded to each other like old acquaintances. Another extended his hands to accept the Mask like he was welcoming a lost child. Clearly, these were Elders of the Medicine Mask society, here to safeguard their treasure. I had little doubt that it would protect itself from here on, at least in their capable grasp.

We were all exhausted and starting to put ourselves together when a call came in to Dana Lambert. It was Jaap Simon, who had made an arrangement with a fine old B&B about a quarter-mile from where we stood. "I can't think of a B&B that's open at midnight on a Sunday," I said, but there it was, golden lights blazing. Jaap had booked us five rooms. An early breakfast was underway as we arrived.

2

We were all beat. We were also completely wired. Sleep for any of us was a long way off. I forget who asked if anybody felt like a walk, but four of us took the offer. Only The Ghost stayed in, presumably for more of his meditating and stretching. That was his decompression. He really is a mystical character. With him there is a ritual for everything. He had taken a few lives that night, too, and there would be a period of penance. We did it during our stroll.

On still summer nights Canandaigua has the delightful feeling of hidden energy, of understated life behind the veneer of the human environment. Its sites and buildings well with significance like dewdrops waiting to be touched to spill their contents.

It was also delightful to be with these three friends. It's a once-in-awhile thing for us all to be together, and that night we were exhilarated by the sense of an adventure shared and survived. No one suspected that anything could be open at 2 AM on a Sunday, yet as we descended the main street with its overview of the lake, we could see what seemed to be a source of light and human activity on a cross street and spotted a few people stepping toward it. *What the...?* we all seemed to think at once. We stepped the block-and-a-half toward their destiny, an odd-looking enterprise that had caught my attention earlier that evening on our way into town. Its shingle-sign, its narrow storefront, and its neon window-art had made me think of a tattoo parlor. It was instead a sidestreet pub. We entered more out of curiosity than thirst.

Had the front window not been so cluttered with neon signs and posters we'd have known we'd enter at the toe line of the dartboard. As it was, the backstroke of one of the players tickled Danny's right ear.

The place was a lot deeper than it was wide, and I had the sense of a vibrant life going on in its recesses. We waited to order by the bar, and I found myself studying the three chunky, gritty young men pitching their "arraz." My time in the Isles has exposed me to the terminology of the game.

I wasn't watching them because they were good dartists. They were closer to chuckers – people just hoping to hit the board. But they were such types that I found them fascinating.

All were denimed, one even in overalls, which was retro when I was a college kid. They had florid complexions and auburn beards and manes. Their builds and coloring were so similar that you'd have presumed them members of the same tribe if you spotted them together in Europe 2500 years earlier. I presumed they were farm kids, but you can never tell by dress. It was as if for them, the 70s had never died. Was Stealer's Wheel making a comeback?

They were drinking concoctions out of tall plastic cups, and I noticed them go through a round quickly. One of them kept calling for a single one of the two bartenders to make his drink. "I wanna *tase'* my liquor," he called. "I wanna *tase'* it." But they were outliers here. Most of the clientele was artsy, and they all seemed to understand something about each other.

We took our drinks and set out to look around. The establishment dimmed and seemed to grow in intrigue as we went deeper into it. We found a second horseshoe bar, like the first coming out of the same wall to our right, the west. This one took up a lot of space and left an avenue of only four feet or so between the elbows of its frisky drinkers and a line of two-top tables pressed against the wall. Past that were the rest rooms and a dance floor that I imagine really hopped on the right nights. Years later, I would discover, the place would be busted for its 4 AM closings. It was in remarkable form for a Sunday.

We moved four stools so we could face each other at the center of the back bar. We were all unexpectedly lightheaded, laughing deliriously after the tension of the evening. Even Danny broke his rule and joined us for a few sips of wine. I looked around as we spoke.

The people in this place continued to fascinate me. Maybe it was a factor of the night we'd had, but I shouldn't have been surprised that the clientele was eclectic. The western Finger Lakes are in the old Burned-over District, a region proverbial for alternative religions and ahead-of-their-time political ideas, including Abolition, Feminism, and Women's Suffrage. Off-the-center thinking still permeates the region, mixing oddly with a more staid and agricultural population.

I was having trouble taking my eyes off two young women in devout conversation at one of the small tables against the wall. I was under 40 at the time, don't forget, and still capable of being fascinated by Muggle women. And with all the intrigue of this town and the night we had just experienced, I had no certainty that these were Muggles.

The woman facing in my direction seemed to be doing all the talking, though I couldn't hear a word of it. She had broad blue eyes and a mane of thick brown hair cut to fall to her shoulders. Her features were rounded and puckish. She wasn't a classic beauty, but there was something sexy about those eyes, and those deep, flat lips. She believed in herself, that was for sure. The woman with her was a blonde. I could only see her back.

Maybe it was their apparent courtship of each other that I found so fascinating. There was magic in the big blues of the one I could see, just a sort of a dance with the expressions and a little twirl of her delicate tongue as she made her points. There was surely something between them. I couldn't hear a word, but I fancied that they were sharing secrets, as if each knew the other's avowed lover and were finding attractions to each other that night. It was then that the blonde nodded as if with laughter, and I could see her in profile. It was almost surely the young woman from Saratoga Springs, the one who had set me up so perfectly after our hit on the witches that seemed so far in the past but that was actually the night before. If someone sent her or anyone made to look like her to an unlikely spot across the state when I just happened to be there – and after such an ordeal! – it was a message, and a challenge, even a taunt.

"I see somebody I gotta talk to," I said to my friends, making meaningful eye contact. I knew they'd be watching my back.

As I approached the small circular table I noticed the untouched wine glass in front of the speaker. Nothing had been sipped from it, and there were no signs that those sensual lips had pressed against it. The woman's arms didn't rest on the table, and she was curled into the wall where no passerby in the narrow walking space might bump her. Then it hit me: One of them might be an apparition, "A Transfer," as we sometimes call it in our College-themed slang, or even "a Special Student." I almost passed a hand onto one or the other of them to see which one it was, but that would have given away the fact that I knew something, but not enough. This was the oddest sensation. Which one was I supposed to watch? It felt like another setup. I was glad to have my three formidable friends ten feet away. I craned around the speaker once as discreetly as I could. The blonde was indeed the young woman from the Saratoga pub who had called herself Kayley. She was raptly looking into the face of the speaker as if taking leads from it – or controlling it.

I gave the wine glass a little clink with my pint as if sharing a toast with a ghostly holder. I tried to read Kayley's – I'm sure that wasn't her name – expression behind her dipping mane. She kept her eyes down like she was too shy or guilty to notice to me. Then I took a seat beside her friend. "Having trouble with your double?" I said, peering at her. "Mind if I kvetch with your fetch?"

"There's one more step," said the brown-haired woman beside me with what I could have sworn was the voice of the blonde. It astonished me. There was something staticky, metallic, fake about the sound of it, but no one anywhere but right where I was would have noticed.

"Where's Wee Willie?" I said, still feeling the blows but not dreading them. He liked hitting by surprise, and I was ready.

"You have to transfer another item," said the brown-haired woman, keeping her big blues on the blonde.

"I work for Jaap Simon," I said.

"He says you weren't when you made your little mess."

"So are you working for *Him*?" I said, meaning no one but the obvious. I got that sinking feeling of aloneness again.

"His interests are involved."

"I'll get back to you," I said, getting up. The phone inside my vest pocket rang, and the apparent speaker nodded to me to answer it. I recognized Jaap Simon's number. At the same instant, I noticed my three friends getting calls. Looking amused, all three picked up and met each others' glances. I rejoined them. It was indeed a conference call. I recognized Jaap Simon's number.

"Jaap," I said, "is this on the level?"

"It is, Eric," said what I'm sure was Jaap's voice.

"Who put out the APB on that Transcript?" said Nadia.

"I'm sorry again about the difficulties this evening," said Jaap. "Nobody saw that coming."

"This was supposed to be a done deal," said Dana.

"Sometimes… there are things none of us can anticipate," said Jaap. "This *is* our business."

Another call came in for Danny, and I saw him switch to the other line. He seemed content to let us focus on our conversation.

"Come back and we'll talk about it," said Jaap. "Right now your job is to get some rest."

Danny was on his phone at least thirty seconds after we cut off with Jaap, and he came back to us with just about the same resolution. We knew he'd been conferring with his dad who in turn had been networking with the Northeastern Elders, and specifically the Longhouse People whose Mask had been recovered. "It seems like things can get back to being civilized," he said, "but Eric's got a trip to the woodshed."

I looked about glumly, letting my eyes stray. I noticed that my two former table-mates were already gone, and I cursed again to myself. I had meant to study them to see if I could get any clues from the way they moved that might help me read the phenomenon and maybe be better prepared for it if I encountered it again. I still wasn't sure which was the emanation, if either.

So. Me. A special delivery. A peace keeping mission. For Puff. Pick something up from him and get it somewhere else.

I sat with the others for last call and pondered the options. For some crazy reason the impressions I have of that night and that pub – Cloün – all come back to me as purple. The walls were all purple, and most people wore clothing that didn't clash with it.

Puff had a chance here to send a message. He could show everybody how tough and unforgiving he is. He might also show people that he was professional and diplomatic.

I honestly thought Puff had nothing to lose with either one. Everybody thought he was just so *bad* that every move he made was interpreted with either genuflection or awe. If he let somebody off, they were devoutly relieved and impressed with his transcendence. If somebody went missing and people got the feeling it was in his interests to have done it, it made him look dreadful. He really did have the mojo over everybody. This could be a face-saving trip for both of us.

So: Jaap Simon, the guy everybody knows I work for, gives me an errand with Puff. Puff accepts it as a peace offering. It's a bit of a bother, but everybody goes home happy. Head home in a day or two, wrap up a few loose ends, prepare for a trip of moderate but indeterminate length, and go for it. All good.

It still felt like a set-up. I knew someone I had to talk to.

3

"I agree that it's problematic, dear boy," commenced Bella, lifting the mimosa and bowing under her broad sun hat to sip it. "We went all through that a few days ago."

Once I'd settled down back in Saratoga Springs I'd streaked to find Bella. It was a Friday morning, and I could only catch her in one of her routine August poses, holding down a six-top with two others on the sun-splashed deck of an elegant restaurant on Broadway Avenue. From the couple's positions at the other corner of the table and the purses and clothing on the empty chairs, I got the feeling that I'd come in at the tail end of a brunch that was expecting people back. That made me think I had to get to the point quickly. I'd taken the chair beside Bella, but I was worrying how much of things I could lay out this publicly. I let on as such.

"Oh, Sam and Shelby are just up for the track, said Bella. "They don't know anything about Smoggy!" That was her nickame for Puff, another spin on the dragon-motif, this one out of Tolkien: Smaug. She's the only person in the College other than yours truly who refers with the slightest irreverence to the entity I call Puff. Maybe she was right about her table-mates five feet away. Neither looked College, and they seemed unlikely to be paying attention to our words even if they were. They had barely nodded when Bella had introduced me and were making a steady point of ignoring me. The man – dark, blocky, and middle-sized – was dressed for the golf course. I could see him heading to the Golf & Polo Club. The woman – pale, petite, pretty, and brown-haired – was dressed for tennis. I could see her having just stepped off the courts at the Gideon Putnam. They didn't look like old-money Anglo snobs, at least the guy didn't, but they had some reason for thinking that the average person they met was most likely not up to their cut.

"Things got a lot screwier after our last conversation," I said, leaning in. "They weren't as simple as they looked."

"That's because of the intervention of an unknown party, maybe more than one. Maybe we should have seen that coming, but nobody did."

"We got through it, but I have some worries about part two of the arrangement."

"You mean going to see Smoggy?"

I nodded.

"I'm the last person who would want to see anything happen to you, Eric, but I don't see it coming in this case. I mean, think about it. If Smoggy goes around knocking people off that he invites to come see him, pretty soon nobody comes to see him. And he has a lot more enemies than anybody needs. Desperate ones. That's something nobody wants to get started. No, a lot of people know you're going to see him. And you better come back or it's going to look really bad."

"It would," I said wryly. But it made sense.

Friday mornings in Saratoga always fill me with an envy, and Friday happy hours are legendary. I studied a half-empty glass and its tiny parasol of a stirrer. I drifted into thinking about how easy it would have been to slip into Bella's languorous day: brunch, mimosas, the track (she was an irreformable bettor), maybe a nap, and a long evening out. I usually like to get a lot more done with my day, but hers looked tempting in the shadow of my visit to Puff. The day was going to be tame and sunny all through, and the town has such an energy at that time of year. Glamorous, interesting people are everywhere, especially in August. The world really does come to Saratoga in race season.

I took a walk down Broadway to Congress Park, the intricate, bowl-like space of springs, fountains, and Neoclassical features. No matter what kind of human-made commotion is in force here or anywhere, the park to me always feels placid. It's a little ceremony to stroll through it, and I always do whenever I leave or return to Saratoga Springs. It's where I say hello or goodbye to this wonderful village I have loved so much, as if I want its images to be among the last memories I may ever have or the ones to greet me when I touch back down. It's where I go when I have thinking to do. I studied the ducks, so placid in their mini-streams and lagoons. I heard a rhythm band warming up for an impromptu session. Members of the fencing club were out.

I thought Puff didn't want to mess with me, at least publicly. I thought his attempt to nail me might have been that Fox-and-Ox show right after Danny and I did for the witches. I'd turned out to be more than he'd bargained for. That made him wary of me. Since almost nobody but him and the three people involved knew much for sure about that incident, he could let that failure slide and keep his moxie with the College. He would like it that way.

He had good reasons not to try to hurt me after that. If I really got desperate and outraged, I might be going after him, and I might able to hurt him. Emperors, after all, dread assassins more than they do armies.

I decided to accept Jaap's offer and go through with the whole plan, including this meeting with Puff. I went to my home to pack a bag for a trip so I could leave on a moment's notice. There was someone else I had to talk to. I have sort of a groupie.

# Chapter 17

# Elena

1

There may be only one person on the planet who sincerely, absolutely loves me. I haven't brought her up yet because she hasn't come into the story of this war, that book, or my meeting with Puff, but now she does. It's time I told you about Elena. I met her on one of my missions for Jaap Simon.

I'd been with Jaap at that point for several years. My life, my fortunes, my adventures… They had come a long way. I'd gotten my base settled in Saratoga Springs and had a very happy, deceptively successful life. I hadn't discovered all the abilities you are used to seeing. I was accustomed to using what I have described to you as "the Hammer Hand," a very serviceable weapon and tool but no thermal lance like I have now on my right. My left was a nice defensive implement, a sort of blocking, shocking device. I had only recently discovered my levitational abilities, the Glide. I had never tried drifting downward from a significant height.

I had made a pickup of a small object in the Swiss Alps. I was touring southern Denmark and Germany with it on me. This might seem strange to you, but it isn't really. Sometimes when you have one of Jaap's deliveries, you beeline it for the airport. Sometimes when you have one of Jaap's deliveries, you act exactly like you don't. You act like a tourist. This confuses people who might be tracking you. Above all, you mix it up. Don't always do the obvious thing. Don't never do the obvious thing. Sometimes, do something in between. That was one of the tweeners.

I spent a bit of time in Dresden near the Czech border. I found it an interesting city. There had been a settlement in its site on the Elbe River since at least the Middle Ages. By the 1500s it was an important city and the home of the Electors (roughly, "kings") of the province of Saxony. Dresden was the scene of one of the most devastating and debatably unjust aerial bombardments of civilian targets in history. Estimates on the low side mention 25,000 people killed at a point in time – February, 1945 – that World War II was assuredly lost for the German cause.

The grand city had been one of Europe's treasures. Just from that perspective, destroying it was a stroke not just against the Germans, but against civilization, even humanity. You talk about the Chimies... My head was hurting from them in almost every bit of that city. It took me quite a while to find an inn far enough from the core to escape the voices.

I shot down to the Black Forest region and spent a couple days journaling, hiking, and getting into the local beer and cuisine. German cooking is a lot healthier than it's stereotyped by most Americans. The Germans love fruit and vegetables. They love local ingredients. Most of them hate processed stuff like so many Americans are hooked on. They also love sport. They're hikers, cyclists, runners... I would have made a good German in that regard. I've already told you that being in shape is vital to maintaining and using some of my abilities, the Glide especially.

The item I had wasn't supposed to be "heavily recruited," as we sometimes say, but I think that was a blind. I'm pretty sure from the fallout that this was one of the most important items I have ever transported. I think it could have been Raedwald's Runestone. I think that could have been the item Jaap Simon had loaned to Carl Jung. It had had an errant destiny in the 20th century, and it had taken Jaap some time after Jung's death in 1961 to get it back. I didn't know what it was at first.

When I'm transporting something for Jaap Simon, I always feel like I know what it isn't: something legally or morally dangerous to transport. I don't always know what it is. We've got a good understanding that way. There's usually a ceremony of validation for the item before I haul it off, and usually I'm there for it, but with that one, Jaap seemed to have it all covered. He said to just pick up what his old friend handed me. I did have to fight off those wingy-stingers I've mentioned earlier, right after I picked the thing up. That was the episode in which I told you about really finding my defensive Glow. That should have been a clue, thought I didn't take it.

Whatever it was fit into a package that could have held a cell phone. It was dense, and nothing in it rattled. I guessed it was a jewel or ornament. I had it on me for weeks. Usually I kept it on me in a security pouch that fit right under the arm. I got good at sleeping with it.

Jaap didn't say anything about not looking at it, and something told me to do it with this one. I can still see it in my palm in the afternoon sunlight spilling through a window in my room at an inn in Stuttgart. It was a semi-translucent ovoid lozenge, probably made of amber. It was etched with a symbol I'd have sworn was a rune, one of the old Germanic/Scandinavian letters. A little trip to a library revealed that it wasn't one of the acknowledged characters, but there was something haunting about it. I wondered if it was a forgotten rune, one that never made it into the textbooks.

It was a mystery in another way: This item needed to get back to Simon. The items I transport usually go from the seller, or his/her drop-off point, to the buyer, or his/her pickup. Simon never touches them. That's another thing that makes me lean to the theory that this item was personal to Jaap. The only one I know with a back-story like that was the one connected to Jung.

I have to cover up some of these details since I don't want you to know everything. But my flight from Frankfort touched down for a lay-over. I had time for a beer at one of the terminal pubs and enjoyed myself, looking about. I've always found airports fascinating. I like to speculate about all the strangers I'll never see again.

One very attractive young woman sipped white wine ten feet away. She had shoulder-length dark hair and an olive complexion. I presumed she was Greek, Arab, or Italian. She dressed simply: perfectly-fitting jeans, a dark knit top, and a stylish mottled scarf. She was used to being looked at. She kept her eyes on her magazine. I wondered if she spoke English. I fancied her the mistress of a powerful oil sheik. She seemed to feel my eyes on her. For the first time, as I write this, I appreciate what really attractive women must experience every hour they are out in public.

I boarded the plane and stuffed my backpack into the overhead luggage rack. It caused a few grumbles from people who had had to separate their luggage, but it was indeed a single carry-on, and just small enough to qualify. I took my seat at the window.

The exotic young woman I had been observing at the pub was not only on this flight but in the aisle seat in my row, with an empty seat between us. I couldn't help looking her over at every chance.

It seemed only thirty minutes after we had taken off that we all heard a massive thud and felt the plane shudder. It was like we had been in a giant toboggan and skidded over a rock. The plane started to head downward. At least that's how I think it happened. It was terrifying.

The rest of the next few minutes is a blur. The masks dropped. People belted themselves in. I saw the haunted gazes of dozens of people. I was going down with them if I didn't do something.

As I scanned the cabin, I met the black-coffee eyes of the young woman in my row and found her barely off her composure. *Wow*, I remember thinking, *not even the prospect of death will break that ice.*

I wondered if the situation we were in was due to an accident or an act of sabotage or terrorism. I felt the package I was carrying under my shirt and against my chest, and the thought came to me that it could have something to do with this artifact. That would make this outrage an assassination, with dozens of extra lives lost. As if the item itself was answering me, I was suddenly sure it was.

Someone had figured out an easy and indirect way to take out a Linebacker: Drop him and his package out of the sky, though with a bit of collateral damage. Someone was probably waiting on the ground for everything to come down, unless simply preventing anyone else from having the object was part of the picture. That made me only more determined.

I was swept with a sense of affirmation. Belief. I knew I could get out of this, if there was just a little time left. I stood against the sterile curving surface of the cabin and concentrated for a breath or two, focusing on the metal and plastic inches from my forehead, barely noticing the window, like the screen of a tiny TV through which a watery world of green, blue, and white streaked past. Then I pressed my right, my Hammer Hand, against the side of the plane, intending to ram my fingers through it with sheer force. I'd never done anything like that to such material. I didn't even't wonder if it would work.

My extended hand tingled like it was being pressed into sand, but it went through the layers of the hull like a knife through a mass of wet cardboard. The tips of my ring, middle, and index fingers had to have emerged into the blue air. The hull gave so little resistance that I dragged my hand through it like a blade, making a long slash. Even through the turmoil I heard people gasp. I forged in at another point and made a slanting gash with an upstroke that just about met the first. One more pass, and I had the outlines of a near-triangle, most of a doorway with just enough holding it together at the vertices to keep it hanging on. The pastel world outside it tore eerily past through the gaps, and a monstrous howling came through them like the moan of a storm at the foot of a door. The final pass with my energized hand, followed, maybe, with a kick, would make an aperture big enough for me and my pack to step through. I could see people's eyes widen with renewed shock that a human being could do what I had just done. I was surprised myself, but I was determined like you can't believe.

I stepped across the young woman in my row, stood in the aisle, hauled down my pack, and belted it on. A big young man got up and

343

came toward me as if I'd been the cause of this disaster and doing something to impede me might help things. I gave him that, *Buddy, don't make this worse* look, and he stopped ten feet away. At least that's how I think it went.

Then I stepped back into my own aisle to the ghastly outline I'd made. The fuselage hadn't been as thick as I'd thought it might be. The surreal landscape through the slits was slanting ever closer. It felt like any second could be one too many. The only person I might be able to save was the only person close: the young dark-haired woman above whom I loomed.

"I can take one," I said, meeting her eyes and nodding to the soon-to-be open space. I extended my left arm as if to fold her under it. She met my eyes with her own wide browns, and I could see how terrified she had been. She had hid it well. Her hands were shuddering so much that she struggled to unbelt herself. I extended my right, coiled my fingers around her chest-belt, pulled it out a few inches, and pulled through it like it was tissue paper. I hadn't known it would be that easy. The belt fell back around her, and she stood into my embrace. I drew her to the outline I had made in the plane's shell, set my foot against the center of it, cut it through with a pass through a corner, and sent the rest of the panel falling out with a kick. The green hills, the fields, the roads and fences below us, looking almost beside us, hurled past. It was as beautiful as it was terrifying.

"I'll get whoever did this," I said to the handful of people whose eyes I met. Then with the girl folded close, I threw what I envisioned to be a powerful protective glow around us and took a good firm hold of her belt. She clutched my own belt and the straps of my pack. Then I drew us out the space I had made and dove us into empty air, into a world of light, sound, and disorientation. It was an effort of will just to hang onto my wits. I couldn't have heard the girl if she was screaming, but I don't think she was. I think she was at that point more full of wonder than fear.

I was astonished, too.

We were behind the wing, but the fact that we missed getting hit by anything on the tail – which had to have been on us in a flash – has to figure as one more of the lucky coincidences that got me to this point in my life. It must have been a close one. My Glow might have saved us from a blow that fearful, but I wouldn't want to chance it. Maybe it did hit us, and bounced us into chaos, and that's why so many things are blurry. All I remember is spinning and whirling and being too baffled at first to do much except hang on to the young woman. But all the while I fought for control of our descent. I looked upward to the sky and got oriented. That helped me steady us.

We had started, I figure, at around a thousand feet off the ground, which ought to take about ten seconds to hit dirt straight down. I tried to use our momentum to veer us sideways, gaining us time. Once I righted us and got us facing the impending earth, I controlled our fall into a glide, slanting downward in a modified tag-team Superman-pose. Then I took us in an arcing course that absorbed even more of our momentum. It was scary, but it was also sheer arrogance! I had never felt more fear, and I had never felt more power. It was as if one was energizing the other! It was miraculous! I did it because I willed. Where was this power coming from if not from within me?

We knew we were going to survive by the time we were fifty feet from the ground. The girl clutched me like a lover under an umbrella in the rain and started pealing forth with laughter – insane, joyous laughter. She giggled like a child as we slowed to a glide and took more of a standing position so that we could adjust to the landing.

We still came in hard. I could feel the tug of the backpack throwing me off, and I knew I was going to land in a heap. Maybe the girl could do better. I let go of her as we touched and spun out on the soft grass. I came down on the pack and tumbled once or twice. She rolled like a kid leaping off of a swing, and came up on her elbows, her mane half over one eye and dangling bits of grass, smiling wickedly like she wanted to do it all over again. Never had life, had simple breath, seemed more golden! This was Elena.

We raised our heads to look at each other, snickering like lovers finishing an interlude just before they would have been discovered. I suppose the analogy holds. Sharing a magical intrigue no one would believe is just as joyous as sharing an amorous one no one knows.

We spotted a raging column of smoke and sparks over the green hill past us. All those poor people! If only I'd had the power to do something for them! I had to get back to Jaap Simon and figure the picture out. I also had my new aptitude to understand, this sudden quasi-laser that had taken over my right hand at a moment of dire need. Was I going to be able to do that again?

It seems to me that there are few parts of Europe from which you are any more than a walk from a village. We could see church steeples in several directions around us and headed off toward the one that looked the nearest. We walked like a couple who had discovered each other in the fields, or, because of my heavy pack, like a wanderer led in from the wild by a village lass.

It took us ten minutes to reach the village. We talked, of course. We got in a few delirious basics of each other's lives.

My first impressions of the woman's looks – exotic – and her manner – so composed – in the airport bar had started me out presuming that she might not be a native English speaker. She was Elena Alexandra Neofitus, a hair stylist born and currently living in New York City. She was returning from Amsterdam after the last stage of an affair with a British filmmaker.

She, of course, asked me what I had done. She looked at me like I was an X-Man, like some sort of super-hero. I told her that I can do a few things, and that I like to keep quiet about them. I told her I'd tell her more when we had time to settle.

My first step in the village was to take us to a pub, where we raised a toast to life, miraculous life. My stein met her wine glass for a tap. The next step was getting us a place to stay. The third was setting out to find her some basic living essentials like toothbrushes and undies. We were both lightheaded and still delirious to be alive. I don't remember a happier afternoon.

Evening found us again at the pub below our B&B, this time for some serious relaxing. It was about 10:30 on a Wednesday, and these pubs usually close early. But the whole town was on alert because of the nearby crash, and the pub was happy to serve late. That was the first moment we really started to converse. Until then, even throughout the afternoon, I'd only heard her draw breath or laugh. She struck me as superhumanly reserved. She was also fun to look at.

Her height, about 5' 3", would have kept her from being a model. I found out why she was never to be an actress, as well as why she had talked so little during the afternoon: She had a surprisingly high voice. When she concentrated she could avoid its peaks and valleys, but she knew about it. She was protective about it, too. It wasn't the baby-voice that some bimbos put on that appeal to some men (not one of whom I know personally). It was all her. Her tone was even a little screechy when she laughed or cried out with astonishment, which she did when she drank.

By midnight we were back to the realization that life once again lay before us, and we started to think of next moves. Mine was to get back to the States – on a boat! – and have a long meeting with Jaap Simon and a few sage heads from his outfit.

Elena, who went lightheaded after the third white wine… Her first instinct was to call the press and tell the world about our miraculous escape. I tried to tell her everyone would think she was crazy, but that didn't bother her. I only talked her out of the idea by threatening to kick her out of the B&B and never speaking to her again.

That was when I told her about the College. About me, my abilities, my work, and my need to stay underground with it. I had to. She had seen it all in action anyway. I left her with that meditation, found a pay phone from which I could just keep an eye on her at the bar, and called Jaap Simon.

I found him awake as always, which surprised me, though I am used to it now. I told him I still had the package and he didn't seem to care. He had heard about the crash. He asked me how I was. He seemed shaken. I'd been told that he liked me and had a twinkle in the eye when he talked about me, but it never really impressed me till then.

He asked me how I'd made it. I told him I tore a hole in the side of the plane with one of the abilities I possess and controlled the fall to the ground with another. I told him there were no survivors who would tell the tale. I didn't tell him about Elena. He said just to get myself put together as well as I could and then get back to the Capital District. We'd have a pow-wow when I had settled.

I turned back to Elena, thrilled not to see her with any reporters. She was being courted by a pair of local studs who retreated when I reappeared. I've found since that Elena loves holding court – and also that she can keep a good secret.

We stayed up till two talking. Or was it four? I told her more about me. I had to. She had seen me in action. She had seen the Gleam, the Glow, and the Glide. I also told her the outlines of what I knew then about the College.

She told me about herself. Her parents, both native Cypriots, had given her her looks. Her father, a soccer player who had opened a restaurant, and her mother, a singer/dancer, had moved to the Big Apple in the 1960s. Both heavy smokers, both had passed by her early twenties. She had gone to a tough high school. She had a pattern of expectable behavior: shoplifting (though she was never caught), cutting (her skin), drinking… Men had been chasing her since her early teens, almost none of them wanting anything but the obvious. The gay ones – and her father – had been the only males who ever seemed to have any concern about her as a person. She told me about "the woman thing." She was straight, she said, she just needed to be with certain women now and then.

As you would have expected – you are, after all, reading a book which you expect to conform to certain patterns – we made love, probably around four in the morning. I knew I was going to want to at two that afternoon when she rolled to a stop in that meadow and came up looking like she did under her green-flecked mane. I didn't even think about whether it would be good or bad for this beautiful, damaged, complicated young woman. I was celebrating my own resurgence. We were celebrating life. She had a beautiful body.

You're wondering why I would even question it? Making love with her? Even by that point in my life I was starting to be aware that I was in a different zone than most other people. I could no longer just get it on with women because they were hot and I could land them. I had to look out for them. I will develop that for you at more length in pages to come.

So you're undoubtedly wondering about the ramifications of surviving a plane crash when all the passengers and crew are supposed to be dead. Well, let me tell you a bit about how the process works.

Elena had to make some phone calls. She had to reintroduce herself to the world. She had to go in for a few interviews. Jaap Simon actually spoke to her and coached her through it all. They seemed to have something in common quickly and to become friends over the phone.

Elena was happy enough to tell the Muggle suits that she had never boarded the plane and that she was sorry that whoever had taken her belongings and her ticket had gotten such a harsh message about theft. I do believe there were some heads shaking "at the office," as it were. I think they'd have been happy to believe in the concept of an Elena body-double deciding to pull a fast one that didn't end up so well. There were people who had spotted her or her double – how would you tell? – boarding the plane, because how could you forget Elena? But the suits seemed happy enough to consider this a mystery they didn't have to explain. I've told you before that this is a useful and easily-exploitable feature of those who run the contemporary world.

As for me… The Muggles were happy enough to let me stay among the dead. My pack was gone, and there were no traces of me other than boarding the plane. Jaap Simon had told me that it might come in really handy to fall off of the grid, drop a social security number, and start all over. "You were going to have to do this someday anyway," he said. "This just gives you a fifty year head start."

I don't know to this day what really brought us down. The official cause of it has even been attributed to something that could have been the incision I made in the plane's fuselage, but that has to be a cover. I still think someone in the College could be involved.

As far as my family was concerned, well, I had been gone to them for years, so my loss to them was less than you would expect from a regular contributor. I missed them all, but it was way better for them to stay completely out of my occult scrapes. If some of the people who want to get to me even knew about people I loved, it could end up being bad. Fortunately most of the people who want to get to me aren't detectives.

There would have to be a name change and a new identity, but that's not as hard as you might think. Jaap can pull a lot of strings. I came up with a name whose ring I liked, including my real first name, and that was that. I had to inform just a few of my College friends of the little alteration in things and beg their understanding.

I figured it was time to commit to living close but not too close to Jaap's Schenectady office. I established a firmer base in Saratoga County, specifically by buying that old farmhouse I told you about earlier. Since then, a number of changes have come over me, including ones you might not expect. Losing all my family in such a quick stroke has been only one of them. Christmases, Easters… Weddings, graduations, funerals… I hope you didn't think I'd lose all those pangs once I became a Collegian. It hurt me so much for the first few years that I could hardly talk about it. I did visit my grandmother once in an intensive care ward in her last days and told her the full story. I'm sure I'll tell you about that someday. It was truly poignant. She brightened up. She was actually delighted for me to have done so well and ducked time the way I had. I told her to keep everything our little secret, and she sparkled. I think it really brightened her last days. I knew that if she talked, anyway, no one would believe her. But so far my whole family has gone about their lives thinking I was lost in my 30s – and pissed that I had dropped out years before that. One of these days I may look up brother Phil and just let him in on a few things. Toward the end.

Elena was also happy to get out of New York City. 'Toga town, as we sometimes call it, has loads of opportunities for good stylists, and before long Elena was living near me.

Elena is one of my very few Townie confidantes. She's probably the only person on the planet who knows my College ins and outs. She's one of the few Muggles truly in our circle. She's very popular, actually. She goes to Mixers. She hears the talk. She knows all about Puff. She's also the only one who really, with all her heart, loves me.

Not only did I save her life, but I have always been good to her. I have cared about her as a person. I have never tried to take advantage of her sexually, which is what most men have always tried to do. Immediately. We've had our moments, particularly when we met. There are reasons that our relationship has lapsed back into the Platonic and has by now become a devoted friendship.

Elena would be dangerous to love, at least in that wretched, fully-committed, possessive way Eros has on you. She has a dark side. She's amazingly confessional about it, particularly her history of self-abuse. She flinches when she talks about the "cutting," even though she's the one who brings it up. She squirms just a little as she shows you the scars, faint white streaks on her olive-toned forearms. She drinks a lot more white wine than anyone I want to get involved with.

Elena is bisexual. She's always been very up front about "the woman thing" in an offhanded way. She has to be with certain women some of the time. She meets them and she knows. It's always seemed mysterious and charming to me. And I've always just wanted her to be happy, so I've never cared what she does to let herself loose. If I'm not giving her everything she needs, I've got no right to care. But for any male who soul-fully loved Elena, it would be stressful to know from the start that there was a component to her that he could never fulfill. I can't tell you how it would torment me knowing about those nights that she would be lost to me, but with another. I'm 70 as I write this. I'm out of the world of conquests and romances. I still know what it would feel like, at least for me.

Though I know those days of self-abuse are over – but for the white wine – those are all things that bespeak an insecurity about a person that would make them a bad match for me in the knock-down and drag-out of a long affair. You have to be a tough cookie to put up with my solitary nature – my travel, my adventures, those times I need to walk by myself. But Elena would be dangerous to love for other reasons.

There's a self-sabotaging streak within Elena that doesn't look like it will ever be mediated. There's a hollow that may never be filled with true self-esteem. People like that can take down the people who passionately love them, because they don't really love themselves.

Our relationship very quickly became that of teacher and student, or brother and little sister, because it was apparent right away that we weren't headed for the type of relationship every woman who has ever liked me thinks she wants. That was evident on my first sojourn away from Elena, which I kept secret because there was a bit of hazard to it. I could tell it was hazardous because it was the first million-dollar payday I was ever offered. (Of course it didn't come in a check!)

Elena had seen my power. She was willing to believe in a lot of other things that were counterintuitive. One of them was that I could be keeping my word to her. Another was that I could actually be looking out more for her than for me. She wasn't used to people like that.

Since then, Elena's become a friend, a sidekick, a house-sitter, arm candy… We've been basically siblings since she came to Saratoga. She is one of the few people on the planet who'll take a risk for me. Besides, she loves Yodie and Savvin.

As I write this, Elena's a stylist who still lives in Saratoga Springs. She's still sensuous and radiantly attractive, maybe even moreso since her girly 20s. She has a compact, toned body, and she loves the gym and long Adirondack hikes. She takes marvelous care of her skin and hair.

Her smile utterly smolders. She is one of those rare people who photograph even better than they look. She doesn't wear a lot of makeup, and her features are so regular and symmetrical – I mean, right off a coin or statue – that you sometimes have to see her made-up – and in one of those photos! – to get how fetching she really is.

Elena didn't last more than a semester in a community college, but she is truly an intelligent woman. She has a real passion for history, culture, and architecture. Yet she has to fight a battle: She constantly feels diminished. I think it's that voice.

High and just a little squeaky under stress – and, coupled with her petite size – that voice causes her to seem girlish to others and makes her feel constantly trivialized. It's the one thing I've found her touchy about. When you deal with her, you have to be wary never to discount any of her ideas without seeming to consider them.

Elena was married for a heartbeat not that long ago. A fairly elegant Spaniard got a crush on her when she came with me on one of my low-pressure continental sojourns. He followed her back to Saratoga Springs and got a job as a beer rep. He did very well at it. I actually liked the guy. He had a jealous streak, though. Her continued friendship with me seems to have been one problem. Him demanding that she drop it might have been another.

Elena, I think, loves me more as a friend and brother now than as a lover. I'm completely OK with that. I love her too much to put her through a relationship with me just so I can have some sex. She knows she has a lifelong caretaker in me. A wealthy one. A powerful one. I can make a lot of problems go away.

So. Bump us back a few years. To the time of this meeting with Puff. Early August 1993.

I had to tell Elena about the second half of the double-deal, the solo pickup with Puff. I had the feeling it wasn't going to be easy.

I had her over for dinner on the second Thursday of the month, a surprisingly cool night for early August. I made a fire. I fixed one of my vegetarian stir-fries based on local produce. We sipped wine and coffee in my tower. We nibbled on dried papayas and apricots.

Around 9:30 I broached the idea of a little business trip. I asked her to watch my place for a period of uncertain length. I expected it to be only a few days, but… I told her that Yodie and Savvin were going to need some care. I showed her where I kept some of my money, all of which was hers if… just in case.

She asked where I was going. I set out a little fine dark chocolate. That's the way you get Elena relaxed. Loves chocolate.

She freaked. She tore it all out of me: the hit on the witches, the fight in the parking lot, the make-up chore, the double-deal, the first delivery, the cross-state nightmare-ride, then the next set of instructions, then a personal solo visit to… you know who. The Magic Dragon.

She cried. She screamed. She sat on my lap and hugged me. She kissed me, the Chardonnay on her breath. She begged me not to go. She begged me to quit the business and disappear. She said she'd follow me wherever I went.

I was touched. I didn't agree to let her come with me.

# Chapter 18
# *PRINCEPS AERIS*

1

I sat on a broad low wall overlooking a developing waterfront. My forearms rested on my denim-clad knees. My sneakered heels tapped the brick that supported me.

To my right was the harbor on the river. I could see what I knew to be a historic fort in the distance, already fading into the creamy light where sky met water. Past it all was the Atlantic and the seeping indigo of encroaching night.

A pannier beside me promised an aquarium, a visitor center, and a history museum to come. Ten feet below, a pair of broad concrete stairs converged on a landing where a young couple toiled with a toddler and a carriage. Ten feet below that was a lounging area with a few families and couples seated at wood-and-stone tables. Nearer the water was the sturdy dock that went past me in either direction. To my left sprawled a boardwalk promenade, with mostly stylish shops and restaurants and one wood-framed building, the last of its kind, a dated house of horrors. It was there that, in minutes, I was to meet with Himself. The Big Guy. Puff.

I had known the recently-trendy coastal city I was headed to for half the month. I'd known the day for a week. I'd known the spot and the rough hour – a late August sunset – since that afternoon.

Elena paced behind me. I still couldn't believe she had followed me. She had flown here on her own without a plan and found me on my cell phone. I didn't want to involve her in this, but I didn't have the heart to just ignore her. She is the most loyal, obstinate, courageous woman who

357

may ever have lived. She had followed me to the zero hour.

We had spent a few days trying to sightsee and relax. I had taken her to a hip seafood restaurant the night before. She could hardly eat. And she loves seafood. She cried beside me most of the night. Finally I said to her that if I was in as much trouble as she thought, I was going to need my sleep. She sobbed more quietly, and I got my four or so hours.

I was having many a fine reflection as I looked out over the bay. At our last talk, Jaap Simon had let on that Danny and I were in hot water with Puff. He had few insights on why Puff wanted me alone to patch up the matter with a delivery, but he felt pretty sure that things were on the level. He couldn't order me to go since I was a private contractor, but he was hoping I would accept. It was vital for maintaining peaceful commerce in the College. I was also consoled by my conversation with Bella.

People are still terrified when they have to go meet with Puff. They're more scared than most people meeting with their boss, not only because this guy might really kill you, but nobody knows if he has any clout over what happens to you after. I kid you not. This is the kind of reputation Puff has. You'd think people in the College who'd seen everything would stop being superstitious, but it's just the opposite for many of them. They've seen so much past the ordinary that their credence for anything else that might be out there goes up, especially when it comes to Puff.

I admit to having some apprehension. As with that high school bully, the talk alone can be intimidating. And almost any Collegian could give you a headache on his or her own turf with a couple of weeks to plan. But I wasn't as worried as everybody else. Maybe I'm naive – I'm sure I am – but I thought the odds were good that all Puff wanted to do do was woof and look tough and that would be that. Besides, I think I can handle myself. I can inflict prohibitive damage.

"*Why* do you have to do this?" said Elena for at least the twentieth time, pacing on the promenade behind me.

"It's a mortal offense if you don't," I said. "Then he'd have to make a statement. He'd hunt you all over the world." *Besides,* I almost added, *I don't think this is a hazing. An expulsion.* But Elena's not up with all the slang, trusted Townie as she is. "I don't think this is a hit," is what I said.

"How can you be sure?"

"If he starts hitting people he asks to come to see him… Have fun playing by yourself. Puff."

"Why do you keep calling him that?" said Elena. "You're only making him madder."

She was right about that. It didn't help anything to rile this guy. It added to the complication of him saving face with the College since so many people had heard me call him that, and I didn't seem to be able to stop myself from doing it. There was no doubt about it: I had been stepping on his toes, starting fifty years ago. Now I had to make good on it.

I looked out over the ocean to my left in the general direction of Puff's fun house. I saw something odd. A sea-green, chalky sphere, probably a disc, shot right out of the front like a huff of smoke or a dandelion clock. It grew in size abruptly as it neared and hovered a few seconds in the air fifty feet from me like a stopwatch waiting for me to read it. Then it shot straight back. Time's a wastin.

The apparition had amazed me. Describing its texture is impossible. Its qualities of light and shade were totally different from those of the natural twilight scene in front of me. It was as if there was an invisible glass pane like the flat screen of a laptop between me and the 3D visual scene in front of me. The animated effect had been on it, shooting like a dot out of a point below and to my left and quickly expanding, suggesting both that it flew and moved closer. Then it had hovered at a size that would suggest a smooth, five-foot-across chalk frisbee.

That part of things fit a pattern. I had heard that Puff had his summons for people, and it didn't surprise me that they might be inscrutable. He loves being ominous, as well as contrapuntal. I wondered if Elena could have seen it.

"I had best get a mosey on," I said, without making much of a move.

"Why can't you just... Not go?"

"I could drop out," I said, reflecting over the water. "Jaap said I had that option. Go back to being a Townie. A Muggle. Stop using the degree. Get a real job. Burn the transcripts as they say. As long as they really do that, people let them alone. They get to keep just one thing they love."

"You have a real job," she said. "You could live in Saratoga Springs and just do your tours. You could do really well."

"I'd have to make more of a show of it than that," I said with a laugh. "I'd have to make a grand statement that everyone in the College could get. Puff would rub it in. I'd have to fake my death. I'd have to sacrifice. A fire, everything. Yodie, Savvin... I'd have to move to the wilderness or the inner city or some little town in the boonies. I'd have to live a completely undistinguished and outwardly penitent life like somebody in witness protection. Like Guinevere in the nunnery. That's what it would take to convince people."

I turned to her. "That would be so cowardly. It would be a total defeat, a total denial. I'd rather take my shot."

A second smoky circle, this one haint blue, shot out of the beachside building to my left. It made a similar abrupt swooping loop and froze itself in the air. It looked bigger – or closer – than the one before it. Then it shot back to its source, shrinking and curling in to my left.

I was less surprised by the second apparition, and I had studied its movements better. It had definitely moved from left to right across my visual field, but whether it zipped closer to me or simply grew bigger, that I couldn't tell you. Its speed and abruptness would have been nothing to draw in a cartoon. You see the same effect on your computer screen everyday. But in real life its movements were unnatural. It was completely out of place against the peaceful twilight. It really did look like a chalky, size-shifting dot superimposed on the environment before me. It was Puff's way of telling me to stop stalling.

"You'd be alive," said Elena, taking me by surprise, following up on a reply to a minute-old comment. "I could stay with you."

I looked at her with astonishment. I laughed in a way that I hoped would be comforting. "I'm not as good company as you think," I said. "When I get broke and old, I'm not going to be interesting to anybody."

"I'm already broke," she said. "And someday I will be old. We could look after each other. We could make it."

I was looking out over the ocean. I was touched. I had never guessed the depth of her feeling. I always thought you had to be getting it on to feel that way about someone. I was also beginning to get a pattern.

When a Mongol army surrounded a fortified town, it set up a white tent in plain sight. This was an announcement that the rulers of the city could save all their people if they gave up and became vassals to the Khan. It stood for a day or so as sort of a grace period. The next signal they sent was a red tent, meaning that the warriors would be killed, but the noncombatants and the city itself would be spared. After a few days of this, up went the black tent. This meant the obvious, that the city would be destroyed and everyone in it killed. Men, women, children... Far from simple brutality, this was a method. Killing thousands was a good way to get millions to play ball. It saved the Khan's troops. It saved time and treasure. That was always Puff's modus operandi: Win without confrontation.

"I can't give it all up now," I said, looking out over the bay. "I'm too far in. Besides, there's something he wants. He needs somebody to do it for him or he'd have done it himself already."

A third smoky sphere came out of the fun house and shot itself my way. The biggest one yet, this one looked like it was about eight feet across, a perfect disc in a raging pinkish/lavender shade, and it stopped dead just a dozen yards from my perch. It was chalky, but it also looked like a watercolor image painted on a window through which I was overlooking a natural mural of waterfront, buildings, trees, and early evening sky.

"Do you see that?" I said to Elena, pointing, almost instantly sorry. She did a double-take, terrified. She doesn't see "magic" very often. Then the thing shot straight back to its source so fast that it might just have disappeared. If its look and movements conveyed emotion, I could have fancied that it was pouting.

"What was that?" she said.

"My ticket to a command performance," I said into the air before me. I sat another few heartbeats, thinking. Then I leaned forward like I was skydiving and did a spread-armed chest-flop into the air over the wall. The collar of my weathered, yellow canvas Patagonia shirt clapped against my right ear in the rush. I dropped a few yards, caught myself, spun up and around, and hovered ten feet out from Elena, upright in the air.

"Besides…" I said, arms folded, looking back with a grin so cavalier that I hoped it would be reassuring. "Who's gonna mess with this?"

2

I swung out over the dock in a smooth arc, enjoying the new view of the brickwork and then the gold-tinged wakes below me, the brush of the air around me, and the gleam the setting sun passed over the bay. I had soared fifty feet or so out, in full view of anyone who might be look-ing. I had made the move casually, with no sound or ceremony. I was fairly sure almost none of the forty or so people in the sprawling walkway outside the funhouse would notice. Then I swooped back toward the shoreline and zeroed in on the gaping howler of a face at the front of the building that represented my point of entrance.

From over the water I got a scan of Puff's fun house – that's not what he called it – that very few of the board-walkers would have gotten. It was a social and architectural fossil. Someone had taken a wood-framed, beachfront Victorian-style house, done multiple additions, painted it all black, and hired muralists of 50s Sunday-funnies-aptitude to deck it with vampire-castles, psycho-chainsaw-artists, killer klowns, and bosomy, ter-rified, cartoon-women.

The last of a cheesy breed, it would have been a dinosaur in the 1970s, and its survival on this gentrified waterfront was another sign of someone who could pull Muggle strings. Because of the untoward add-ons and the undoubted wiring issues, someone would have paid dues to get this structure to pass code. Only a historic property designation would keep it where it was much longer. It was obviously just a front for Puff's activities anyway, and one that would have suited what I presume to be his off-beat taste. He loves tweaking the mainstream.

The entrance was a double door through the yellow-tinged teeth and lips of a leering, balding, black-and-purple goblin too big to be appreci-ated from the boardwalk. As I soared in from a perspective no ticket-buyer ever gets, it reminded me of the Buddha in his laughing pose, except that this would be a yawn we were entering – or a gulp.

I thought back on those discs that had belched, evidently, right out of the doors. I couldn't say much about his color symbolism other than that Puff likes poofy pastels. But the fact that they were vaporous and emanated from the mouth of a giant ghoul gave me the sense of the structure itself as a hat for the head of a vast subterranean smoker whose body stretched rods under the earth. He controlled his exhalations, cut loose with a guff, and sent those smoky marshmallows anywhere Puff wanted them to go.

Everyone associates Puff with the underground. I'd heard that he has a couple home bases around the world, always freaky looking places that have a lot more space underneath. I can't tell you if that serves some purpose for him or if he just likes copying the imagery of the Devil, but these sites are widely recognized in the College, and no matter what continent you are on, you know right where to go for your audition. I fancied that all his sites around the world could be linked by a network of tunnels. If Puff can pull that off he has more of my respect.

I coasted in slantwise, slowing to a skip, a walk, then a stop at the end of the line of Muggle customers. I could see a couple holding their breath and staring at me as if they had seen something they couldn't believe. I was acting so naturally after the Chaplinesque landing that none of them thought it could have been anything but their imagination. I stifled a laugh.

When I was a punk just developing my abilities I used to love doing stuff like that. It's amazing how often I got away without being spotted. I got to know group observation patterns pretty well. When people hang out waiting for something, only a couple will look anywhere but eye level, in the direction of other people. That night, I didn't need to be risking any more trouble for myself. I think I was unconsciously still tweaking Puff. Either that or glorying in a last hurrah.

I stepped up behind a young Asian-looking family and waited like I was in line for a ticket. Their six-year-old stared at me. He may have been the only one who really noticed my flight. His mother beside him was ministering to something with his younger sister. His dad was looking ahead to the ticket booth.

I stepped into the lobby, with gaping ghouls on every paintable space. A handful of windows in the wall could have been used for ticket-taking, but only one was in use. It was to the center-right.

I doubted I'd see Puff here, since no one else has anywhere, despite what they say. I was sure some sort of test was waiting. Puff has the reputation of knowing someone's pressure points. My advantage was that I knew that. If I saw something that stressed me it was likely to be one of his constructions.

While the Devil, too, was thought to be a good prober, the ability to read a few things about a mind or two isn't that rare in the College. It's common enough that most of us learn to police our thoughts during negotiations and not dwell on what we need to conceal. Most of us learn to tell when we are being probed, too. We get good at fogging the attempt.

Just as the father in front of me got to the open ticket booth, another window opened ten feet to the left. I stepped over to it. The ticket-taker was a handsome young man, a tall, slender kid who must have been on the lookout for me. He had short dark hair and dark eyes and a very aquiline nose. He looked like one of those sharp kids who is way ahead of his years.

"Ticket for one?" he said.

"I was invited," I said.

The young guy looked at me like I was weird. "Your name?"

"There's only one on the list."

"And what name would that be?"

"I think I'm in the wrong place."

"What kind of a place are you looking for?"

"Why don't I just come back when you're keeping a little better track of things?" I said, making eye-contact with a grin. *Just like Puff*, I thought. *Even the help are snots.*

"Let me just see what I can do," the lad said crisply, closing the window. Puff would cream him if he let me fulfill the letter of the invitation and get off without the audience, and I had just called him on it. I smiled to myself. *Another new friend. Have I got the touch…?*

I heard something to my left and looked to see that a panel, really just a knobless, inward-folding door, had opened in the glossy wall. Its seams had been obscured by a steadfast Batman lunging for a harlequinesque Joker. The countenance of my new friend was partly illumined behind it. I stepped into a bare, closet-sized space and heard the door latch behind me. A short, dim stairs ahead of me led down a narrow windowless passage. The speakeasy motif was fully in play. "Be my guest," said the lad behind me in the tone of someone presenting an apartment.

Normally one would trust the agent showing the space, but my hackles were up. I thought about setting on my Glow before following the opened palm down the stairs. Without it, something simple could kill me: a pitfall, a pouncing predator, even a knife in this kid's hand… I was ready to arm up in a flash if something sprang out at me. I almost hoped, if anything did have to pay a price, that it would be a serious assassin and not one of Puff's hired locals.

The stairway was wide, with wooden rails on each side. My companion stepped beside me and reached the end of it ahead of me. He pressed some kind of latch on the wall and let the panel spring inward, revealing that this had been just a shortcut to a lower level of the fun house. I stepped in among the patrons being deliciously terrorized by the puppets and maniacs and dizzied by the sloping floors and distorted mirrors. It was dim, disorienting, and possibly even dangerous. Wait till the first lawsuit!

My new friend was suddenly beside me. I looked to him, and he just made an antic little point toward something about head-height in the dim, shifting corridor. I followed his eyes and noticed nothing at first, probably expecting another door or another person. I followed the man's finger again and saw something like a fist-sized soap bubble floating in the air and trembling against its own weight. Only its reflective qualities kept it visible. The light of this place was churning and shifting like a disco.

I did a double-take. In this hall of disorientation, a few airborne surprises wouldn't be unexpected. The goal of the place was to school all the senses but taste and to befuddle from three dimensions and all directions. But a large bubble lasting more than a few seconds in this turbulent environment seemed impossible. It was obviously one more of Puff's invitation-cards, and this one was slowly receding. I followed, moving into and against the thin stream of touring humanity. They must have thought I worked there if they noticed me at all. They were on the lookout, anyway, for the mildly-threatening amusements. The bubble I followed... that I'm sure none of them noticed.

The wobbly sphere stopped about shoulder-height six inches from a spot on a plain paneled wall. To get to it I had to pass between two people, the Japanese-looking father and the kid who had seen me swooping in from the bay. I recognized him by his soccer jersey. If the father remarked inwardly about the mystery of spotting me here it was probably only to wonder how I beat him to the spot. The average patron would expect emergency apertures and escape-hatches, as well as staff and inspectors. The kid still looked at me with a bit of awe.

I reached around the bubble and pressed gently. The panel turned out to be another of their unobtrusive doors with one of those clever latches that took a pair of timed shoves to let loose, which would lessen the chance that a leaning patron might open it by a bump. I watched it pop gently inward to reveal a ten-foot slanting ramp that was illuminated like most of this place, indirectly, by the glare off of shiny walls, ceilings, and floors. I waited for the bubble to drift in and then followed. I could see light coming from another room at the base of the passage, but it still felt creepy to hear the panel close behind me.

I tried to keep track of myself. I had taken two short, interior descents, but was, I suspected, only a full level below the street, and still right under the building I'd entered.

I came to a simple wood-paneled room about twelve by twelve, with three mismatched doors on each wall around me. Its light source was a faint lamp with a cheap-looking stained glass shade. It rested on a small wooden table by the wall with a porch-style rattan chair with a well-worn cushion beside it. The furnishings and the whole environment reminded me of a group home.

Each door looked like it came from a reuse facility and was a hundred years old. The bubble – which had taken on a purple glint – stopped before the one to the left. I turned the knob, opened the door cautiously, and let the bubble drift inward through a short, paneled, descending corridor to another spare, carpeted room with, again, three doors, one on each wall. The bubble picked its favorite, and I opened it to get quite the surprise.

I stepped in at the corner of a fairly busy interior chamber with a low ceiling. This felt and looked like the basement bar of a commercial establishment, and one the town fathers did not officially know about. On the wall across from me were three more mismatched old doors, and I looked behind me to notice that I had entered through one of three.

Clearly, this was the plan of the place, to be a second-hand maze of misdirection. No one who found the way to this point by accident would be able to find the way out on the run. This was always Puff's game, anyway. He loves bamboozling you.

I was at first surprised to suspect that the whole waterfront could be honeycombed with levels of these irregular chambers. I caught myself instantly: Why was that so unusual? This was a 400-year-old city, surely mined with the architectural relics of Prohibition, prostitution, several wars, and the Underground Railroad.

This broad, cluttered space, possibly sixty by sixty, was no more ornately furnished than anything else I had seen here, but it had a few tables, broad square booths, and comfortable-looking chairs. People, mostly men, were drinking, playing cards, and watching the mounted TVs. I didn't study them much where they were. I was too shocked by the servers.

The three I noticed crisscrossing the space with their trays were exceptionally burly men, balding, bearded, or mustached… and dressed in women's clothing! Nothing could be funnier or, strangely, more challenging, than the sight of these hirsute wide-bodies so clearly tutti-frutti. As I stood gaping, one white-mustached Germanic-looking gent passed me wearing a jade-green dirndl. He was probably only 5'11" tall, but he had to weigh 260. His blocky arms and massive elbows swelled out the sleeves. His legs were comically furry. I was radically uncomfortable. Was it part of Puff getting his guests off their game? Or was this just him? A gender-bender? The correspondents with the Medieval presentations of Satan, the arch-god of the Inquisitors, were mounting. The Devil is a hermaphrodite, they say, and like the Greek Bacchus who gave him a lot of his image in the Western mind, he stands for testing all the boundaries. Or was this just part of Puff's plan for me?

It was about then that I expected someone to come up to me with a portable artifact, the one I was supposed to be escorting. No one approached me at all. I figured more journeying was ahead. I looked for my guiding bubble and spotted it nowhere. I went over other things I remembered and tried to guess my position relative to where I had entered. I was no longer confident that I was still right under Puff's fun house. I had the sense of a substantial underground, at least laterally, and I was sure I hadn't seen all of it.

One really big Black server passed me, his tray folded under one of his long, blocky arms sprouting from the open-topped dress, his pecs looking almost like breasts. He looked like he could have been an NBA power forward twenty years earlier. I was about to ask him something but he seemed on a mission, and he headed into what must have been a kitchen.

Just as I was thinking about ordering a beer, the big Black server set down his tray and came up to me. He looked like a thicker-bodied, natural-haired Dennis Rodman. He smiled just a little and stuck out a cigar-sized index past me to my left like he was giving me directions. I followed it in time to see it snake out and pop the big bubble that had evidently been with me all along. He met my eyes, gave a little jerk of his head, and led me toward the wall with the doors. I don't remember which one he opened, but it led to another short slanting passage and another spare, carpeted room with, again, three doors. Another level!

I stepped through the door the server opened and came to another basement bar so much like the first that I had to study it to be sure I wasn't back where I had just been. The cross-dressing servers settled it; they – and their dresses! – were different. Surely this was a completely underground club in more ways than the obvious. It ran against any imaginable codes.

A big red-bearded guy in a sun dress came up and motioned me to follow him. Other than the dress, he reminded me of the notorious 70s Oakland Raiders defensive tackle Ben Davidson. Except for things like, "This way," and "Watch your head," he didn't say much. I'd pick his accent for Texas and his life-goal for Hell's Angel. We passed through a third – or were we back to the first? – stripped-down lounge, and I spotted more normal-looking loungers and more curious servers. I continued to be shocked by the size and formidability of these men. They had big, beefy torsos. What was the message of the cross-dressing? Most of the ones I noticed were European-looking whites, but there the homogeneity ended. They looked like Slavs, Germans, Mediterraneans... I can't tell you how bizarre this seemed to me. They paid me little notice.

The last room I remember was what felt like the "waiting room." Whatever its purpose, I was dropped off, and I just waited. I was expecting someone to appear and lead me to the Lord of the Fruits in all his discordant pomposity, but minutes passed. This last room was the oddest of all.

It was irregularly shaped like some bedrooms I'd seen made out of onetime attics. This ceiling sloped to a corner that was only four or so feet high. The walls were as bare as in any of the other rooms, but each was painted, and a different color: deep, dandelion-maize; rich, clayey turquoise; a pea-soup green; a thick and glinty purple. All the colors had a McDonald's tone, I realized; they glistened; they were fulsome. Maybe there was some Four Quarters/compass symbolism going on, but I couldn't get it.

That room was the first I had come to with only two doors. There were overstuffed, faux-leather couches here, too, soft, swooshie, and mismatched. There were enough of them for any sort of depravity. At least the one I was on looked clean.

The only item of furniture besides the wonky couches was a sort of rectangular box, most likely of wood, that someone had carpeted on all sides like it was a sofa. I'd seen a multipurpose piece of furniture like it in college community rooms where people did a lot of drinking, lounging, and even roughhousing. You could set things on it; you could sit on it.

I looked around the room for magazines or anything at all to read and found absolutely nothing. It may surprise you that I would be feeling as natural as if I was in a waiting room at the dentist's. In Puff's lair, I should have had every sense on edge, but I had long forgotten my initial fears, fascinated as I was by all the curiosities. All I can tell you is that I had lost a bit of focus in every sense. My odds of finding my way out without guidance were by then astronomical.

If I hadn't spent so much time, energy, and meditation refocusing this experience, I might have thought I had dreamed it all. I realize now that this power of "the fog," of slowly affecting someone's consciousness and making them think they're in a dream, might be one of Puff's prime skills. It's a weighty one, if you think about it, at least against human beings.

You know how captivated you can get within a dream. You can be horrified, entranced, delighted… And none of it is real. And dreams are surreal and foggy, no matter how some of them grip you. What if someone could harness a force that could make you take basic reality to be inconsequential? To gradually make you think you were dreaming? You would be helpless against any real danger around you. Even if you saw it coming, you would never take it seriously. I can tell you now in retrospect how dangerous a state that would be be, dreaming awake. I was doing it.

Just as I was thinking that I should have brought my sketch book – does time have any meaning in an interchange like that? – I noticed something on the carpeted lounge-table/seat that I thought I would have spotted before. It was a very curious book – old, wood-bound, broad, and thick. It was also locked shut by a contraption that appeared to have been wrought for it, a metal band bolted to the lacquered cover and folded around it like a belt. An ornate lock was mounted like a buckle at the center of what would seem to have been the front cover. Someone who wanted to read it would have had to open its cover with a key like it was a door.

Before my dream-mind could remark to itself on the strangeness of something suddenly appearing on a surface that I at least thought had been bare, I found the book in my hand. It was hefty. I inspected it.

No writing or imagery was anywhere on the cover, the spine, the band, or the lock. I had no clue what the book's contents might be. I presumed at least due to the style of the metalwork that it was of European medieval or Renaissance workmanship. I was sure only that it was old and important, and that somebody wanted it to stay shut most of the time.

The possibility came to me that this could have been an original copy of a pioneering and famous work of art, literature, or science. Could it have been a translation of a lost Greek epic, a First Folio of *Hamlet*, one of Da Vinci's sketchbooks…? Could it have been one of the Aztec codices saved by one of the Jesuits? Any one of them would be priceless.

Just as quickly I considered the chance that it was something of greater significance than its history or price. It could have been a powerful old grimoire, a spell-book, or a work of significance to the Alchemical/Rosicrucian thought that permeated some departments of our College. If somebody thought it was even a faint counterbalance to that Medicine Mask we had managed to deliver through such harrowing circumstances, it was clearly important. Because of the players involved and the circumstances, the occult theme made more sense.

Before I started calculating that there might be a good reason to leave this item closed, I took it up and weighed a means of opening it. There was enough wiggle between the band and the edges of the pages for me to fit in a fingertip. Surely my Gleam, the Axe-Hand, could cut through the metal holding its cover shut without mentionable damage to the pages. Just then, up came a broad, olive-complected, mustached man in a backless pantsuit. He looked like a Lebanese Olympic wrestler, the coal-black fur of his back curling up his neck. How he got in, I did not notice. Neither of the doors to my left had opened. I didn't even suspect that this was Puff. He wouldn't put himself within ten feet of me without five bodyguards.

The man spoke to me. Whatever he said was a garble, as if he was speaking through water or in a different language – or as if I couldn't hear anything outside my own thoughts. I judged from his motions that he was demanding me to hand him the book I held, if not criticizing me for even thinking about opening it. Something about that made me bristle. I didn't like the way he was talking to me, I hated being underground, and I was tired of all this indirection. The impulse came over me to get out of there – that minute. Exactly how I was going to do that was unclear. I don't remember my thought processes any better than that.

I threw the Glow over myself. If the man was a Collegian, he surely spotted the change.

I guess I was planning to tear my way out to the open air in the shortest course possible: upward, and through the material of the building. I was going to levitate to the ceiling and carve a body-sized space through it with my laser Axe-hand, the right. I was going to soar up through it, shoot to the next ceiling, and keep going the same way through every level of material – much to the shock of anyone on a floor – till I forged through the roof of the place and came into the open sky. I'd never tried a move like that before, but it ought to be possible. Anybody who got in my way was getting trouble. Other than the simple toxicity of my Glow, which people can feel a foot out, I don't have any gentle weapons.

With those impressions, I felt myself soaring upward as if the structure around me didn't exist, or at least failed to offer any impediment. It was like the Glow that usually accompanies my levitation had suddenly become as corrosive as the Gleam that energizes my right hand. This has never happened before and I am not sure it happened then. But I felt myself rising.

I got the image of myself as a human form inside a giant flower that seemed to echo an old LP cover in my memory. (I have since found that my image was a morph of two Moody Blues covers I must have seen, either "…Lost Chord" or "…Threshold of a Dream…") The impression was of soaring growth, of something semi-natural blossoming and even erupting upward out of a dim background. As if watching myself from afar, I saw myself in it, clothed as I was, bursting through the fuming, vegetative petals of a growth so rapid it was almost an explosion, almost like I was the pistil at the center of the bloom. I saw myself surging forth into the evening sky like a speeded-up transition of a moth from its cocoon. I saw myself like a Biblical prophet, a Moses in a Blakean engraving, holding a single tablet in the crook of an arm. *What?*

I felt something. The book was with me. It was folded in close to my body in my left hand and elbow. I must have been holding it when I threw on the Glow. Why had I taken it? If I wanted to bail out of that situation, from an entanglement with the College, with Puff, I had just brought it all with me! And how had I torn through all the floors above me?

The next thing I remember is waking up bolted to a wall in a basement, two hounds yapping at me from a foot away, with a creak in my back from slumping atop an ancient book whose cover read, *PRINCEPS AERIS*.

2

## Death of a Man Found in Car
### Published 6:00 pm EST, Thursday, August 26, 1993

Police are asking the public for information in the death of a man found behind the wheel of a car in a casino parking lot. Police believe the man was mauled to death by an exotic animal, Verona Police Chief Marcus Kirk said.

64-year-old Hewson Jacobs was found early Monday morning in a car parked at Turning Stone Resort Casino in Verona. His face was lacerated so severely that he drowned in his own blood, police said. Police could not say how he could have driven his car with those kinds of wounds to his face.

Police are investigating the case as a homicide and believe Jacobs was mauled to death by an animal that could have escaped from a zoo. His wounds were not like those made by any animal native to New York State. Jacobs' car was covered in scratches.

Jacobs, of Nedrow, 7 miles south of Syracuse, was employed as a teacher and interpreter of Onondaga culture, authorities said.

Jacobs was last seen Sunday morning at the National Shrine of the North American Martyrs in Auriesville. He phoned his son and daughter that afternoon to say that he had to meet someone at the Saint Kateri National Shrine and Historic Site in Fonda.

Police were still investigating the case.

The End of *The Prince of the Air*

Next: *The King of the Cats*

# ART AND ARTISTS

Except for plates attributed directly to others, publisher Mark Donnelly, Ph. D., refinished everything into what we see. Dr. Donnelly has an artist's eye, a flair for the arcane, a knack for Photoshop, and a spritely wit.

The Cover: Matthew Joshua Knisley's rousing front cover features our Wizard in his manifesting guise which deliberately echoes classic occult images including DaVinci's "Vitruvian Man," the angel-form of Blake's "Glad Day," and Pamela Coleman Smith's "the Magician" card of the Rider-Waite-Smith tarot deck. Matt's back cover features his own image of the Wizard's hand. The spine is Matt's incomparable handiwork.
Our version of the Rider-Waite-Smith card the Ace of Swords, used mostly as a spacer/a. k. a., a "dingbat": Drawn by artist David Heisch. The locked book **PRINCEPS AERIS**: Crafted by publisher Mark Donnelly.

## Chapter Plates:

Plate 1, "Rousting Witches": Juan Gines de Pasamonte and Esteban Dhuy fused photographs taken by Juan and the author into this illustration of a scene from the text. The model for our Wizard deliberately copies the pose of the Knight of Swords from the Rider-Waite-Smith deck. We use imagery from the Swords suit so much because it is widely taken to represent the Greek/Elizabethan element Air.

Plate 2, *Who Knew That Was Starting a War?*: Juan Gines de Pasamonte and Esteban Dhuy incorporated a photograph taken by Jake Govenettio to make our Wizard. The pair crafted the form of his attacker and all other circumstances in the plate.

.

Plate 3, "The Invisible College": Matthew Joshua Knisley's design includes his own Eye of Providence, his own prophetic ravens, his own echo of John Dee's intricate symbol Monas Heiroglyophica, and a treatment of the movable temple-castle in the famous Rosicrucian-themed illustration often called Collegium Fraternitatis.

Plate 4, "The *Source*": This plate mixes photographs taken by the author, including that of our model for the character of Dana Lambert, which was treated by Matthew Joshua Knisley. Raedwald's Runestone is the author's creation in every sense. Though most Iron Age kings would have had something like it, the item is not known to exist.

Plate 5, "The Occult Economy": Brutus' pugium, Charlemagne's francisca, Dracula's diadem, and the fabulous Runestone are mentioned in the chapter.

Plate 6, "The Tower": The images are photographs taken by the author (including those of one of his own cats portraying those of the Wizard), plus the riding crop/chess piece created by Juan Gines de Pasamonte.

Plate 7, "Something About Witches": Matthew Joshua Knisley's production features alchemical/mystical symbols of his own choice. If you want to know what they mean, ask him. He is quite the mystic.

Plate 8, "The Two Byrons": Matthew Joshua Knisley posterized the face of Lord Byron in his "Corsair" pose and placed it upon the body of the Page of Swords of the Rider-Waite-Smith tarot deck. The cigarette and sneakers are his idea.

Plate 9, "Beam, Gleam, Glow and Glide": Juan Gines de Pasamonte took the photo of the model for our Wizard in the pose of the Magician on the Rider-Waite-Smith tarot card and set it inside the same card's border.

That Magician's belt evokes the ouroboros, the tail-biting snake, which we have suggested with our floating image, a well-known Hermetic-Cabalist/Alchemical design using two dragons.

Plate 10, "The Chimies": Images of Glastonbury Tor and Chartres Cathedral underlie Juan Gines de Pasamonte's treatments of the mystery-presences the narrator hears. Juan's "Hopewell Highway," the dead straight 60-mile pathway between two ancient Ohio earthworks, is included. It's all meant to evoke the layers of significance to the types of sites at which the narrator's presences are most active.

Plate 11, "The Magickal Battle of Britain": The Sutton Hoo helmet underlies the Runestone, an RAF fighter plane, and the image of our model for Dana Lambert.

Plate 12, "Blood Drives": This is a representation of the Aztec child-sacrificer Tlaloc suggested in Chapter 1, the title page of King James I's book on witchcraft, and an old woodcut of witches dancing to the Devil. This is an illustration for a work of fiction. Its point is to embody topics mentioned in the chapter. We by no means intend to link all witches to either Satan or sacrifice, though, should there happen to be a Devil, child-sacrifice would surely be on his list of delights.

Plate 13, "The Magic Dragon": Julie Marechal took this picture in 2019 in the flats along the Cattaraugus Creek in Zoar Valley, NY, at a spirited annual party/performance, the inimitable *Amphibian*. The symmetrical columns that appear in the center left are mysterious. Every *Amphibian* features light, smoke, costumes, and chaos, but never props that Classical. Up to twenty pictures were taken in the same area, and none held columns or anything that might suggest them. Could this be a psychic photograph?

Plate 14, "Snake Hill": Matthew Joshua Knisley illustrated the character Danny Montour's clash with a monstrous attacker and set it under the backdrop of his glorious, symbolic Medicine Mask.

Plate 15, "The Iron Trail": Juan Gines de Pasamonte's treatments of "the Hopewell Highway" and pterosaur-like forms were set over the author's photograph of Logan's Monument atop Auburn's Fort Hill Cemetery. It's all meant to suggest the lost sacred landscape of New York State and its manifestations in supernatural folklore today.

Plate 16, "Lady Justice": Matthew Joshua Knisley interpreted this scene at the Ontario County Courthouse with his ascending wizard under the auspices of his Mask. The author has long been fascinated by this politically powerful, folklorically-energetic site.

Chapter Plate 17, "Elena": The central image of the Rider-Waite-Smith tarot card "The World" was set atop our Runestone.

Plate 18, PRINCEPS AERIS: The author's photograph of another of Amphibian's charismatic denizens was placed atop Julie Marechal's picture and decked with the publisher's interpretation of the locked grimoire.

# THE AUTHOR

Mason Winfield studied English and Classics at Denison University, earned a master's degree in British literature at Boston College, and studied poetry and fiction at SUNY Buffalo with professor emeritus and MacArthur grant recipient Irving Feldman. For thirteen years he taught English at The Gow School (South Wales, NY), during which time he chaired the English department, won a 50K cross-country ski marathon, and was ranked several times among the Buffalo, NY, area's top ten tennis players. He has written or edited fifteen books, including the regional sensation *Shadows of the Western Door* (1997) and *Iroquois Supernatural*, a book on the traditions of the Six Longhouse Nations (Inner Traditions International/Bear & Company, 2011) co-authored with Michael Bastine. Several of his books of upstate folklore and paranormal tradition may be found at the website of Western New York Wares: *www.buffalobooks.com*. Mason is the founder of Western New York's original supernatural tourism company, Haunted History Ghost Walks, Inc.